GIS CONCEPTS

AND

ArcGIS METHODS

2nd Edition, July 2005

David M. Theobald, Ph.D.

Natural Resource Ecology Laboratory

Colorado State University

GIS Concepts and ArcGIS Methods

Copyright

Copyright © 2005 by David M. Theobald. All rights reserved.

Trademarks

ArcGIS, ArcMap, ArcCatalog, ArcToolbox, ArcView, ArcInfo, Spatial Analyst, Shapefile, Image Analysis, 3D Analyst, and Avenue are registered trademarks of Environmental Systems Research Institute, Inc.

Publisher

Conservation Planning Technologies, 1113 West Olive Street, Fort Collins, Colorado, 80521, USA. Phone: 970.980.1183.

For book inquiries, please visit the following website:

> http://www.consplan.com

Published in the United States of America

ISBN 0-9679208-3-3 (paper)

CHAPTER 7

Raster basics   *223*

Preface

A relatively recent trend in the geographical information systems (GIS) industry is *desktop GIS* that utilizes graphical user interface components, and ArcGIS v8 is the most recent version of software produced by Environmental Systems Research Institute (ESRI). A natural outgrowth of desktop GIS is that the user base has become broader and more diverse. One of the consequences of the broadening of the user base is that documentation has become more general and less technical, even though the software is becoming more flexible and powerful. Much of the reasoning has been lost from user manuals behind why a certain option should be selected or which algorithm should be used. There are numerous good GIS textbooks that discuss basic concepts, but increasingly many users of GIS software are not aware of this foundation.

In the GIS field, as in other areas that are strongly influenced by technology, there seem to be two types of books available. First, *training* books provide a mechanical tutorial for specific software products. *Educational* textbooks, on the other hand, provide a conceptual basis and understanding for generic methods and techniques, and lend scientific rigor to the content. Students in formal GIS courses are provided general descriptions of analytical procedures through textbooks, but are left to determine which algorithm has been implemented and how it works. The result is that users frequently understand general principles, but lack knowledge of specific, technical details.

Six years ago I wrote the precursor to this book — *GIS Concepts and ArcView Methods* — to fill the void between textbooks and user manuals by fusing a grounded presentation of *ArcView* GIS software. Encouraged by the success of that book and stimulated by the significant changes that ArcGIS has brought, I have written the present one — *GIS Concepts and ArcGIS Methods* — in very much the same spirit, but addressing ESRI's recent flagship software, *ArcGIS*. As the book title suggests, I have attempted to organize and frame the methods and techniques used in ArcGIS within the context of GIS concepts and principles. I attempt to describe *why* you should choose a particular method or technique, in addition to how to do it — without crossing the line where the forest is lost for the trees. This **2nd Edition** has been revised and updated to include changes made to ArcGIS up to *v9.1*.

I welcome and encourage feedback on my book, so it can be improved over time. Please write me at David.Theobald@colostate.edu and visit the book's website at: www.consplan.com.

Cheers!

Dave Theobald
Colorado State University, Fort Collins, Colorado, USA
July 2005

Book organization

This book is organized roughly from basic to advanced concepts. I have chosen to provide fairly detailed information even in introductory chapters so that the text provides a full, cohesive reference book. As a result, some of the information may be a bit too detailed for first-time users of ArcGIS and GIS in general. Please simply note that "there is something more there" and refer back to it at a later reading.

Chapter 1 introduces some basic geographical concepts and describes terms and concepts specific to ArcGIS. Chapter 2 describes data models and structures and provides detailed discussion about shapefiles and geodatabases. Chapter 3 provides a review of projections and concludes with specific projections supported in ArcGIS. Chapter 4 describes the basic steps of visualizing geographic phenomena with maps and printing maps. Chapter 5 describes the numerous ways you can query map and attribute data. Chapter 6 describes in detail how to create and edit both spatial and attribute data, including procedures for topological and non-topological editing. Chapter 7 describes raster-based modeling and the Spatial Analyst extension, and Chapter 8 provides an in-depth section on the Raster Calculator. Chapter 9 describes how to analyze a single layer, while Chapter 10 describes how to analyze the relationships and features between two or more layers. Chapter 11 (new with the 2nd Edition) describes spatial modeling, geoprocessing, the ModelBuilder window, and the basics of how to program geoprocessing objects with Python scripts.

Technical details are provided as footnotes at the end of each chapter, as are numerous citations to primary and secondary references. I have also commented on parallels to ArcView v3.x throughout in various footnotes. I conclude most sections with step-by-step instructions, rather than including them directly in the text.

Acknowledgements

I wish to thank my students who have helped me to continue to learn over the years and my colleagues at the Natural Resource Ecology Lab for providing such a stimulating and fun environment. I also am grateful to my numerous colleagues and friends for heartfelt discussions about ways to promote sustainable living and about the important role GIS can play. Thanks to Nate Peterson and Anne Smith who provided helpful feedback on earlier drafts. To Pam and Charlie—although I have tested your patience and good will yet again, you have responded with encouragement and support. I thank you for your love and understanding while I was periodically absorbed writing this book.

## CHAPTER 1

Introduction to GIS and ArcGIS

1.1 What is special about GIS?

Geographic Information Systems (GIS) have emerged as a key technology to manipulate and analyze geographic data. Although there are many roots of GIS (and they are often intertwined), there are a few that are worth mentioning here. The term GIS was first coined in the early 1960s by Roger Tomlinson during his work with the Canada Land Inventory (CLI). At that time, a system was needed to analyze the data collected by the CLI to support the development of land management plans for rural areas of Canada. In the United States, the Bureau of the Census developed the DIME-GBF data structure and street database in 1967 in preparation for the 1970 census, and the TIGER topological data structure in 1988. Howard Fisher established the Laboratory for Computer Graphics and Spatial Analysis at Harvard University in 1964, and work accomplished in the 1970s and early 1980s had a major influence on the development of GIS. A number of software packages were developed there: SYMAP, CALFORM, SYMVU, GRID, POLYVRT, and ODYSSEY. Jack Dangermond, a Harvard Lab graduate, founded Environmental Systems Research Institute (ESRI) in 1969. Many of the ideas used to develop ARC/INFO, first released in the early 1980s, originated from ODYSSEY.[1]

1.1.1 GIS defined

GIS are commonly defined as information systems that manage, manipulate, and analyze spatial data. GIS are used to produce information that is useful in decision-making, historically in the natural resource management area, but increasingly for business, health, marketing, and other fields. A key characteristic of GIS is the explicit linkage between geographic features represented on a map with attribute data that describe the geographic feature. GIS are typically distinguished from other systems that manipulate spatial data, such as Computer-Aided Design (CAD), by their ability to perform complex spatial operations and analyses.

But a comprehensive definition of GIS must include the users of GIS—and so ESRI president Jack Dangermond's "3Ws of Geography" is helpful here: *what* is where, *why* is it there, and *why* do I care. By emphasizing the interconnected grouping of data, algorithms, display, management, *and* people, GIS can be seen as a coordinated system. This system includes the combination of software, hardware, and geographic data. Visualization and analysis of geographic data is the key to transforming geographic data into powerful, useful information.

Generally, there are four groups of functions that GIS software and hardware provide: input, management, analysis, and output. Geographic data are *input* into a GIS through a variety of mechanisms. A common form of data collection is through digitizing or scanning existing paper maps. For example, the US Geological Survey creates Digital Line Graphs by digitizing its topographic series to create political boundaries, roads, contour lines, etc., while Digital Raster Graphics are created by scanning topographic maps to create geo-referenced images that can serve as a reference or base for other geographic data. Increasingly, data are collected by Global Positioning Systems (GPS) to create high-quality data about features such as parcel boundaries, roads, wildlife movement, fire boundaries, etc. Data are also collected through remote sensing methods that include satellite imagery (e.g., Landsat or SPOT) and aerial photography.

Once these geographic data are input into a GIS, they require *management*. There can be massive volumes of data that would quickly overwhelm users without tools to handle large geographic data sets. Data need to be stored in such a manner that they can be easily maintained and retrieved.

The heart of a GIS is *analysis*: the creation of information from data. Geographic information is created by a user's queries of an individual data set, through overlaying a number of different layers of geographic data, and through complex modeling and simulation.

The most common way to visualize the results of queries and analyses is through map *output*. A map can be output via a printer or large-format plotter, included in an electronic report (e.g., in PDF format), or exported as an interactive map (e.g., through dynamic HTML). Graphs and

---

1. See the NCGIA's Core Curriculum project, History of GIS module: http://www.geog.ubc.ca/courses/klink/ gis.notes/ncgia/u23.html#UNIT23

summary statistics are often created and output in a report. A powerful way to use GIS is to project maps onto a screen to facilitate collection, interpretation, and decision making by groups of scientists and land managers (Figure 1.1).

FIGURE 1.1. Scientists using GIS to develop a conservation plan for the Southern Rockies Ecoregional Plan.

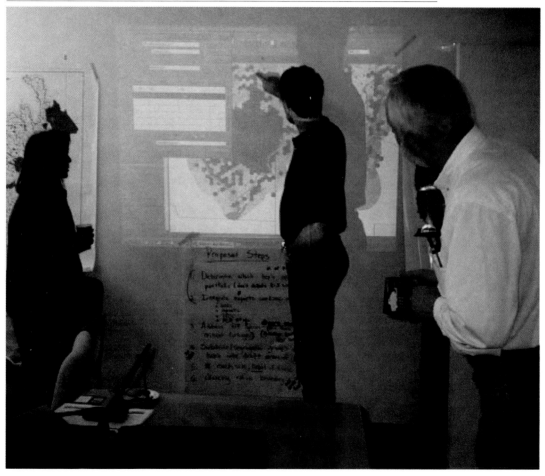

1.1.2 Maps and more...

Geographic data is typically displayed in a map form. Indeed, the metaphor of a "smart" or electronic map is often made to describe GIS and its display of geographic data. The analogy is useful to some degree, especially to describe the electronic medium used to portray spatial data, and the "smart" moniker hints at the information that lies (virtually) behind the map.

However, there are a number of ways that the metaphor breaks down—that geographic data manipulated by GIS are much more than just electronic maps.

To illustrate this point, imagine that you are interested in forests, and, in particular, the location of patches of quaking aspen in Colorado (Figure 1.2). First, because geographic data can be manipulated in a GIS, they can be displayed in various ways. This provides the user with the ability to examine not just *the* map, but many possible maps by varying the way features are portrayed through different symbols, or the way the data are classified into different categories. A second difference is that typically there are many different attributes associated with spatial features. Not only can all of these be accessed, but they can also be interactively queried to answer questions like: "What vegetation type is here?" "Where are patches of aspen located?" "How many acres of patches of aspen are there?" Moreover, the spatial location of features can be compared to one another, so questions about distance and direction can be answered. That is, are aspen patches clustered together, or are they scattered throughout the landscape? Third, data can be transformed into information that fits a user's context through a rich set of analytical tools. The relationship between different attributes can be examined to investigate, for example, the spatial arrangement of aspen clones with respect to soil type, aspect, or time since disturbance. Fourth, geographic data in a GIS do not suffer, as they do in paper maps, from the fundamental trade-off between spatial detail and geographic coverage (although because most geographic data are derived from paper maps, they typically can only represent features to a certain resolution).

FIGURE 1.2. A map of land cover types in Colorado, USA. Patches of quaking aspen are displayed in bright yellow, and county boundaries (black lines) are shown for reference.[2]

1.1.3 Spatial analysis

Another characteristic commonly used to describe GIS and differentiate it from other spatial technologies is that it allows users to conduct advanced *spatial analysis*, including the "big three Cs" — connectivity, containment, and contiguity. Most analyses are based on relationships between and among geographic features. The set of spatial relationships are called *spatial relations*[3], and there are three types: *topological, directional, and proximal.* Topologically, two or more features can be equivalent (spatially), partially equivalent (meaning that they overlap one another or cross one another), contained (one feature is wholly inside another), adjacent (two features share a common boundary or meet at a point), or separate (disjoint or not adjacent). (Also see Figure 1.3.) Note that the relationships most

---

2. Data source: the Colorado Gap Analysis Project, 2000.

3. A classic paper on spatial relations is: Freeman, J. 1975. The modeling of spatial relations. *Computer Graphics and Image Processing* 4: 156-171.

closely associated with advanced GIS analyses—connectivity, containment, and contiguity—are all topological relationships. Directional relations include relative relationships such as foreground/background (also known as in front of/behind), above/below, left/right; and absolute relationships such as north, south, east, west, and azimuthal (compass) bearings. Occasionally above/below is used to describe some topological relationship as well, for example, Lake Mead (formed by Hoover Dam) is above Lake Havasu (formed by Parker Dam) on the Colorado River. Proximity relations include relative measures such as near and far, and absolute such as measured distances (e.g., Lake Tahoe is about 250 kilometers from San Francisco).

FIGURE 1.3. Examples of topologic relationships: *equivalent* (top left, two polygons of Lake Tahoe, CA on top of one another); *partial equivalent* (top right, Lake Tahoe overlaps parts of 5 counties); *contained* (bottom left, two islands are wholly inside Lake Mono and Lake Mono is wholly within Mono County); *adjacent* (bottom right, Placer County is adjacent to Washoe, Carson City, Douglas, and El Dorado counties); *separate* (bottom right, Washoe County is disjoint from El Dorado County).

Spatial analyses range from simple to advanced and typically rely on some combination of spatial relations. For example, location analysis enables you to query "What is here?", which uses a combination of equivalent (Is this city at the same location as the user-defined location?) and containment (Which polygon is the user-defined location within?) relations. Nearest-neighbor analysis utilizes adjacency relations. It is used, for example, when all the counties adjacent to a disease outbreak need to be determined. Proximity analysis uses the concept of a buffer around an object to determine what features are within a certain distance of another feature. This assists us in answering questions like: which houses are further away than a three-mile radius of a fire station? What areas are sensitive to encroachment in parks and protected areas? (see Figure 1.4).

FIGURE 1.4. Spatial analysis can be used to examine how parks and protected areas may be effected by non-compatible land uses in adjacent areas. Jardin Botanico outside San Miguel de Allende, Mexico.

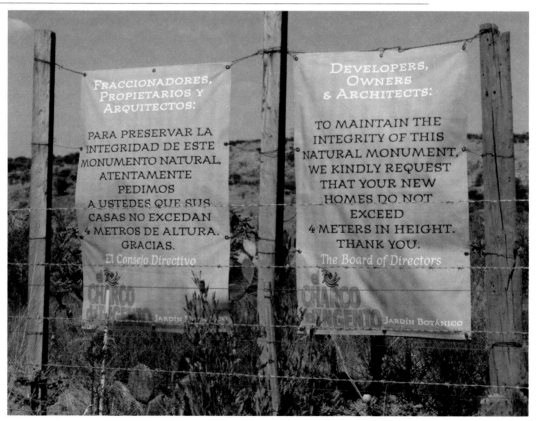

1.2 Evolution of interface design

GIS have evolved dramatically since their inception in the 1960s and 1970s. In some of the pioneering GIS, there was no separation between geographic data and the tools to query and analyze them (e.g., POLYVRT[5]). After the era of computing that required punch-cards and batch processing, command-line interfaces were developed that allowed users to type in commands. To output or print maps, clever use of different characters was made to represent different shades of grey (e.g., SYMAP).

The most recent interface innovation has been a shift to what is called *desktop GIS*, which takes advantage of powerful desktop computers and graphical user interface design. ArcGIS is called a *desktop GIS* because the applications are based around a point-and-click graphical user interface (GUI). Desktop GIS simplifies user interaction by providing an easy-to-use interface and packaging common analyses that are accessible from menus and dialogs. This type of user interaction is a much different approach than a *command-line* interface, which is typically more difficult to learn, remember, and use, especially for beginning users — but is easily programmable and extendable for advanced users. ESRI's flagship product, ARC/INFO (up to v7.X) was considered to be a *toolbox GIS* and relied exclusively on a command-line interface and scripting. However, beginning with the release of ArcView (v3.x) and the recent releases of ArcGIS Desktop (v8 and v9) — and the suite of applications ArcMap, ArcCatalog, and ArcToolbox — mark a significant adoption of GUI-based technology. Interestingly, the command-line interface and scripting has been revived and brought back in v9. This provides users a number of ways to interfaces to interact with ArcGIS.

Prior to the release of v3.0, ArcView had limited editing, query, and analytical functions commonly found in other industry-standard GIS. It was used mostly for map production and as a tool to query and view maps. However, v3.x of ArcView has advanced GIS capabilities. Although ArcView (v3.x) is still sold and supported by ESRI, ArcGIS (v8.x) takes advantage of Microsoft® Windows® user interface standards and a consistent programming platform to standardize all ESRI products at v8.x. ArcGIS Desktop v9 builds on the consistent platform and provides easier and more advanced ways to build models, process data, and create custom tools that can be directly integrated into the Desktop applications.

---

4. Data source: the Colorado Gap Analysis Project, 2000.
5. Peucker, T.K. and Chrisman, N. 1975. Geographic data structures. *The American Cartographer* 2: 55-69.

1.3 Desktop ArcGIS

1.3.1 Overview

ArcGIS is actually comprised of two distinct but coordinated applications or software products: *ArcMap* and *ArcCatalog*.[6] ArcMap is the application used primarily to examine data, query attributes, conduct spatial analysis, and design maps for output. ArcCatalog is the application used to browse and manage spatial data. Think of it as a specialized Microsoft® Windows® Explorer, but it can be used to search for spatial data, preview it, create and manage meta-data (to describe where the data came from, its projection, attributes, scale, accuracy, etc.), and conduct basic processing of spatial data. *ArcToolbox* is a dockable window containing a set of tools that can be integrated directly into ArcMap or ArcCatalog. The tools in ArcToolbox allow data to be imported and converted into different formats and to be re-projected, and provide tools to conduct spatial analysis (see Table 1.1). The advantage of having somewhat separate but overlapping functionality in different applications is that the tool can be targeted better to the task at hand. However, the disadvantage is that you must understand which application is best for which task.[7]

Within each application, there are three levels or degrees of functionality, ranging from basic to advanced. These levels are called ArcView, ArcEditor, and ArcInfo. The distinction between the applications and the level of functionality can be confusing, especially because prior to ArcGIS, ArcView (v3.x) and ArcInfo (v7.x) were applications themselves. The names for the levels of functionality are a legacy of the past: the application ArcView (v3.x) was considered to be more of a data viewer (hence the name) and so was considered to be the "little brother" to the application ArcInfo (v7.x). So, the ArcView level of ArcGIS provides basic functionality such as making maps, querying data, and analyzing spatial relationships, with some limitation on creating and editing certain types of data (see Table 1.2). At the intermediate ArcEditor level, you can do the same as the ArcView level, but you can edit some additional data formats. At the advanced ArcInfo level, you can also edit some additional data formats and some additional analysis tools are available as well. Also, ArcInfo Workstation (a command-line interface based on the legacy ArcInfo v7.x) is available at the ArcInfo level of ArcGIS. Although conceptually it may not be so straightforward to keep the names of applications and functionality levels apart, it is easy to determine the level of functionality when you are using a given application—the level will follow the application name in the Window title bar (e.g., *ArcMap - ArcView*). The level of functionality is administered by the ArcGIS license manager.

---

6. At v8, ArcGIS is comprised of three applications -- ArcToolbox was its own standalone application. ArcView v3 was contained all within a single application.

7. Another disadvantage is that you may not be able to change the properties of a dataset (i.e. that needs write-access) through one application (e.g., ArcToolbox) if it is already being accessed through another application (e.g., ArcMap).

Of course, if you have not purchased a license for the ArcEditor or ArcInfo level, then the advanced level of functionality will not be available.

TABLE 1.1. Which application should you use for a given task? (++ primarily, + secondarily). *Available only at ArcInfo level.

Task	ArcMap	ArcCatalog	ArcToolbox
Input			
- creating new layers		++	
- heads-up digitizing	++		
- importing data	+		++
Management			
- copying and moving datasets	+	++	
- setting projection information		+	++
- metadata		++	
- searching	+	++	
- re-projecting	+		++
- building topology		+	++
Analysis			
- query	++	+	
- buffering	++		++
- geo-processing	++		++
- overlay	++		++*
- modeling	+		++
Output			
- map design and layout	++		
- export to *.e00			++*
- export to graphics	++		
- export to interactive map	++		
- export to other map formats	+	+	++
- print to plotter	++		

1.3.2 ArcMap basics

The main use of *ArcMap* is viewing spatial data by creating and querying a map, hence the name. The main document that ArcMap works with is called the *map docu-ment*, stored in a file with extension *.mxd.[8] It is important to realize that the map document stores the layers, symbology, and layout, but does *not* store the actual geographic data. Rather, the map document simply "points to" the various files that are being accessed in ArcMap. After the Arc-Map application has been started, you can either open an existing map document or create a new one.

Each map document is composed of at least two panels (Figure 1.5 & 1.6). The *table of contents* is shown on the left, and the *map display* (or map view) is shown on the right. The table of contents lists the layers that are contained within the map document. Each *layer* is identified by a name, which, by default, is the same as the filename (names can be changed in the Table of Contents by a soft-click). To the left of the name is the visibility check box — you can control the visibility (whether the layer is drawn or not) by checking or un-checking it. To the left of the visibility check box is the layer expansion box (+ or -), which you can use to control whether the symbology for a layer is displayed or not underneath the layer name. Layers are drawn in a bottom-to-top order, so that layers at the top of the table of contents list are drawn on top of lower layers. You can change the draw order by clicking on the name and dragging it up or down to the desired order. Layers can be grouped together using a *group layer*, which is particularly useful to organize a group of similar layers. Multiple layers can be selected by shift-click and ctrl-click. Context menus for each layer can be accessed by right-clicking on a layer name. Many operations that are specific to a given layer are accessed in this way (e.g., opening the attribute table, copying or deleting a layer, setting and viewing properties, etc.). You can also bring up the Properties dialog by double-clicking on the layer name.

Two additional panels or windows related to geoprocessing can be docked into the interface. The ArcToolbox window can be docked (or allowed to float) allowing easy access to a variety of tools. The command-line interface can also be docked allowing users to type in commands. These windows can be added to ArcMap either through buttons on the standard toolbar or through the Window menu.

---

8. A map document (*.mxd) essentially replaces ArcView v3.x project files (*.apr).

FIGURE 1.5. A typical ArcMap map document (v9), with table of contents (left), Toolbox (center), map display (right), and command line interface (bottom). Add or remove these windows through the Windows menu.

FIGURE 1.6. A typical ArcMap map document (v8), with table of contents (left) and map display (right).

Opening an existing map document.

1. Select File -> Open....
2. Navigate to desired folder.
3. Select *.mxd file.
4. Click Open.

TABLE 1.2. Functions that are available for each application at the ArcView, ArcEditor, and ArcInfo levels. The levels build from ArcView on up (so if a function is available in ArcView, then it is also available in ArcEditor and ArcInfo as well).

Application	ArcView	ArcEditor	ArcInfo
ArcMap	Display shapefiles, coverages, geodatabase, GRIDs Edit shapefiles and simple geodatabases	Edit coverages and geodatabase	ArcPlot - command-line mapping ArcEdit - command-line editing
ArcCatalog		Define geodatabase schema	
ArcTools	Define projection information Project shapefiles and geodatabases Import *.e00 files		Project GRIDs and coverages AML scripting

Typically at the bottom of the table of contents are three tabs:[9] *display* and *source* and *selection*. The appearance of the layers in the table of contents changes with each tab. In the display tab, layer names are shown in the draw order of the layers, and layers can be re-ordered only in this tab (click-and-drag). If you click on a layer's name, then the number of selected features will be listed in the lower-left corner of the map document.[10] (If no features are selected, then the message will be blank. In the source tab, layers are organized by the source location (folder/pathname) -- but the layer name is still used. Also, clicking on a layer in the source tab will cause the number of features to be listed below. Note that tables can be added to an ArcMap document, but can be accessed only through the *source* tab. In the selection tab, layers are listed with checks if they are selectable layers. If any features are selected, then the layer is "bolded" and the number of features are provided in parentheses.

Layers (and grouped layers) are organized within a *data frame*, and they share the same coordinate system (e.g., latitude/longitude, UTM, or Albers Equal Area). The coordinate system will default to the first layer added to the data frame (though this can be changed through the data frame properties dialog). All layers within a data frame will then be on the fly projected to the same coordinate system. Note that multiple layers in a data frame can reference the same dataset. Also, layers can be copied from one map document to pasted into another map document. See Chapter 3 for more discussion about coordinate systems. The default data frame is called *Layers*. Occasionally, you may want to have multiple data frames

---

9. By default in v9.1, but only two tabs in prior versions.

10. But to get the total number of features in the layer, you must open the attribute table, yuk! Also, to get the actual dataset name that a layer points to, you must go to the source tab in the Layer Properties dialog -- only the path name is displayed in the source tab (the layer name is not the same as the source or filename).

in a map document, to create a map complete with inset or overview maps, for example. When there is more than one data frame in a map document, the active data frame is shown by the **bolded** data frame name. Data frames can also be expanded or contracted to control the complexity of the table of contents. You can switch between the views using the **View** menu item, or by using the tabs (display, source) at the lower-left corner of the map display.[11]

The layers are shown in the map display to the right side of the map document. There are two types of displays: *data view* and *layout view*. Data view is used when you want to "browse" the data—that is, to examine and query the spatial data. Only one data frame can be visible at a time (the active one), and cartographic elements such as legends and scale bars are hidden when in data view.

An additional button is located at the bottom of the data frame (to the right of the data view and layout view tabs), that *pauses drawing* so that you can make changes to the symbology of numerous layers without re-drawing occurring. Click the button again to restart drawing.[12]

Two other ways to "view" your maps are through the overview and magnify windows. The *overview window* provides the spatial context by showing the full extent of the map with the current spatial extent outlined displayed in red on the map.

 The *magnifier window* allows you to essentially move a magnifying glass over your map for closer inspection.

The layout view is used to compose a map, to complement the geographic features with other cartographic elements such as legends, scale bars, and north arrows; and usually for exporting and printing. All data frames are visible when in layout view, and multiple data frames are often used to create

---

11. Multiple data views can be used in a roughly similar fashion as views in ArcView v3.x. However, there is only one layout view in ArcMap, in contrast to the possibility of many layouts in ArcView v3.x.

12. Pressing F9 also pauses drawing. Press F9 again to resume drawing.

a complex map layout showing different aspects of the same geographic area, or perhaps to include an inset map.

Opening overview & magnification windows

1. Select Window -> Overview... or Window -> Magnifier....

2. Click and drag on floating window.

Surrounding the table of contents and map display areas are a variety of menus, buttons, and tools. The *cursor coordinates* of the current location of the cursor (in the active data frame coordinate system) are displayed at the bottom of the application window, and the coordinate units (e.g., lat/long vs. UTM coordinates) can be changed in the Data Frame Properties.

Setting cursor coordinate system

1. Select View -> Data Frame Properties....

2. Click General tab.

3. Set Display: drop-down list to desired units.

There are two ways that data can be added from the *Catalog* to an existing or new map document. The first is to add data directly from the map catalog to a map document. Data are inserted into the table of contents ordered from top to bottom by point, line, polygon, and then raster.[13] A second way to add data is to locate a dataset using ArcCatalog, click on the dataset icon, and then drag it into a map document. A *layer file* (*.lyr) stores a specific representation or symbology of a dataset (and any relates or joins), but does not store the data itself (see Table 1.3). You can also create a *folder connection* to streamline the catalog so that it only includes folders where you have spatial datasets located. For example, if you only have data on **c:\data**, then create a folder connection to this folder, then remove the **c:** folder connection to make adding data faster. If you have data in multiple folders, you can create multiple folder

---

13. By default, new maps are immediately visible (drawn), but this option can be changed in ArcMap by selecting **Tools -> Options**, clicking on the Applications tab, then unchecking the New Layer Visibility box.

---

connections and add them to the top level of the Catalog so that your most frequently used data locations are convenient to access. A folder connection is similar to a working directory, but allows multiple directories to be rapidly accessible.

Adding data to map document

1. Select File -> Add Data....
2. Navigate to desired folder.
3. Select dataset(s).
4. Click Add.

A wide variety of data types are supported in ArcGIS. Some of the more frequently used ones include: shapefiles, geodatabases, coverages, TINs, and GRIDs. In addition, datasets that are available on the Internet can be added directly into a map document. These datasets, called *map services*, need to be served by ArcIMS, a separate ESRI product that is part of the broader ArcGIS Desktop family. An ArcIMS *image service* takes snapshots of the map on the server and then sends an image over the Internet. Because a static image of a map is served, the symbology cannot be changed. Also, if the map service contains raster data, then the coordinate system of your data frame and the map service must be the same; otherwise, the raster layer will not be displayed. An ArcIMS *feature service* streams the actual features themselves so symbology can be changed. Feature services cannot contain raster-based data, however. When datasets are added to a map document in this way (i.e. "served"), the data itself is not downloaded onto your hard-drive, rather, you work with a "live" service over the Internet. The advantages of map services are that you do not have to store and manage the data yourself, and you are sure to be accessing the most up-to-date dataset. The disadvantage is that the layer will become unavailable if the service or server goes down. Also, depending on your Internet connection speed, map display and query can be slow at times.

TABLE 1.3. Commonly used datasets, layers, and their icons.

Name	Type	Dataset	Layer
Shapefile	point	places.shp	places.lyr
	line	Rivers.shp	rivers.lyr
	polygon	LAKES.shp	lakes.lyr
Coverage	coverage	states	states.lyr
	arc	arc	
	point	label	
	polygon	polygon	
GRID		dem30	dem30.lyr
TIN		tin_study	tin_stud...
Geodatabase		yellowsto...	

Once a layer has been added to a map document, a common task is to manipulate the data with a "tool." The Tool bar (or tool palette) contains a number of commonly used tools. The top eight tools are navigational tools, which allow you to change the view on your data. You can interactively zoom in or out, zoom in or out a predefined amount, pan (re-center), go to the full extent, and go back to the previous extent or forward to the next extent. Note that you can also use a *spatial bookmark*, which allows you to name and store spatial extents, and to quickly navigate to particular parts of a map.

The bottom six tools allow you to interact with the features and their attributes in various ways. First, you can select specific features using the *Selection* tool (.). Next, you can select and move graphics using the plain arrow tool. The *Identify* tool ( ) allows you to click on a feature and get various attributes about it. The *Find* tool ( ) allows you to quickly search for text in the attribute table. The *Measure* tool ( ) can be used to measure distances on the map by interactively defining straight-line segments (double-click to end). The *Hyperlink* tool ( ) can be used to access hyperlinks that are attached to features, for instance, to bring up an picture taken at a certain location.

Setting a spatial bookmark

1. Navigate to a desired spatial extent.
2. Select View -> Bookmarks -> Create....
3. Type in a name.
4. Click OK.

1.3.3 ArcCatalog basics

ArcCatalog is used to manage your data: to find particular datasets on your hard-drive, to copy and move datasets around your system, and to document your geographic datasets with meta-data. ArcCatalog can be best thought of as a specialized Microsoft® Windows® Explorer-like application designed especially to handle geographic data. Not surprisingly then, the ArcCatalog application looks familiar, with the *catalog tree* to the left and the *catalog display* to the right (Figure 1.7). One of the most useful aspects of this application is that because a single geographic dataset is often composed of multiple files in multiple folders (e.g., a coverage or a GRID), copying and deleting them cannot be done using the standard Windows Explorer. Rather, ArcCatalog can deal with these complex data structures properly.

FIGURE 1.7. A typical ArcCatalog dialog, with the catalog tree (left), ArcToolbox (center), and catalog display (right).

Use the catalog tree to navigate your hard-drive or network to find a folder where your desired data reside. There are three views (or tabs) of the catalog display. The *contents view* shows the recognized datasets available, and you can show them with icons, as a list with icons and types, or as thumbnails. Again, you can bring up a context menu by right-clicking on a dataset to bring up a number of actions specific to a given dataset. One of these actions is to open the properties dialog (double-clicking will also show this), which is where you can see and change a number of parameters (Figure 1.8). General properties such as a dataset's name are described here. In the *fields tab*, you can find out the data types and size of each of your fields. By selecting the shape field, you can either examine the coordinate system of a dataset or specify it by clicking on the button to the right of the spatial reference row (and then saving it to a *.prj) file. In the *index tab*, you can also examine or create an index file associated with a specific attribute to speed up queries and display. (Note that if the fields are greyed out, then it is likely that your data set is read-only.)

> ### *Indexing the shape field*
>
> 1. In ArcCatalog, navigate to the desired folder.
>
> 2. Double-click on shapefile to open up the Properties dialog.
>
> 3. Click on the **Index** tab.
>
> 4. Click on the **Add** button at the bottom of the dialog (if greyed out, make sure layer is not open in another application and ensure you have write-access).
>
> 5. Click **OK**.

FIGURE 1.8. The three tabs of the properties dialog in ArcCatalog.

The *preview view* allows you to browse a map or the attribute table for a selected layer (Figure 1.9). The *metadata view* allows you to examine meta-data that describes various factors about your map.

FIGURE 1.9. ArcCatalog with the preview tab showing in the catalog display (right). Note that the navigation (zoom in, zoom out, pan, full extent) and identify tools at the center-right are now available to use, so that you can zoom into an area of interest and then query for an attribute value.

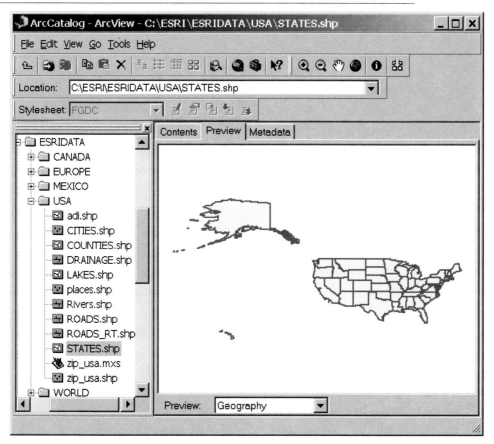

An interesting and useful function available in ArcCatalog is the *search tool* (Figure 1.10), which allows datasets to be located by specifying the name, geographic location, date created/modified, or keywords in meta-data. Once you have located a dataset(s) that you would like to work with, you can "drag and drop" it directly from ArcCatalog into ArcMap.

FIGURE 1.10. The ArcCatalog search tool dialog.

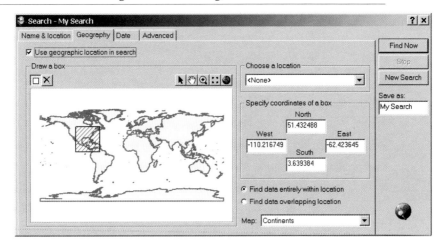

1.3.3.1 Meta-data

Meta-data is often described as "data about data". That is, it is additional documentation about a spatial dataset that describes things such as its coordinate system, spatial extent, descriptions of attributes, how and when the data were created, and who to contact for further information. ArcCatalog automatically maintains the technical meta-data such as coordinate system and spatial extent. It falls to your shoulders to enter other meta-data, such as a general description of the dataset, why you created, and what are proper (and potentially improper) uses. This may seem to be a heavy responsibility, but hard-won words of advice (a.k.a. the *documentation mantra*) about meta-data are: *document early, frequently, and thoroughly*. Taking two minutes to document now is worth two days of angst later. ArcCatalog provides tools to maintain meta-data.

Editing meta-data

1. In ArcCatalog, navigate to the desired folder.

2. Select the dataset of interest.

3. Click on the Metadata tab.

4. If the Meta-data toolbar is not displayed ("Stylesheet"... above), then click View -> Toolbars -> Metadata.

5. Click on the edit metadata button (📝). (Note: if it is greyed out, check to see if the file is read-only.)

6. Modify meta-data.

7. Click OK.

1.3.4 Geoprocessing

Geoprocessing is defined as the processing of geographic information through an operation that generates desired information, typically in the form of a new spatial dataset but also as a simple statistical value or a table. In addition, a series of muliple operations can also be conducted. In this chapter geoprocessing is introduced, and Chapter 11 provides a more detailed discussion of geoprocessing within the context of spatial modelling.

Each operation or process is called a *command* or a tool, and ArcGIS provides numerous commands and tools through the native interface. The most common way to access these tools is through ArcToolbox, which organizes tools within toolsets and toolboxes. A *toolset* can contain tools, other toolsets, scripts, and models. A *toolbox* is similar to a toolset in that it can contain tools, other toolsets, scripts, and models -- but a toolbox cannot contain other toolboxes. In addition, users can create their own operations by writing a *script*, which is a set of instructions stored in a file and typically interpreted (but can be compiled) at run time. A script can be as simple as calling a single tool, but typically it automates a more complex series of operations. Another way to group tools by creating a model. In ArcGIS, a *model* is composed of one or more commands or tools that are strung together in a specific way through a new application within ArcGIS called ModelBuilder.

In ArcGIS, a variety of interfaces are provided that allow access to geoprocessing (here listed loosely in novice to expert). First, a tool can be located and run from the ArcToolbox window. Each tool has a dialog associated with it to provide information about how the tool should be used, what inputs are required (or optional), and what outputs are generated. Note that these dialogs are non-modal, so that you can continue work while the tool is running. When starting

---

a tool from ArcMap, the selected set of features is respected. Also, most of the Wizards that were common in v8 have been removed and replaced by dialogs. Second, a tool can be run from the command-line interface. The name of a tool can be typed interactively, complete with an excellent "in-line-completion", or whole strings can be cut and paste. Third, a model can be created in ModelBuilder that represents and runs a sequence of tools. Fourth, a script or program can be written that runs a variety of geoprocessing tools.

1.3.4.1 ArcToolbox

ArcToolbox provides access to a wide variety of tools. At the ArcView (basic) level, there are analysis tools, conversion tools (both import and export), data management tools, geocoding tools, linear referencing tools, and spatial statistics tools. Additional tools may be available for each extension.

At the ArcInfo level, the basic set of toolboxes are available, but a much richer set of tools, particularly analytical, are available.

1.3.4.2 Command line

The command-line interface is typically used to start an operation when you are familiar with a tool and its parameters. There are two sections to the command-line interface. In the top portion, commands can be typed in (with Intelli-sense). Note that the full list of tools available and their required parameters (including user-created tools) can be accessed here by simply typing in the command line. The bottom part of the command-line dialog box lists out the progress of a tool, and can also be used to get feedback from tools that have been run using other methods as well.

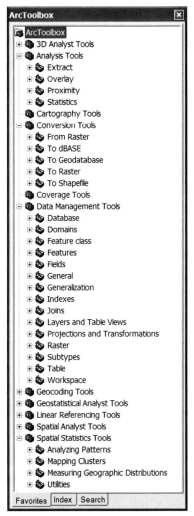

1.3.5 Extensions

In addition to the three ArcGIS applications, a number of *extension* products provide additional capabilities (Table 1.4). Typically, extensions require an additional license. If you have a license for an extension, to get the functionality in ArcMap you need to add the extension (Tools -> Extensions) and then add the toolbar (View -> Toolbars, ...).

TABLE 1.4. Extensions available to provide additional capabilities to ArcGIS.

Name	Functionality
3D Analyst	Allows three-dimensional displays, fly-throughs, visualization and analysis.
ArcReader	Provides browsing of maps (created by ArcGIS Publisher) through a free application.
Data Interoperability	Integrate a variety of spatial data formats by directly using, importing, and exporting numerous feature-based data formats, as well as modeling new customized spatial data formats.

TABLE 1.4. Extensions available to provide additional capabilities to ArcGIS.

Name	Functionality
Geostatistical Analyst	Allows advanced interpolation and geostatistical analysis of surfaces, including kriging.
Maplex	
Network Analyst	Allows routing and planning with networks. Available post v8.2.
Publisher	Allows you to convert a map document into an interactive map readable by ArcReader (a free plug-in).
Schematics	Allows you to represent the connectivity of linear and network data through schematic diagrams.
Spatial Analyst	Allows manipulation, analysis, and modeling of raster-based (GRID) data.
StreetMap (USA and Europe)	Provides street mapping and geocoding dataset.
Tracking Analyst	Provides tracking and analysis of temporal data.

1.3.6 Key changes in v9

A new environment for geoprocessing, modeling, and scripting is provided in v9. ArcToolbox is no longer a standalone application, rather it is a dockable window accessed through ArcMap or ArcCatalog.

1.3.6.1 New features in ArcGIS v9.1

Map document files (and layer and scenes) can be saved so that they are backwards compatible and can be shared with ArcGIS v8.3 (at v9.0 they could not). A new merge tool was created (in Data Management toolbox) to allow multiple inputs into a single feature output. StreetMap is now core functionality that allows all ArcGIS users to perform nationwide geocoding. ArcPress is also now core functionality, allowing high-quality printing. Two new extensions are provided: Network Analyst and Schematics. Network Analyst is typically used for managing and analyzing transportation networks. Schematics allows you to represent the connectivity of linear and network data through schematic diagrams.

1.3.6.2 New features in ArcGIS v9.0

Several new ways are provided to build spatial models and to conduct geoprocessing. First, the ArcToolbox dockable window has a comprehensive set of tools. Note that an image of where a tool is located in ArcToolbox is provided throughout this book to help you visualize the organization of tools. The ModelBuilder application allows you to build models interactively through a "visual programming language", to link a set of operations together, and to share models with other users. All of these tools, including user-generated, are available through the ArcToolbox, a new dockable command-line window, ModelBuilder, and third-party scripting including Python. Raster datasets can be integrated into the geodatabase, either through individual datasets or as groups within a raster catalog. Geodatabases now support open data exchange using XML, which allows all or part of a geodatabase to be exported to an XML file and shared. Support for GPS devices is now provided through the GPS toolbar.

There are variety of new extensions also available, including the ArcGlobe application for making 3D visualizations, Maplex extension that provides high-quality cartographic labelling, the ArcGIS Data Interoperability that provides access to over 65 spatial data formats, the ArcGIS Publisher and ArcReader that packages data better and allows embedding in customized desktop solutions. In Spatial Analyst, raster datasets in GRID format no longer have a file size limit (use to be 2.4 GB).

1.3.7 Key changes in v8

Many new users of ArcGIS are bound to be seasoned users of ArcView v3.x. And many of you (like me) have been cautious to make the transition to ArcGIS. Is v8.x of ArcView essentially the same car as v3.x with a shiny new paint job, or is it a new "tricked-out, souped-up" monster truck? Underneath the hood, the big difference between the new version (v8.x) and the old version (v3.x) of ArcView is that the new version is based on MS COM objects to provide a more stable platform and consistency throughout the applications, extensions, and functionality levels. As advertised, the ArcView version of ArcGIS v8.2 does provide all the functionality of v3.2, and more! But to the tire-kickin' novice driver, the look and feel *is* likely to be fairly different and will require taking it out for a spin or two around the block—before you head out into rush-hour traffic (with your boss in the back seat demanding delivery of a complicated analysis).

The most challenging aspect to making the transition to ArcGIS v8.x is to be able to differentiate terminology versus conceptual differences. The fact that ArcView in v8.x is no longer an application, but rather is a level of functionality has been described in detail above. A big challenge of learning the new software is understanding which application (ArcMap, ArcCatalog, or ArcToolbox) you should use to do a specific task.

In v3.x, a project file (*.apr) contains various documents such as views, tables, charts, scripts, and layouts. In v8.x, the map document (*.mxd) is a single document that contains essentially a number of different views—called *data frames*, but only one layout. A *theme* in v3.x represents spatial data, but in v8.x a *layer* is used. Like a theme, a layer simply points to a specific spatial dataset (e.g., a shapefile). But a layer also can exist outside of the map document as a layer file (*.lyr). The advantage to this is that a legend and "look" of a particular layer can be shared with other users (rather than using *.avl files).

Also, although the idea of an active theme is key in v3.x, it is not directly translatable to v8.x. This is largely due to the use of "context menus" in v8.x that allow you to right-click directly on a layer, rather than having to first set the active theme, then select some menu option. So, in v8.x, you can control the "selectability" of a layer. Selected polygon features are displayed differently as well. In v8.x, the outline of the polygon rather than the interior of the polygon is highlighted (though the selection color for each layer can be set individually). This is straightforward, but for areas with *island polygons* it can be difficult to discern which feature(s) is selected (Figure 1.11).

FIGURE 1.11. Selection of polygons is shown by outline color, but island polygons may not be clear. Fortunately, the number of features selected is shown in the status bar below.

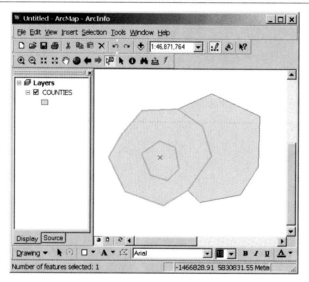

The new version provides some excellent improvements, especially the enhancements on cartographic production. The transparency on all layers (yes, not just GRIDs) in a view can be controlled individually. A wide variety of symbols are available, and tools can customize nearly every aspect of a symbol. Maps can be printed and exported (reliably) to a variety of formats (including PDF and PostScript color separates). Interactive graphs support examining and creating custom classification of data sets. Support for editing feature data is also vastly improved, using the idea of a *sketch*. A key difference between v3.x and v8.x is that the data frame in v8.x recognizes the coordinate system of each of its layers and on-the-fly re-projects them (if different from the data frame's coordinate system). This is a nice feature, but display speed can be a bit slow because of it. Another significant change is the use of Visual Basic for Applications (VBA) rather than Avenue to create custom functions. Some of the more straightforward changes in terminology and common tasks are provided below (Tables 1.5 and 1.6). Also, many of the free v3.x extensions, such as Dialog Designer, Graticules and Measure Grids, Legend Tool, etc. have been absorbed into the core v8.x software.

1.3.7.1 New features in ArcGIS v8.3

The most important change provided in v8.3 of ArcGIS is full implementation of topology for geodatabases.[14] Topology allows users to specify the spatial relationships between features in a much more flexible manner than the previous coverage data structure. The editing tools in ArcMap have been updated as well to make use of the new topological relationships. Linear referencing tools have also been updated to provide similar functionality as dynamic segmentation tools in workstation ArcInfo v7. One of the unfortunate side-effects of these updates is that ArcGIS document files created in v8.3 are not readable by previous versions (though documents created in v8.2 and earlier can be read by ArcGIS v8.3), including: map documents (*.mxd), ArcScene documents (*.sxd), published map files (*.pmf), and personal or multi-user geodatabases created in v8.3 cannot be used in previous versions of ArcGIS.

1.3.7.2 New features in ArcGIS v8.2

ArcGIS v8.2 provides new tools and functionality (some of the highlights are discussed below), but probably most importantly the new release provides core improvements to display speed and stability. For the ArcMap application, the *Spatial Adjustment* tools allow transformation, rubber sheeting, attribute transfer, and edge matching capabilities. New options for labeling and annotation are provided, including export of geodatabase annotation to coverage annotation. Text formatting tags allow "mid-stream" formatting (e.g., "The *Colorado* River"). The *Military Grid Reference System* is now supported. You can now add data from any ArcIMS service that is provided on the Internet. For display of raster data, you can now manually set the minimum and maximum settings.

There are also a number of enhancements to extensions. 3D Analyst provides a new *Animation* tool to create "fly-bys," fade layer visibility, and more. TINs are constructed much faster and new COM interfaces have been added to provide new functionality for custom applications. A large number of new functions are now available for Spatial Analyst, including groundwater, multivariate, and color model conversion functions, and a new functional reference is available. Also, for the Raster Calculator, multi-line expressions, usage (highlight function and right-click), and recent expressions are available. The ESRI Data and Maps CDs were updated so that the metadata is now compatible with ArcIMS 4.0 Metadata server. Also, all Census data were updated with the recent 2000 Census. Using the ArcGIS Publisher extension, maps can be published and viewed through ArcReader software using a similar concept to Adobe Acrobat PDFs and Reader software.

---

14. For a good introduction to topology for ArcView users, see: Childs, C. 2003. ArcGIS for ArcView users. ArcUser July-September. http://www.esri.com/news/arcuser/0703/files/av_topo.pdf

1.3.8 File and path names in ArcGIS

Although most software allows you free reign over the naming of files and folders, with ArcGIS it is wise to cultivate good working habits and follow dogmatically a few naming conventions. Do not use spaces or any non-alphanumeric character — excluding the underscore ("_") character — in the filename *or* the folders that contain your files. Hyphens in particular are a poor choice because unique field names are generated when joining one table to another by appending the <table name>"-"<field name>. Also, do not start a file name or folder with a number.[15]

TABLE 1.5. Changes in terminology from ArcView v3.x to ArcGIS v8.[a]

ArcView v3.x	ArcGIS v8.x
brightness theme	transparency
chart	graph
database theme	geodatabase layer
GRID theme	raster layer
hotlink	hyperlink
layout	layout view
legend file	layer file
project	map document
projection	coordinate system
symbol files	styles
theme	layer
view	data frame

a. Source: ESRI ArcGIS Desktop help, topic: "Transitioning from ArcView v3.2 to ArcGIS v8.x" --> "Terminology reference"...

TABLE 1.6. Changes in common tasks from ArcView v3.x to ArcGIS v8.x.

ArcView v3.x task	ArcGIS application	Menu/button/tool
Add theme...	ArcMap	File->Add data...
Add a field	ArcMap	Table window: Options->Add field...
	ArcCatalog	Properties->Fields...
Apply a legend	ArcMap	Import symbology from layer file
Convert to shapefile...	ArcMap	Context menu: Data-->Export
Create index...	ArcCatalog	Properties-> Fields...
New shapefile...	ArcCatalog	File->New->Shapefile

TABLE 1.6. Changes in common tasks from ArcView v3.x to ArcGIS v8.x.

ArcView v3.x task	ArcGIS application	Menu/button/tool
Promote selected records	ArcMap	Open table, selected
Query builder	ArcMap	Select by attributes
Select by theme	ArcMap	Select by location
Spatial join	ArcMap	Join by location

---

15. These file and path naming conventions also apply when using GRIDs in ArcView v3.x.

Data models and structures

2.1 Representing geographic features

Geographic information systems are concerned with representing geographic features or phenomena: those that occur at or near the Earth's surface. Because we are challenged to deal with the complexity of the world, we have developed ways to simplify it. The key, like all modeling efforts, is to identify the salient characteristics, the essential features—to know what to represent. Then, the task becomes one of how to best represent it. Representing features is necessary, as Lewis Carroll makes obvious:

> *"What a useful thing a pocket-map is!" I remarked. "That's another thing we've learned from your Nation," said Mein Herr, "map-making. But we've carried it much further than you. What do you consider the largest map that would be really useful?" "About six inches to the mile." "Only six inches!" exclaimed Mein Herr. "We very soon got to six yards to the mile. Then we tried a hundred yards to the mile. And then came the grandest idea of all! We actually made a map of the country, on the scale of a mile to the mile!" "Have you used it much?" I enquired. "It has never been spread out, yet," said Mein Herr: "the farmers objected: they said it would cover the whole country, and shut out the sunlight! So we now use the country itself, as its own map, and I assure you it does nearly as well."*
>
> *-- Lewis Carroll -- from Silvio and Bruno Concluded, 1893.*

2.1.1 Where, what, and when

Three aspects are central to understanding the nature of geographic data. Typically, we need to know *where*, or at what place, a geographic phenomena of interest is located. We also need to know specifically *what* we are interested in. There can be many attributes of a place, such as the elevation, the soil type, the amount of annual precipitation, the population density, who owns the land or mineral rights, etc. And although many aspects of a place change very slowly, such as elevation, others change rapidly. So, *when* a particular feature was recorded at a given location, usually specified by date or time, is important as well.

2.1.2 Human cognition of geographic features

Humans commonly view space in two different ways. The first way we view space is as a continuous field of Cartesian coordinates, so that for any given location a value can be described. This view is typically used when thinking about continuous phenomena that vary smoothly over space, such as elevation, temperature, or precipitation. A second view of space is that we typically enumerate various entities or features, such as houses, lakes, roads, or forests. Representing geographic phenomena as entities assumes that they are discrete, clearly bounded objects.

Viewing space as either continuous or discrete is helpful, but to get any practical work done, we need to move beyond simply conceptualizing reality as either entities or fields (see Table 2.1). The next step is to formalize our conceptual model of reality as a *data model*. There are two common data models: *feature* (also called object or entity) and *field*.[1] Feature data models represent geographic features or entities either as points, lines, areas, or networks. Field data models represent geographic phenomenon as a raster or grid of values, typically at equal spaced locations across a surface. Although in the past there was lengthy debate about which approach was better, a more useful perspective is to understand the advantages and disadvantages to both approaches (Table 2.2). More recently, there has been increasing recognition that these conceptualizations are not mutually exclusive, that "at some level... fields and objects can coexist."[2] Object fields have been developed to allow a many-to-many relationship between geographic objects and every location in the field.[3]

---

1. Goodchild, M.F. 1992. Geographical data modeling. *Computers & Geosciences* 18(4): 401-408.
2. Worboys, M.F. 1995. *GIS: a computing perspective.* London: Taylor & Francis.
3. Cova, T.J. and M.F. Goodchild. 2002. Extending geographical representation to include fields of spatial objects. *International Journal of Geographical Information Science* 16(6):509-532.

TABLE 2.1. Space can be conceptualized as either discrete (entities) or continuous (field).

	Entities	**Field**
Reality	Lakes, houses, roads	Watersheds
Data model	Feature (vector)	Field (raster)
Data structure	Coverage, shapefile, geoda-tabase, DLG, etc.	GRID, image, DEM, etc.

TABLE 2.2. Advantages and disadvantages of representing geographic features using features or fields.

Model	Advantages	Disadvantages
Feature	Represent discrete entities (point, line, polygon) Compact data structure Topology easily described Easy coordinate transformation	Complex data structure Overlaying computationally expensive Display time-consuming Spatial modeling difficult
Field	Represent continuous phenomena Simple data structure Simplifies spatial analysis and modeling	Must compromise between resolution and data size Crude raster maps of poor cartographic quality

Finally, there are numerous *data structures* that implement each data model. A data structure is a specific implementation of a data model that specifies the way electronic data is organized or formatted in a computer. Indeed, much of the pioneering efforts in the GIS field were spent working out different ways to implement data models as data structures, and work on these data structures have been hailed as some of the most important contributions to GIScience.[4] This is because the ease or difficulty of different types of display, queries, and spatial analyses hinges on the data structure used to store the geographic features. And, in practice, data are commonly converted from one data model to another to ease modeling or analysis, and from one data structure to another. Typically, data models, data structures, and specific implementations of them (data formats), are discussed separately, but below I discuss them together to highlight the nested or hierarchical relationship. Moreover, a detailed description of common data structures used in ArcGIS (i.e. coverages, shapefiles, geodatabases, GRIDs, and TINs) is provided within the context of data models.

4. Goodchild, M.F. 1992. Geographical Information Science. *International Journal of Geographical Information Systems* 6(1):31-45.

2.2 Feature data structures

Feature data structures represent geographic phenomena as discrete entities. There are a number of fundamental *geographical primitives,* or feature types, in the feature data model: points, lines, areas, networks, and surfaces (some consider volume to be a sixth type). Each of these feature types is represented by different types of data structures: geometric, topologic, network, and surface.

2.2.1 Geometric data structure

Geometric (sometimes called cartographic) data structures represent point, line, and areal features. *Point* features are represented as a single geographic location using *x,y* coordinate pairs. For example, cities are often represented as points, especially in broad-scale, national or regional maps. Imagine that you are on US Interstate 25, driving north from Sante Fe, NM to Denver, CO. Eventually you will likely consider whether you have enough fuel to reach your destination, and in this case, your mental representation of Denver is likely to be as a point.

A *line* feature is recorded as an ordered series of connected line segments, where each line segment has two *x,y* coordinates, or *vertices*. Lines are used to represent features such as rivers, powerlines, and roads, such as I-25 between Santa Fe and Denver.

An *areal* feature, such as a lake, forest, or state is represented as a polygon, an ordered series of a minimum of three connected line segments, but the starting and ending vertices are at the same location. Polygons cannot have self-intersecting boundaries. Even though earlier we considered Denver and Santa Fe to be points, we could also think of them as polygons. For example, as you approach Denver from the south on I-25 (assuming you did have enough fuel), you see the different parts of the city and you may think about how the city has grown and expanded.

Lines and polygons can represent *simple features* or *complex features*. Simple features have one contiguous feature, such as the polygon that represents the State of Colorado. Complex features are often represented by polygons with perforations. For example, if we were interested in the land area of each state, we might want to exclude the Great Salt Lake in Utah, which is a noticeable perforation even from outer space. In this case, Utah would be represented by both an exterior polygon showing the state boundaries, and an interior polygon delimiting the Great Salt Lake.

Complex features also can be comprised of multiple polygons (or lines) that are discontinuous (but usually nearby), which are known as *multi-part* features. For example, while Hawaii is a single state, it is comprised of seven islands (actually there are many additional, smaller islands). Within coverages, these discontinuous, multiple polygon features are known as *regions*. Line features can also be comprised of multiple, discontinuous features. For example, sometimes a stream appears to be discontinuous, being interrupted by geologic strata where the water disappears into the ground, and later resurfaces (e.g., Lost Creek in Colorado).

The geometric data structure is generally considered to be the same as a "*spaghetti*" model or structure.[5] The spaghetti analogy refers to the messy representation of geographic features by a heap of tangled lines that twist, curl, and cross one another — no more structured than a plate of spaghetti. Representing geographic features using a spaghetti data structure poses four distinct problems. First, the lines have little or no relationship to the geographic features they represent. For example, in Figure 2.1 (and Table 2.3), line 1 represents portions of polygons 1 and 2, but there is no direct relationship between the lines and the polygonal features. Another example is that a feature like a lake may be represented by a single line, many lines that run end-to-end, or by a small part of a line (and many lakes may be represented by a single line). Second, the relationships between adjacent features are not explicitly stored, and so advanced analyses are more difficult to conduct. Third, the boundaries of polygons must be represented twice, and so there is data redundancy. Fourth, inconsistencies in the boundaries between adjacent polygons can cause overlaps or gaps.

---

5. Dangermond, J. 1982. A classification of software components commonly used in Geographic Information Systems. *In Proceedings of the US-Australia Workshop on the Design and Implementation of Computer-Based Geographic Information Systems*, Honolulu, HI. Pgs. 70-91.

FIGURE 2.1. An example of geographic features stored in a spaghetti data structure. The entire outside boundary was digitized first (line 1), then the bisecting line (line 2), then the island polygon (line 3) .

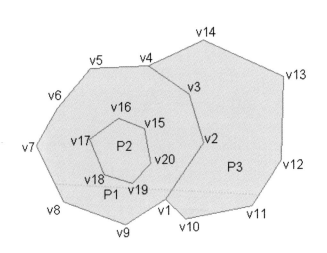

TABLE 2.3. Lines and vertices from Figure 2.1.

Line	Vertices
1	v1, v10, v11, v12, v13, v14, v4, v5, v6, v7, v8, v9, v1
2	v1, v2, v3, v4
3	v15, v20, v19, v18, v17, v16, v15

However, it is important to make a distinction between the spaghetti and geometric data structure. The geometric data structure shares all but the first characteristic with the spaghetti structure. That is, in a geometric data structure there *is* a strong and direct relationship between the feature being represented and the primitive type that represents it, while for the spaghetti data structure this is not necessarily so. For example, a lake (as an areal feature) is represented in a geometric data structure as a polygon, not a tangle of lines. Historically, numerous data structures that were developed for cartography were simply spaghetti data structures, and making a clear distinction between these and ones that represented topological features was important in defining the newly emergent GIS field. However, contemporary claims that non-topologic data structures are not useful in GIS ignores this important distinction, and is central to misunderstanding the difference between non-topological and topological data structures, and especially the utility of shapefiles.[6] As Tor Bernhardsen explains: "...the problems related to spaghetti and topology have changed somewhat during recent years with the advent of new GIS software which treats polygons as independent objects that may overlap and need not fill the plane, and with systems permitting shapes."[7]

2.2.1.1 Shapefiles

A *shapefile* is a geometric data structure that ESRI developed originally for ArcView v1.x (see Figure 2.2 and Table 2.4), but has found much wider application and acceptance and can be used by ArcGIS. In fact, some have recently called shapefiles the *de facto* standard for GIS data.[8] Indeed, because of its simplicity and open structure, many applications, ranging from GIS to global positioning systems (GPS) to desktop publishing, support it.

The shapefile data structure is actually composed of at least three files (*.shp, *.shx, *.dbf). These are *not* stored in a directory format so they *can* be copied around using system-level copy. These files include:

.shp - the shape file, which stores feature geometry (required).

.shx - the shape index, which stores an index to the feature geometry, because each feature may have a different number of coordinates. This means that the *.shp file is a variable-length record. The *.shx file then indexes the *.shp file for faster access.

.dbf - dBASE file that stores the attribute information of features.

.sbn (spatial bin) and *.sbx* (spatial bin index) - store the *spatial index* of the features. When you index on the Shape field, ArcGIS partitions the geographic features in spatial *bins* or rectangular areas. The record number of each feature then is stored into a bin. If you create an index on a theme's Shape field, you will create a spatial index. A spatial index improves performance on identify, all drawing operations, spatial joins, and select by location operations.[9]

.ain and *.aih* - *.ain* stores the attribute index of the active fields in a table or a theme's attribute table. This index improves the speed of joining and linking and simple queries. The *.aih* file is the attribute header file, which contains the name of each field that has been indexed. These files exist only if an index on an attribute field has been created.

The spatial coordinates of shapefiles are stored with *double precision*. That is, the *x* and *y* locations for vertices that represent geometric features are stored using 2 bytes (64 bits). But shapefiles will contain only *single precision* level data (accurate to 1 byte or 32 bits) if the source document was a single-precision coverage (such as a PC ARC/INFO coverage). The spatial

6. Theobald, D.M. 2001. Topology revisited: Representing spatial relations. *International Journal of Geographical Information Science* 15(8): 689-705.
7. Bernhardsen, T. 1999. *Geographic Information Systems: An Introduction.* John Wiley & Sons.
8. Strand, E. 1999. Shapefiles shape GIS data transfer standards. *GeoWorld* (April), pgs 12-13.
9. Ormsby, T. and J. Alvi. 1999. *Extending ArcView GIS.* ESRI Press, Appendix C.

coordinates for a coverage stored in single-precision are stored to seven significant digits, so that a precision of one unit can be maintained for a theme whose extent is 10,000,000 units wide. Coordinates in a double-precision coverage are stored to 15 significant digits. Of course double-precision coverages require additional storage space, but file sizes are generally smaller than twice the size of a single-precision file. Shapefiles also support some extended feature types for *measured* and *3D* shapes. In addition to storing *x,y* coordinates for each vertex in a shapefile, you can store a measure and/or an elevation value at each vertex. This is useful, for example, to store the distances from a starting point along a transect or the elevation of each point.

FIGURE 2.2. An example of geographic features represented in a shapefile data structure showing the polygon feature type. There are 20 vertices (e.g., v1 to v20) and three polygons (e.g., P1, P2, and P3).

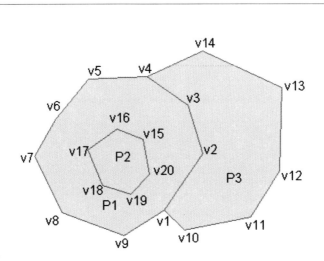

TABLE 2.4. The three features shown in Figure 2.2 are comprised of three polygons, formed by the list of vertices detailed below.

Polygon	Part (ring)	Vertices
P1	1	v1, v9, v8, v7, v6, v4, v3, v2, v1
	2	v15, v16, v17, v18, v19, v20, v15
P2	1	v15, v20, v19, v18, v17, v16, v15
P3	1	v1, v2, v3, v4, v14, v13, v12, v11, v10, v1

There is a lot of confusion regarding topology and shapefiles in the GIS world.[10] To clear up this confusion, it is helpful to know about two aspects of topology: adjacency and planar enforcement. A topological data structure stores topological (adjacency) relationships explicitly in a file, in addition to the geometry (spatial coordinates) and attribute data. In this sense, common GIS data formats such as coverages "have topology," while shapefiles do not. Many people assume that typical GIS analyses, such as adjacency analysis (i.e. find the neighbors adjacent to a particular feature) cannot be accomplished using geometric (non-topological) data structures. And because shapefiles do not store topology, it is assumed, therefore, that these types of analyses cannot be achieved with shapefile data.

This reasoning is incorrect! Topology can be generated *on the fly*, rather than being explicitly stored. For example, two polygons can be determined to be adjacent by finding a common vertex (or vertices).[11] In fact, one has to remember that the topological data files themselves must be created somehow in the first place! Beginning with ArcGIS v8.3, geodatabases employ rules that are applied dynamically, rather than explicitly storing spatial relationships (see section 2.2.5.1). Moreover, computationally efficient overlay selections rely on spatial indexing, not topology.

Although ESRI shapefiles are a non-topological data structure, they are more accurately classified as a geometric, rather than a spaghetti data structure. There is a direct relationship between geographic features and their object, or "shape" representation. Also, complex polygons can be represented because shapefiles store rings (e.g., polygon 1 is represented by two rings in Figure 2.2) with their vertices in clockwise order. This allows shapefiles to know what is "inside" and what is "outside" a polygon.[12] The bottom line is that ArcGIS and shapefiles *do* support most analyses that require adjacency information and with reasonable performance. However, for very large files and certain functions (e.g., dissolving adjacent polygons with similar attribute values), storage of explicit adjacency is necessary.

The second important aspect of topology to consider is whether the spatial data have had planar topology enforced during their creation and subsequent editing. A consequence of planar enforcement is that there is one and only one geographical feature at any x,y location. This means that lines that cross one another cross at a node, and that polygons are space-filling and exhaustive. One important and useful consequence of a planar-enforced theme is that the sum of the area of the individual polygons equals the area of the extent of all polygons (not including the universe polygon). If polygons overlap or if there are gaps between them, summations may be erroneous. A topologically-correct polygon coverage has no overlapping polygons, nor does it have areas surrounded by polygons without a polygon in the middle–

---

10. Theobald, D.M. 2001. Understanding topology and shapefiles. *ArcUser* (Spring): 24-26. www.esri.com/news/arcuser/0401/topo.html.

11. Worboys, M.F. 1995. *GIS: A computing perspective*. Taylor & Francis.

12. ESRI, 1998. *ESRI shapefile technical description*. ArcView White Paper Series.

commonly called a *gap*. Also, maps created from data with slight gaps and overlaps are not pleasing to the eye.

Most shapefiles are topologically correct in this planar graph sense because shapefiles are commonly derived directly from coverages. However, because shapefiles can be edited in ArcView v3.x and ArcGIS, which do not *require* topology to be enforced, you need to be careful when assuming that a shapefile is topologically correct. However, ArcGIS *does* provide powerful editing tools that make it easy to maintain planar topology and update attribute information about the geometry of features (e.g., area/perimeter and length).

Even though the vast majority of geographic data sets are planar enforced, for some situations it can be useful to break the restrictions of planar topology. For example, some geographic features overlap, such as winter range and severe winter range for elk. That is, a single location may be considered to have both winter range and severe winter range. Some geographic features are represented as discontinuous polygons, but are still considered the same feature — think back to the seven islands of Hawaii. Also, a single land ownership parcel is often literally split by a road right-of-way, creating non-contiguous polygons. Whether the two polygons represent a single parcel or two parcels is a very important issue, because development rights are conferred typically on a per-parcel basis.

2.2.2 *Topological data structure*

One of the defining features of GIS is the ability to manipulate topologic data. Generally, topology is defined as the spatial relationships between connecting or adjacent features. A *topological data structure* then *explicitly* stores topological relations in a data file (Figure 2.3 and Table 2.5).

Topological data structures were developed to allow a mathematically robust means of verifying data entry and to increase computational efficiency of complex queries that involved adjacency or containment. A full review of the various data structures that have been developed over the past 30 years is beyond the scope of this book, but a useful comparison of four main topological data structures including POLYVRT, CANSIS, and TIGER is provided in Bonham-Carter's book.[13]

The spatial relations are typically stored as adjacent polygons in a Polygon Topology Table or an Arc Attribute Table, or as connected lines. Also note that the boundaries between polygons are stored only once. In contrast, a *geometric data structure* such as a shapefile simply stores the geometry of features, rather than both the geometry and topology of features. Shapefiles store the common boundaries between adjacent polygons twice.

---

13. Bonham-Carter, G.F. 1996. *Geographic Information Systems for Geoscientists: Modelling with GIS*. Ontario, Canada: Pergamon Press. Also, see Peucker, T.K. and Chrisman, N. 1975. Geographic data structures. *The American Cartographer* 2: 55-69.

The most common implementation of a topological data structure uses some form of *arc-node* topology. The biggest difference between topological and geometric data structures is the extension of the concept of a line to a chain terminated by nodes. The first vertex is called the *start node* (or from node) and the last vertex is called the *end node* (or to node). Chains are linked to other chains through nodes. Because the vertices

of a chain are ordered (which allows the computer to know about the start and end node), the direction of a network can be determined. This allows, for instance, a network of lines representing streams to "flow downhill." For example, chain 1 runs from node N1 to node N2, allowing us to determine that chains 2 and 5 are upstream of chain 1.

Chains are also linked together through nodes in the case of the polygon feature type. Again, because there is a direction to a chain, the left and right adjacent polygons can be determined. For example, in the diagram and table on the following page, you can determine that polygon 1 is adjacent to polygon 2, while polygon 3 is adjacent to only polygon 2.

FIGURE 2.3. An example of geographic features represented in a topological data structure. Nodes are shown with red points.

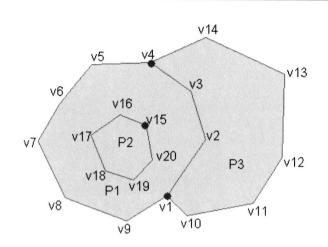

TABLE 2.5. Topology tables for Figure 2.3. The top table below stores the vertices that comprise the individual arcs, and the associated left and right adjacent polygons. The bottom table shows the Polygon Attribute Table.

Arc	Vertices	Left polygon	Right polygon
A1	v15, v16, v17, v18, v19, v20	P1	P2
A2	v4, v5, v6, v7, v8, v9, v1	-	P1
A3	v1, v2, v3, v4	P1	P3
A4	v10, v11, v12, v13, v14, v4	P3	-

Polygon	Adjacent polygon
P1	P2, P3
P2	P1
P3	P2

In addition to explicitly storing adjacent polygons, topological data structures utilize planar graph[14] theory, which requires that polygons are space filling and exhaustive. This means that interior polygons such as P2 in Figure 2.5 are represented as a polygon, not a hole. Also, it means that there are no overlaps among adjacent polygons or gaps between adjacent polygons.

In topological data structures, the geometric feature types (points, lines, areas) are referred to as 0, 1, and 2 cells. The use of the term cells here should not be confused with raster cells, but rather is influenced by mathematical topology that refers to the cellular structure of a map. These cells correspond to their respective dimension — that is, points are considered 0 dimensional, lines are 1 dimensional, and polygons are 2 dimensional objects. Another source of potential confusion is the wide variety of terms often used formally in spatial data standards, and informally by GIS users, such as *chains, arcs,* and *rings.* These terms are described in detail in tables 2.6, 2.7, and 2.8. ArcGIS supports a number of vector data structures, but primarily shapefiles, coverages, and geodatabases.

2.2.2.1 Coverages

A *coverage* is a spatial data structure developed by ESRI for use primarily in ArcInfo. Coverages store geographic data in a topological data structure.[15] A coverage can store multiple feature types (e.g., points, labels, lines, polygons, regions, etc.) simultaneously. The coverage feature types that ArcGIS recognizes are: *points, arcs, labelpoint, polygons, routes, regions,* and *annotation.* Only one feature class at a time can be recognized per layer in ArcMap.

A coverage is actually not a single file, but is a collection of files organized within two directories or folders. The first directory (the "arc" part), named the same as the coverage name, contains files that store the geometry, projection, and log information. A second directory, always named "INFO," holds files for the attribute and topological files (basically all tables) for the coverage, and *all* other coverages at that same level in the directory structure. Because the attribute data for a coverage is stored in a separate directory (the *info* directory), you cannot copy or move these files using system-level copy commands (e.g., **copy <f1> <f2>**). Instead, you need to use the *ArcCatalog* (or copy the entire parent directory, with all the other sibling coverages, of the coverage directory). You can also import ArcInfo export format files (*.e00) using the Import to Coverage utility available through ArcToolbox.[16] However, you cannot export layers to the export (*.e00) format without the ArcInfo version of ArcGIS.

---

14. Corbett, J.P. 1979. *Topological principles in cartography.* Technical Paper 48. US Department of Commerce, Bureau of the Census. Washington, D.C. 50 pgs. In a planar graph, the node and link or chain objects of the graph are represented as though they occur upon a planar surface. Only one node may exist at any given point on the surface, and links or chains intersect only at nodes.

15. Morehouse, S. 1992. The ARC/INFO geographic information system. *Computers & Geosciences* 18: 435-441.

16. GRIDs in *.e00 files can also be imported using this tool.

Also, you can use ArcCatalog (ArcEditor or ArcInfo version) to clean and build a coverage to enforce topology.

TABLE 2.6. Definitions of point vector data structures (sub-classes are distinguished by italics below).

Geometric (G)	Topologic (T)	Shapefile	Coverage
Point - specifies a location through x,y or x,y,z coordinates. There are three types: *Entity point* - identifies the location of point features (or areal features collapsed to a point) *Label point* - used to display map and chart text (e.g., annotation) *Area point* - represents an area, including attribute information	Node - a topological junction of two or more links or chains, or an end point of a link or chain	Point - a single location specified by x,y *PointM* (measured point) - an x,y point that stores a third variable (m), and is used to represent time, distance, or any other measure (such as events). *PointZ* (3D point) - an x,y point that stores a z (elevation) value *Multipoint* - represents a set of points *MultipointM* *MultipointZ*	Points - a single location specified by x,y Labelpoints - a point that identifies a features center for labeling, which are guaranteed to fall within polygons, unlike true centroid. Tics - points that are used to help georeference a coverage Nodes - points where two lines are coincident

TABLE 2.7. Definitions of line vector data structures (sub-classes are distinguished by italics below).

Geometric (G)	Topologic (T)	Shapefile	Coverage
<u>Segment</u> - straight line connecting two points	<u>Link</u> - a topological connection between two nodes	<u>Line</u> - a single geometric line segment defined by two points. Lines may intersect other lines. LineM LineZ	
<u>String</u> - an ordered sequence of connected, non-branching line segments	<u>Chain</u> - a directed, non branching sequence of non-crossing line segments and/or arcs bounded by nodes *Complete chain* - references left and right polygons and start and end nodes *Area chain* - references left and right polygons but not the start and end nodes *Network chain* - references start and end nodes but not left and right polygons	<u>Polyline</u> - a set of one or more parts. Each part contains one or more contiguous lines. Parts are discontinuous. Polylines may intersect other polylines. *PolylineM* (dynamic segmentation) - a measured polyline contains measures used to locate data that describe parts along a route PolylineZ	<u>Arcs</u> - Arcs represent linear features such as streams, streets and contours. Note this term is NOT consistent with SDTS terms. ARC/INFO arcs are similar to chains. <u>Routes</u> - are linear features composed of one or more arcs or parts of an arc.
<u>Arc</u> - a curve defined by mathematical functions		<u>Circle</u> - a geometric circle <u>Oval</u> - a geometric ellipse <u>Rectangle</u> - a geometric rectangle	
<u>G-ring</u> - a sequence of non-intersecting strings and/or arcs, with closure. A ring represents a closed boundary, but not the interior area inside the closed boundary.	<u>GT-ring</u> - a ring created from a sequence of non-intersecting complete or area chains, with closure	<u>Polyline</u> - a polyline where the first and last point are the same	

TABLE 2.8. Definitions of polygon vector data structures (sub-classes are distinguished by italics below).

Geometric (G)	Topologic (T)	Shapefile	Coverage
G-polygon - an area consisting of an interior area, one outer G-ring and zero or more non intersecting, non-nested inner G-rings. No ring, inner or outer, must be co-linear with or intersect any other ring of the same G-polygon	GT-polygon - the boundary of a GT-polygon may be defined by GT-rings created from its bounding chains. A GT-polygon may also be associated with its chains (either the bounding set, or the complete set) by direct reference to these chains. The complete set of chains associated with a GT-polygon may also be found by examining the polygon references on the chains. Universe polygon - the part of the universe that is outside the perimeter of the area covered by other GT-polygons. This polygon completes the adjacency relationships of the perimeter polygons.	Polygon - an area that consists of a set of *directed* rings. Each ring is a set of non-self-intersecting polylines that close back to the first vertex. A polygon can be made up of several disjunct polygons -- similar to a region (e.g., the Hawaiian Islands would be one feature). Because clockwise-ordered rings are used, "inside" and "outside" can be determined (as you walk along the ring the inside is to the right). *PolygonM* *PolygonZ*	Polygon - Polygons represent areas enclosed by specific boundaries, such as countries, states, land parcels and soil types. The boundaries of polygons in a coverage can be displayed irrespective of whether the coverage contains arc features. Region - Regions represent complex areas that overlap, features that are composed of many polygons (disjoint), and multiple classes of features that share common boundaries

2.2.3 Network

Certain applications, such as transportation services, route planning, hydrological analysis, and utility management, require a special type of topologic data structure, called the *network data model*. Networks are built from nodes and lines, or more precisely chains (often called "edges" in graph theory), and explicitly represent how lines intersect one another (Figure 2.4 and Table 2.9). Importantly, networks typically do *not* represent two-dimensional (2D) features. For example, transportation systems, with their interconnected network of interstates, highways, and local roads are represented as a network. Another example of geographic system that is typically represented as a network is a *hydrologic network* that shows the location of streams and rivers, as well as the flow direction. Flow direction is represented using "from-to" topology, so that a stream reach is represented by a single chain (or edge), which is oriented to run upstream (from node being lower than to node), ending at a confluence(s) or at a headwater. Thus, a confluence can be defined as a node where two from nodes and one to node are collocated. Areal features such as lakes and ponds, however, cannot be explicitly represented. Instead, special line segments called *artificial paths* are often used.[17] Note that although the third dimension (elevation) profoundly influences the behavior of hydrologic systems, to date it has not been fully incorporated into spatial network models.

FIGURE 2.4. Example of a network data structure. Nodes are labeled by letters, and edges are labeled by numbers. Note that the table could have a fourth column to represent the weight or cost to traverse each edge and that the arcs are directed upstream.

17. For example, see the USGS National Hydrography Dataset's data model: http://nhd.usgs.gov

TABLE 2.9. The edge table for Figure 2.4.

Edge	From Node	To Node
1	C	B
6	C	A
7	E	C
9	F	E
11	J	F
14	L	K
15	E	D
16	F	G
17	J	H
18	K	J
19	K	I

2.2.3.1 Geometric network

In ArcGIS, the geodatabase model (described on the next page) provides for a special type of geodatabase called a *geometric network*. Networks are represented as one-dimensional non-planar graphs. These data structures are called geometric networks because connectivity is based on geometric coincidence. Networks are composed of *edges* and *junctions* (nodes). A simple edge always has one junction at each end. For example, a stream reach is represented as an edge, ending at a junction (confluence) at each end. A complex edge may have an additional junction feature somewhere between the end junctions. Flow direction along an edge is calculated by distinguishing sources and sinks. Water flows from a source to a sink in a hydrologic network. You can also attribute edges with a weight, which can be used to calculate the cost of traversing a network feature. For example, this can be used to differentiate the lengths of different stream reaches. You can then conduct a number of trace analyses, for example, to find all the upstream features from a particular point on a hydrologic network (Figure 2.5). (Please see the discussion on geodatabases later in this chapter for further description of geometric networks.)

FIGURE 2.5. Example of geometric network analysis using hydrology data. The stream is flowing from top right to bottom left (shown by arrows). Upstream reaches of the dam (red triangle) are selected (cyan) using upstream tracing (left). Downstream reaches selected using downstream tracing (right).

2.2.4 Surface

A *surface data structure* represents a surface as a 2.5D structure, where each location has one and only one z-value (e.g., elevation). This contrasts with a true 3D data structure where each location can have multiple z-values. Probably the most commonly-used data structure for surfaces is the Digital Elevation Model (DEM) data structure which is based on a field-data model (discussed later in this chapter).

2.2.4.1 Triangulated Irregular Network

TINs (Triangulated Irregular Networks) use a feature data model to represent surfaces. TINs represent surfaces using a network of irregularly shaped triangles that are contiguous and non-overlapping (Figure 2.6). TINs are typically based on point-based elevation values. The actual sample points serve as the nodes of the triangles, and planar surfaces fit through the triangle. Because triangles are very fast to draw using computer graphic rendering technology, TINs are used for draping attributes onto surfaces to enable oblique perspectives and "fly-by" animations. You will need to have the 3D Analyst extension to create and analyze these data (though you can view an existing TIN in ArcMap).

FIGURE 2.6. Example of a TIN data structure representing the elevation surface near Yellowstone National. Park, Wyoming.

2.2.5 *Object-oriented data structure*

A relatively recent advance in GIS has been the *object-oriented* data structure. Rather than simplifying complex geographic features as either points, lines, or areas, object-oriented approaches attempt to better represent the complexity of real-world features. In particular, object-oriented techniques allow not only the *state* of a feature (i.e. what it is), but also the *behavior* of a feature (i.e. what it does) to be captured. Similar geographic features are grouped together as a class, and in addition to defining intra-class relationships, inter-class relationships can be defined as well.[18] Imagine that you have a database that contains building objects and parcel objects. It would make little sense for two buildings to overlap or be located within the same parcel, so behavioral rules could prohibit placing buildings so that they overlap. Also, it does not make sense that a building can be located in a street or right-of-way parcel, and so this situation could also be prohibited through establishing a spatial relationship between features.

2.2.5.1 *Geodatabases*

Geographic databases, or *geodatabases*, build on the shapefile and coverage data structures by providing a number of advanced capabilities. Geodatabases store geographic information inside a database management system (DBMS) following the relational data model where an object and its attributes are stored as a row in a table. The power of storing objects in a geodatabase is the ability to represent and emulate real-world features and behavior—to put the behavior in with the data, rather than building behavior in through an application. Referring back to the parcel example, while a polygon shapefile can represent the geometry of a land ownership parcel (and some attributes as well), a geodatabase can also represent

---

18. Zeiler, M. 1999. *Modeling our world: The ESRI guide to geodatabase design.* Redlands, California: ESRI Press.

relationships between parcels and other features so that a parcel cannot overlap with another and only one building can occur in a parcel. Although at first blush geodatabases can appear to be quite complex (and indeed the innards often are), there are three primary advantages to geodatabases.

First, all types of data can be stored together in a geodatabase, including feature, CAD, raster, attributes, addresses, annotation, etc. This makes sharing data straightforward (just one file to locate!), and these data can be managed seamlessly. So, for large data sets, data are no longer needed to be partitioned into map tiles. Also, because these comprehensive datasets are stored and managed within a commercial, off-the-shelf database management system, multiple and iterative editing sessions can be long (up to months!) and different versions can be tracked.

Second, "smart" features, rules, and relationships can be implemented. Vector features can have two (x, y), three (x, y, z), or four dimensions (x, y, z, m); line segments can be represented by true curves (circular, elliptical, Bezier); and networks can be implemented. Rules that define spatial relationships between features can be established, including methods to enforce planar topology, as well as rules to specify relationships between attribute objects.

Third, ArcGIS *data models* that are specific to different industries or applications have been developed (and additional ones can be created). This provides an easy way for industry-wide standards to be incorporated into a framework to capture the behavior of real-world objects.[19] Currently, a number of data models are available, including: forestry, geology, hydrology[20], land use parcels, petroleum, pipelines, etc.

Note that there are two types of geodatabases: *personal* and *multi-user* geodatabases. Personal geodatabases allow many users to read a geodatabase, but only a single editor, and are stored in a Microsoft® Access database. Multi-user geodatabases (which allow versioning) require a database management system, such as Oracle or Informix. At the ArcView level, only simple personal databases (e.g., points, lines, areas) can be edited, and more complex features with topology require an advanced level (ArcEditor or ArcInfo).

Geodatabases are organized as a hierarchical collection of datasets, feature classes, object classes, and relationship classes (Table 2.10). There are three types of datasets: feature, raster, and TIN. A *feature dataset* shares a common coordinate system (also called *XY domain* or spatial extent) and contains feature classes (i.e. point, line, area, network). Although feature classes can exist outside of a feature dataset, using topological constraints between features can be done only within a feature dataset (because they must share the same coordinate system). A *feature class* is a collection of features that share the same type of geometry (roughly

19. For example, the ArcGIS Land Parcel data model, described in ArcNews 24(3): 6-9. http://www.esri.com/news/arcnews/fall02articles/tofc-fall02.html. Also, ESRI's ArcGIS data models provide a number of templates for different industries and applications: http://www.esri.com/software/arcgisdatamodels/index.html.
20. See: Maidment, D. 2002. ArcHydro: GIS for water resources. ESRI Press. Also, see: Maidment, D. and D. Djokic (eds.). 2000. Hydrologic and hydraulic modeling support with Geographic Information Systems. ESRI Press.

comparable to point, polyline, and polygon shapefiles). An *object class* is a table that stores descriptive information about a particular type of feature (e.g., parcels) rather than to an individual instance of a feature (e.g., a particular parcel) as an attribute table does. A *relationship class* stores relationships between features or objects so that dependencies between features and behavior can be modeled.

TABLE 2.10. A comparison of the organizational structure of vector datasets.

	Shapefile	**Coverage**	**Geodatabase**
Collections of datasets	Folder of shapefiles	ArcInfo Workspace	Geodatabase
Datasets	One feature class	Coverage	Collection of classes
Collections of features	Feature class	Feature class	Features of same type
Features	Point, Multipoint Polyline Polygon	Primary: Point or label, arc and node Secondary: polygon, tic, link, section, annotation Compound: region and route	Point, multipoint Polyline Polygon Network Annotation

Feature types in geodatabases implement a full range of geometry types. In addition to point and multi-point features, *network junctions* (where two or more *network edges* meet) are available. Single- and multi-part polylines can be implemented, and in addition to straight-line segments, circular, elliptical, and Bezier curves are available, as well as edges that form a one-dimensional *geometric network*. Polygons are formed from one or more rings. A *ring* is a closed, non-intersecting *path*. A path is a simple, connected series of polylines.

Rather than building topology based on arc-node relationships (as in the coverage model), geodatabases[21] employ spatial relationship and integrity rules established between feature geometry. Specifying topology directly on feature types allows multiple layers (feature classes) to be coincident with one another, a wider-range of spatial relationships to be enforced (Table 2.11), direct control over which layers will have topology or which will not, and increased display and editing performance.[22] Topological relationships can be best considered to be spatial constraints or a set of integrity rules. These rules build on the basic spatial relations between two features: equals (spatially equivalent, where all constituent vertices are the identical), contains (a feature is wholly within another), within (inside, but can touch), crosses (e.g., two lines intersect), overlaps, disjoint (spatially separate), or touches (boundaries

---

21. Actually, topology is fully implemented in ArcGIS v8.3.
22. For a good overview article, see: ArcNews Summer 2002 issue: http://www.esri.com/news/arcnews/summer02articles/arcgis83-brings.html.

intersect). Using these basic relationships, rules can be specified, such as: *polygons must not overlap* or *lines must not have dangles*. Note that instead of the coverage model where geometry is a collection of arcs, nodes, and label points, each feature in a geodatabase is represented by a single shape (or geometry) and can exist on its own. For example, a parcel is represented as a polygon, not as a combination of arcs and nodes. This allows more rapid display, query, and editing of features.

In addition to constraints for features, attribute values can be constrained through *attribute domains* to minimize data-entry errors and to ensure data integrity. A *range domain* can be specified for numeric fields that represent quantitative data, which prescribe the minimum and maximum values.[23] A *coded domain* can be specified for non-numeric fields that represent qualitative data (e.g., nominal classes), which prescribe a set of valid values. For example, a field representing the number of housing units in a county could be constrained using a range domain of 0 to 1,000,000, while a field representing land use types could be constrained using a coded domain of valid classes such as: commercial, residential, agricultural, transportation, forested, mining, etc.

TABLE 2.11. Topology types with geodatabase (supported at v8.3 of ArcGIS).

Type	Description	Graphic
Arc-node	Line features can share end points	
Node	Line features can share end point vertices with point features	
Point event	Point features can share vertices with line features	

---

23. At v8.2, range domains must be validated in a step after data entry.

TABLE 2.11. Topology types with geodatabase (supported at v8.3 of ArcGIS).

Type	Description	Graphic
Polygon	Area features can share boundaries	
Region	Area features can overlap with other area features	
Route	Line features can share segments with other line features	

2.2.6 *Spatial index*

Although *spatial indexing* is not a data structure per se, it is key to providing adequate performance for spatial queries and analysis of data stored in a feature data structure. Spatial indexing increases the speed of graphical display, spatial queries, and analyses. For example, if you have zoomed into a small portion of a map, then ArcGIS uses the spatial index to find the features that fall within that display area *before* they are drawn.

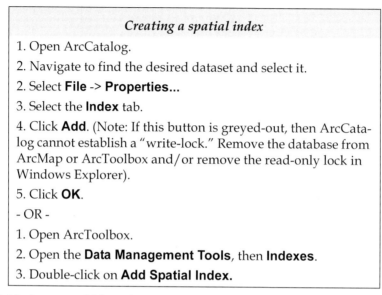

Creating a spatial index

1. Open ArcCatalog.

2. Navigate to find the desired dataset and select it.

2. Select **File** -> **Properties...**

3. Select the **Index** tab.

4. Click **Add**. (Note: If this button is greyed-out, then ArcCatalog cannot establish a "write-lock." Remove the database from ArcMap or ArcToolbox and/or remove the read-only lock in Windows Explorer).

5. Click **OK**.

- OR -

1. Open ArcToolbox.

2. Open the **Data Management Tools**, then **Indexes**.

3. Double-click on **Add Spatial Index**.

How do spatial indexes work? Imagine you just opened a new, 100-piece puzzle and you set out to complete it as fast as possible. What are your strategies? If you are like most puzzlers, then you might use shape (border pieces first) and color and pattern to group (visually or literally) pieces to reduce the number of possible combinations that need to be carefully compared (i.e., picked up and tried with another). As the puzzle comes together, notice that the rate which pieces are added increases dramatically as the number of pieces declines--that is, it is slow going in the beginning punctuated by a flurry of activity at the end. Why is this? With 100 pieces, there are nearly 5,000 possible combinations to compare all pieces. But if the puzzle was separated into even just 4 groups (e.g., the border pieces and the red, black, and white pieces), there would be about 1,200 possible combinations—nearly a five-fold reduction! And if the puzzle could be separated further into 10 groups of 10, there would be only 495 possible combinations—the puzzle would be a piece o' cake at this point.

Although there are a variety of approaches to index space, generally spatial indexing works by reducing the number of possible combinations to compare by separating features into groups, just like a puzzle. Geographic features are grouped or partitioned into spatial *bins* or rectangular areas (also known as grids—not to be confused with GRID, a raster data structure).[24] A list of the geographic features that fall within each bin is then recorded. Often, *minimum bounding rectangles* (MBRs) are used as an approximation of the more detailed

---

24. Rigaux, P., M. Scholl, and A. Voisard. 2002. *Spatial databases with application to GIS*. Morgan Kaufmann Publishers.

geographic features to further reduce the time it takes to find adjacent features. When the features need to be accessed, first the bins that are needed are found, then the features in those bins are accessed.

2.2.7 Supported feature data structures

In addition to shapefiles, coverages, and geodatabases, a number of other spatial data formats are directly supported by ArcGIS. That is, these do not need to be imported or converted somehow to be usable. See Table 2.12 for a summary of supported feature data structures.

TABLE 2.12. Supported feature data formats.

Name	Description
ArcIMS Feature Service, ArcIMS Map Service	ArcIMS Feature Service streams features over the Internet, so a Feature Service layer works the same as any other feature layer.
Coverages	Both Workstation and PC ArcINFO coverages.
DGN	MicroStation design file, supported to v8.
DWG	AutoCAD drawing file. Note that a CAD layer can be georeferenced by using the Transformation tab in the Properties dialog (through v2004).
DXF	CAD interchange files. Note that ASCII, binary, and partial drawing interchange files that comply with DXF are supported.
Geodatabases	Discussed above.
Geography network	Adds data from ESRI's geography network.
OLE DB	Allows access to OLE DB providers.
PMF	ESRI's published map format (*.pmf), which can be created using ArcGIS Publisher extension and read with ArcReader.
SDC	Smart Data Compression dataset is an encrypted and compressed format used by ESRI to provide StreetMap data.
SDE layer	ArcSDE (spatial database engine) layers are treated as geodatabase feature classes and tables. Not available with ArcView functionality.
Shapefiles	Discussed above.
Text files	Tabular data that contain x,y coordinates can be added as a point layer. The table can be in comma-delimited files (*.asc, *.csv, *.txt) or tab-delimited (*.tab).
TIN	Described above.
VPF	The Vector Product Format (VPF) can be read in ArcCatalog. For more information, visit: http://www.nima.mil/vpfproto/

2.3 Field data structures

Continuous geographic phenomena, such as elevation, are usually represented using the *field data model*. These are typically represented using a raster data structure.[25] A raster contains a matrix or mesh of *cells* (or *pixels*) that represent a particular numeric value, such as a brightness value or a land cover type. A GRID is an ESRI-developed implementation of a raster data structure. There are two types of GRIDs: *integer GRIDs* and *real GRIDs*. Integer values can be used to represent nominal, ordinal, and ratio data. Cells that have the same integer values have the same attributes. Integer GRIDs can also be used to represent continuous phenomena. Floating-point values are used to represent truly continuous phenomena, but require much more disk space because they cannot be run-length encoded.[26] In addition to GRID data, images, such as remotely sensed satellite images, scanned aerial photographs, or US Geological Survey's Digital Raster Graphics (scanned, georeferenced images of topographic maps) are common examples of raster data. See Table 2.13 for an overview of supported raster data formats.[27] Chapter 7 provides a detailed discussion of raster datasets and analysis, in particular raster datasets, raster dataset bands, and raster catalogs.

TABLE 2.13. Supported raster data formats.

Name	Description
ArcIMS Image Service	An ArcIMS Image Service delivers snapshots of data over the Internet as an image.
Arc Digitized Raster Graphics (*.img, *.ovr, *.lgg-legend)	Geographically referenced arc-second raster map. Compressed (CADRG).
BMP (*.bmp)	Windows bitmap images: 1, 4, 8, or 24 bits per pixel. Compressed BMP files are not supported.
BIL, BIP, BSQ (*.bil, *.bip, *.bsq; *.hdr-header; *.clr-colormap; *.stx-statistics)	Single and multi-band images: band sequential (multi-band image), band interleaved by line, band interleaved by pixel. Header file describes layout of image data.
Controlled Image Base (*.cib)	US Department of Defense's Controlled Image Base (CIB) are georeferenced, grayscale images similar to digital orthophoto quads.
Compressed ARC Digitized Raster Graphics (CADRG)	CADRG Image Support extension
DTED (Digital Terrain Elevation Data) (*.dt1, etc)	Created by NIMA (National Imagery and Mapping Agency), level 0, 1, and 2

25. For a thorough introduction to raster data structures, see: Holroyd, F. and S.B.M. Bell. 1992. Raster GIS: Models of raster encoding. *Computers & Geosciences* 18(4): 419-426.

26. In contrast to ArcView v3.x, attribute tables can be created for floating-point GRIDs in ArcGIS.

27. Also see ESRI's Extendable Image Formats for ArcView GIS 3.1 and 3.2 White Paper: http://www.esri.com/library/whitepapers/pdfs/eximgav.pdf

TABLE 2.13. Supported raster data formats.

ER Mapper (*.ers)	ER mapper format
ERDAS (GIS file: *.gis; Imagine file: *.img; raw *.raw)	ERDAS Rev 7.3 and 7.4 *.lan and *.gis files
GIF (*.gif)	ArcGIS can create GIF images — high quality, lossless compression.
GRID, SDE raster	ESRI format that supports 32-bit integer and 32-bit floating point raster grids. Without Spatial Analyst extension, a GRID is viewed as a single band image and looks for *.clr color map file.
Hierarchical Data Format (HDF)	National Center for Supercomputing Application's Hierarchical Data Format. There is no direct translator currently, but see: http://hdf.ncsa.uiuc.edu/
IMPELL (*.rlc)	IMPELL Bitmap format which uses run-length compression used for scanned monochrome images
Intergraph raster file	Both .CIT or .COT
JPEG (*.jpg)	Standard compression technique for storing full color and gray scale images. Requires JPEG image extension (comes standard)
MrSid (*.sid)	LizardTech's format -- a multi-resolution wavelet-based image format for high compression and fast access.
NITF	National Image Transfer Format, NITF 2.0 and 2.1.
Portable Network Graphics (*.png)	High-quality, lossless compression of graphics — a replacement for GIF. Supports 64-bit color, indexed-color images up to 256.
Sun (*.rs, *.ras, *.sun)	Sun rasterfiles for monochrome, grayscale, pseudocolor, and true color. Uses either 1, 8, 24, or 32 bits per pixel. These support a byte-level run-encoding scheme.
TIFF (*.tif, *.tff, *.tiff)	Tag Image File Format - supports black and white (1 bit), grayscale (4, 8, 16, 24, or 32 bits), pseudocolor (4, 8, or 16), and true colors in compressed or uncompressed format. Multi-band images with 8 bits per band, unlimited number of bands. Requires TIFF 6.0 Image Support extension. GeoTIFF 1.0 supported if the file is present. Also supports LZW compression.

2.4 Non-spatial (attribute) data

Recall that one of the key features of GIS is the explicit linkage between a geographic feature at a place and its attributes. Attributes are stored in tables, which rely on a relational database structure. Data in a *relational table* are stored as ordered rows or records. Each record has the same number of columns or fields, and there is a record for each geographic feature. Each field represents a single attribute. Returning to the earlier example of a map of aspen patches in Chapter 1, the table for the dataset might have, for each patch, attributes such as ID, name, condition, age class, tree size, acres, and aspect. Tables are stored in a database, such as INFO, dBase, Access, and Oracle.

2.4.1 Data types

It is important to understand the types of attribute data that can be stored, managed, analyzed, and displayed in GIS. Generally, attribute data is either qualitative or quantitative. *Qualitative* information tells you what things exist, while *quantitative* information measures the magnitude of things. There are five data types (one qualitative and four quantitative): nominal, ordinal, interval, ratio, and cyclic. The data types that are used most commonly are nominal and ratio.

2.4.1.1 Nominal

The *nominal* data type is used for qualitative data, and phenomena within a class are assumed to be relatively homogenous. This type is also associated with class or categorical data. In the example of the aspen map (Figure 1.2), name and ID (e.g., "Routt-1") would be considered nominal data types. Land cover and land use data are also typical examples of nominal data. Usually nominal data are stored using a field of type string (e.g., "forest," "wetland," "tundra"). However, nominal data are occasionally stored as integer values (e.g., 1=forest, 2=wetland, 3=tundra). Do not confuse the field data type (string vs. number) with the measurement level (nominal vs. ratio) it represents. Even though nominal data can be (and often are) stored in a numerical field, it is still nominal data. Dividing 3 by 2 (i.e. tundra divided by wetland) when using nominal data is nonsensical. This is sometimes difficult to remember when nominal data are stored in a numerical field, especially when using an integer GRID to represent nominal data.

2.4.1.2 Ordinal

The *ordinal* data type is used to partition features along some continuum. It is also called rank data. The aspen condition field, with classes of poor, good, and excellent is an example of ordinal data. Also, population density classes such as low, medium, and high, and wildfire hazard ratings of low, medium, high, and extreme are other examples of ordinal data. Again, mathematical operations (e.g., low divided by high) and statistical summaries (e.g., the average) on these data make no sense, though the median class (where an equal number of attributes are higher ranked and lower ranked) is a useful surrogate for the central value.

2.4.1.3 Interval

The *interval* data type is also used to organize features along a continuum, and the intervals between groups have meaning—but the numbers do not have an absolute scale. Temperature is a good example of the interval data type. Because the 0 value for temperature is arbitrary, it does not make sense to say that 60°F is twice as hot as 30°F.

2.4.1.4 Ratio

The *ratio* data type is used to organize values along a continuum where the values *do* have an absolute meaning. The number of acres in the aspen patch is a good example of ratio data. Another example is the number of people per county. With ratio data, it does make sense to conduct computations such as county A has 2.7 times the population of county B, and statistical summaries such as the average population by county in the US in 2000 is 87,630.5.

2.4.1.5 Cyclical

The *cyclical* data type is used to characterize directional attributes, such as aspect, degrees on a compass, etc. The reason why this data type is different from ratio is that, although it does make sense to compute and average aspect, you cannot simply average values. For example, although the average of 178° and 182° is 180° (south), the average aspect of 350° and 10° is 180°, but it should be 0° (north). Another example of cyclical data occurs when months in the year are represented as the integers 1 through 12. That is, the colder months (for the northern hemisphere) are typically considered to be 11, 12, 1, and 2 (November through February). These are discontinuous as ratio data, but are actually cyclical where 1 (January) follows 12 (December).

2.4.2 *Relating tables*

Relational tables are useful because they organize attributes in a straightforward way, and data from another table can be related using a relational join. *Joining* and *relating* allow you to associate any two tables to access additional data about geographic features. Typically, tables are joined to display additional data that is not currently in a layer's attribute table. The key to relating tables is that they must have a *common field*. For example, typically, an attribute table contains a unique ID field, such as a name (e.g., Larimer County), but more commonly a number (e.g., a county FIPS code: 8069). If a separate table with additional attribute data (e.g., 2000 Census data) also has the unique ID field, then the two can be related. In ArcGIS, you can either *join* or *relate* two tables. Joining brings the two tables together "virtually," so they appear as one but remain two separate files. The map document saves the virtual join and re-establishes the join when you open it. Relating, however, establishes a linkage between two tables, but they remain separate.[28] There are four types of relates: one-to-one, many-to-one, one-to-many, and many-to-many (Table 2.14). In ArcGIS, the common fields do not need to have the same name, but the two fields do need to be the same *type* (e.g., string or number).[29] You can join numbers to numbers, strings to strings, Boolean to Boolean, and dates to dates. The table name is inserted in front of the field names in the resulting joined table.[30]

---

28. This is like *link* in ArcView v3.x.

29. Previous releases of ArcInfo (commands JOINITEM or RELATE) required common names as well.

30. This is done for clarity in viewing a table, but also to ensure that fields have unique names within a table. In ArcView v3.x, identically named fields can occur and can be a pesty problem.

> ### *Joining and relating tables*
>
> 1. In ArcMap, right-click on the name of the desired layer (in the Table of Contents).
>
> 2. Select **Joins and Relates** -> **Join...** (or Relate...).
>
> 3. Choose the common field in Step 1.
>
> 4. Choose the table to join in Step 2.
>
> 5. Select the common field for the joined table in Step 3.
>
> 4. Click **OK**.

TABLE 2.14. Relate types. Tables can be joined for one-to-one and many-to-one types. Tables can be related for one-to-many and many-to-one types.

Type	Table A	Table B	Result
One-to-one	Value A1	Value B1	Value A1 B1
	1 a	1 A	1 a A
	2 b	2 B	2 b B
	3 c	3 C	3 c C
	4 d	4 D	4 d D
	5 e	5 E	5 e E
Many-to-one	Value A1	Value B1	Value A1 B1
	1 a	1 A	1 a A
	1 b	2 B	1 b A
	2 c	3 C	2 c B
	4 d	4 D	4 d D
	4 e	5 E	4 e D

TABLE 2.14. Relate types. Tables can be joined for one-to-one and many-to-one types. Tables can be related for one-to-many and many-to-one types.

One-to-many	Value A1		Value B1		
	1	a	1	A	
	2	b	1	B	
	3	c	3	C	
	4	d	3	D	
	5	e	3	E	
Many-to-many	Value A1		Value B1		
	1	a	1	A	
	1	b	1	B	
	2	c	1	C	
	3	d	2	D	
	3	e	2	E	

2.4.3 Tables in ArcGIS

In ArcGIS, you can work with tables in both ArcCatalog and ArcMap. ArcCatalog is used primarily to access the properties of fields of attribute tables and to view other existing tables, but tables can also (and only) be created in ArcCatalog. ArcMap is used primarily to work with existing tables, especially to view and edit data (Figure 2.7). Tables that are not associated with a layer are accessed through the Source view of the table of contents (and again, through its context menu).[31]

Opening an attribute table

1. Open ArcMap.
2. Right-click on the name of the layer in the Table of Contents.
3. Select **Open Attribute Table.**

Previewing an attribute table

1. Open ArcCatalog.
2. Navigate to a desired location and select a dataset.
3. Select the **Preview** tab.
4. Select the Table type from the "Preview:" drop-down list.

FIGURE 2.7. Example of a feature attribute table for a shapefile.

FID	Shape*	NAME	STATE_NAME	ST
0	Polygon	Lake of the Woods	Minnesota	27
1	Polygon	Ferry	Washington	53
2	Polygon	Stevens	Washington	53
3	Polygon	Okanogan	Washington	53
4	Polygon	Pend Oreille	Washington	53
5	Polygon	Boundary	Idaho	16
6	Polygon	Lincoln	Montana	30
7	Polygon	Flathead	Montana	30
8	Polygon	Glacier	Montana	30
9	Polygon	Toole	Montana	30
10	Polygon	Liberty	Montana	30
11	Polygon	Hill	Montana	30
12	Polygon	Sheridan	Montana	30
13	Polygon	Divide	North Dakota	38
14	Polygon	Burke	North Dakota	38
15	Polygon	Renville	North Dakota	38
16	Polygon	Bottineau	North Dakota	38
17	Polygon	Rolette	North Dakota	38
18	Polygon	Towner	North Dakota	38
19	Polygon	Cavalier	North Dakota	38
20	Polygon	Pembina	North Dakota	38
21	Polygon	Kittson	Minnesota	27
22	Polygon	Roseau	Minnesota	27
23	Polygon	Blaine	Montana	30

Record: 1   Show: All Selected   Records (0 out of 3140 Selected.)   Options

The number of selected and total records is displayed at the bottom of the table, and you can go directly to a specific record number by entering it. The "All" and "Selected" buttons allow you to display all the records or just the selected records. Also, the context menu is opened by clicking on the "Options" button. Through this menu, the table can be exported and a field can be added[32], among other things. Existing fields cannot be modified, however, so it is best to delete a field, then add a new field to replace it.

Find & Replace...
Select By Attributes...
Select All
Clear Selection
Switch Selection
Add Field...
Related Tables
Create Graph...
Add Table to Layout
Reload Cache
Export...
Appearance...

---

31. If you are having trouble opening a table that has another table related to it, make sure that filenames conform to the file and path naming conventions—only alphanumeric and underscore are allowed (no spaces).

There are seven *field types* to store data on numerical values, text, dates, and BLOBs (binary large ogjects). Numeric field types include: short integer, long integer, float (i.e. short real), and double (i.e. long real). A *short integer* can store whole numbers from -32,768 to 32,768 (it uses 2 bytes or 16 bits). A *long integer* can store numbers ranging from -2,147,483,648 to 2,147,483,648 (using 4 bytes). To store numbers with values to the right of the decimal place (fractions or real numbers), you need to use either float or double field types. A *float* can store a value up to 7 significant digits (using 4 bytes). A double can store a value up to 15 significant digits (using 8 bytes). For integer fields (short and long), specify the *precision*, which is the total number of digits stored in a field. For real numerical fields (float and double), specify both the precision and the *scale*, which is the total number of decimal places stored in a field. Be sure to set the fields large enough to hold the desired values, otherwise numbers may be rounded or converted. Note that ArcGIS will attempt to change the type of field if the precision and/or scale exceeds the limits of a particular numeric type. Text fields store a series of alphanumeric symbols and you can specify the length of the field (up to 255 characters). A *date* field stores dates and times in a particular format, usually: mm/dd/yyyy hh:mm:ss. A *BLOB* (binary large object) can store a variety of items in a Geodatabase as a long sequence of binary numbers, such as images or multimedia.

Deleting an existing field

1. With a table open, right-click on field to delete.
2. Select **Delete Field**.

---

32. A field can also be added using ArcCatalog through the Fields tab of the Properties dialog.

> ### *Adding a field*
> 1. With a table open, click on the **Options** button.
> 2. Select **Add Field...**.

2.4.3.1 *Changing the appearance of a table*

An attribute table has a record for each geographic feature showing its associated attributes. There is a column for each field, and the field name is displayed at the top of the column. If a field is indexed, then the name has an asterisk (*) to the right of it. A column can be widened or narrowed by clicking on the vertical black bar to the right of the column name, then dragging to the desired location. A column can also be moved to a different location as well, by clicking on the name and dragging it to the desired location. To keep a column in view when scrolling across a table, *freeze* the column by right-clicking on the header and select Freeze/Unfreeze Column. Also, you can *sort* (ascending or descending) a column (or multiple columns) through a field's context menu. Through the Fields tab of the Layers Properties dialog, you can set a number of additional properties of fields (Figure 2.8). Aliases can be provided to change the field name to something more meaningful and fields can be completely hidden from view -- but not removed from the dataset -- by setting their visibility off. The *primary display field* can also be set, which is used to organize the results of an Identify query, to label features on a map, and for *map tips*. From the "Options" menu on a table, you can also bring up the Appearance dialog, which allows you to change the font, size, and of the text in a table, the selection color, and the highlighting color.

FIGURE 2.8. Aliases, visibility, and the look of a field can be specified in the Fields tab of the Layer Properties dialog.

Name	Alias	Type	Length	Precision	Scale	Number Format	
☑ FID	FID	Object ID	4	0	0		
☑ Shape		Point					
☑ CAMPSITES_	CAMPSITES_	Double	11	11	0	Numeric	...
☑ CAMPNAME	CAMPNAME	String	30	0	0		
☑ EASTING	EASTING	Double	18	17	5	Numeric	...
☑ NORTHING	NORTHING	Double	18	17	5	Numeric	...
☑ ELEVATION	ELEVATION	Double	11	11	0	Numeric	...
☑ Orientatio	Orientatio	Float	6	5	1		...

Sorting on a field

1. Right-click on a field heading.
2. Select **Sort (Ascending or Descending)**....

> ## *Sorting on multiple fields*
> 1. Arrange columns in left-to-right priority.
> 2. Click on first column.
> 3. Ctrl-click on subsequent columns.
> 4. Right-click on a last field heading.
> 5. Select **Sort (Ascending or Descending)**....

Another useful but under-appreciated feature is the ability to modify the display of numbers in the table. That is, you can change the *number format* to make the display of the number more specific to the values represented in the table. This allows you to represent percentages, add thousand's separators (i.e. commas), change the rounding, specify fractions or angles, etc.

2.4.3.2 Editing a table

In order to edit attribute data, an editing session needs to be started. Edits can then be made directly to a table (click in a table cell and change it to the desired value). To add a record to a table, scroll all the way to the bottom of the table, and then type into the cells in the blank row at the end.

Records can be copied and pasted. To delete a record, select the record (ctrl-click to select multiple records) and then press the Delete key. You can also undo edits during your edit session using Edit->Undo. In order to save edits, the edit session must be closed. Fields cannot be added or deleted during an edit session.

Starting/stopping an edit session

1. Make sure Editor toolbox is opened (if not, select **View -> Toolbars -> Editor**).

2. Select **Editor** (button) **-> Start Editing** (or **Stop Editing**).

2.4.3.3 Importing and exporting

Occasionally you will need to bring tabular data into ArcGIS that is not currently in a database format such as dBASE or INFO. ArcGIS automatically recognizes *.txt, *.csv, and *.asc files as comma delimited, and *.tab files as tab-delimited tables. Note that you cannot edit these text file tables, however. To gain access to these data, simply add the tables to the map document just as you would a coverage or shapefile. Be sure to close the text file (e.g., if you created the file in Microsoft® Excel) before trying to add the data to ArcGIS. Alternatively, you can convert a text file into a dBASE file, and an easy way to convert a spreadsheet is to save it to dBASE IV format. Be sure to double-check your data, however, as some spreadsheet conversion routines (especially MS Excel 97) have some idiosyncrasies.

The first line in the text file must contain the field names for the table, and strings can be either quoted or unquoted. Fields with values containing any non-numeric characters are treated as string fields. Fields with values containing only numbers are treated as numeric fields. (If you want to read numeric values in as strings, enclose the numbers in quotes). Spaces and underscores are the only non-alphanumeric characters that should be used. Although ArcGIS will read *.txt files with field names that contain spaces and are longer than 11 characters, due to dBASE limitations you should keep field names to 10 characters or less and without spaces, brackets, and hyphens. Occasionally you may want to add tabular data that have x,y data, also known as point event data.[33] For example, output files from GPS typically create tabular files with x,y coordinates, such as latitude/longitude, and this provides an easy method to add tabular data as a map layer. Tables can be exported to a variety of data formats, including: text (comma-delimited), dBASE, INFO, geodatabase, and SDE

ArcToolbox

- ArcToolbox
  - 3D Analyst Tools
  - Analysis Tools
  - Cartography Tools
  - Conversion Tools
  - Coverage Tools
  - Data Management Tools
    - Database
    - Domains
    - Feature class
    - Features
    - Fields
    - General
    - Generalization
    - Indexes
    - Joins
    - Layers and Table Views
      - Make Feature Layer
      - Make Query Table
      - Make Raster Catalog Lay
      - Make Raster Layer
      - Make Table View
      - Make XY Event Layer
      - Save To Layer File
      - Select Layer By Attribut
      - Select Layer By Locatioi
    - Projections and Transform;
    - Raster
    - Subtypes
    - Table
    - Workspace
  - Geocoding Tools
  - Geostatistical Analyst Tools

Favorites | Index | Search

---

33. In ArcView v3.x, this was called an event theme.

.

Adding x,y data from a table

1. In ArcMap, select **Tools -> Add XY Data...**.
2. Browse to find desired file.
3. Specify the fields that contain the x and y data.
4. Click **OK**.

Exporting a table

1. In ArcMap, open the table (right-click, **Open Attribute Table...**).
2. Click on **Options** button.
3. Select **Export...**.
4. Click on the Browse button and specify the table type and name.
5. Click **Save**.

2.4.3.4 Attribute domains

The attribute tables associated with geodatabases offer the ability to apply *attribute domains*, which can be used to constrain the allowable values for a field. There are two types of domains: range and coded. *Range domains* can be applied to quantitative data to specify a minimum and maximum value. *Coded domains* can be applied to any type of data, though they most commonly are applied to nominal data types where there are a limited number possible values. The type of domain is specified in ArcCatalog during the creation of the geodatabase.

2.4.4 GRID attribute table

A GRID attribute table (a.k.a. the Value Attribute Table) contains, at a minimum, two fields: *value* and *count*.[34] The value field contains the values of a GRID, and the count field stores the number of cells in a GRID that have that value. A GRID will not have an attribute table if the GRID is a floating-point type or if the GRID was created from a 1-bit image theme.

---

34. In ArcGIS v8.2, fields cannot be added to an attribute table for a raster dataset. Instead, you can join a table to gain additional fields.

2.5 Importing spatial data

In the past, the majority of time "doing GIS" was consumed by simply developing the datasets. Recently there has been an explosion of free (or inexpensive) GIS datasets. These often are in standard formats that ArcGIS can read in directly, but occasionally they need to be imported or converted into a standard ArcGIS format. In addition to the useful and comprehensive data provided in ESRI's Data and Maps CDs, there are many, many sites on the Internet that provide free or low-cost GIS data.[35]

---

35. For example, the US Geological Survey's GISDATA Web mapping portal: http://gisdata.usgs.net/ and the GIS Data Depot: http://www.gisdatadepot.com/

2.5.1 Importing feature data

ArcGIS recognizes a variety of spatial data formats and that can be brought directly into ArcMap or ArcCatalog, but some formats need to be imported into ArcGIS. An ArcINFO license is required to import most formats, and the tools are provided in ArcToolbox to convert these formats to coverages (which can then be later converted to shapefiles or geodatabases).[36] A complete list of supported formats is provided in Table 2.15.

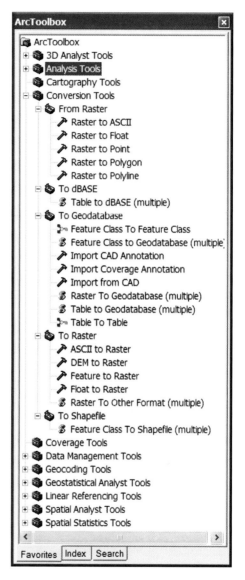

36. ArcINFO export interchange (*.e00) files are no longer supported in ArcView version of v9, you must have an ArcINFO license.

TABLE 2.15. Feature data formats that can be imported into ArcGIS (with ArcINFO license).

Name	Description
AGF	Atlas Geo Files. Import AGF files in ArcToolbox, Conversion Tools, Import to Shapefile.
DFAD	National Imagery and Mapping Agency's format, and Digital Feature Analysis Data (DFAD) levels 1, 2, 1-c, and 3-c are supported. VPF has replaced DFAD.
DIME	US Census Bureau's Dual Independent Map Encoding (DIME) files, created for the 1980 census, and replaced in 1990 with TIGER/Line files.
DLG	US Geological Survey's Digital Line Graph (DLG), providing data on transportation, hydrography, contours, and public land boundaries. See: http://mapping.usgs.gov/standards/
E00	ESRI's ArcINFO export interchange file (*.e00). Available in ArcToolbox. Only coverages and GRIDs can be imported and exported to an e00 file.
ETAK	Etak, Inc.'s format ETAK stores street networks.
GIRAS	The US Geological Survey's Geographic Information Retrieval Analysis System (GIRAS) provides land use and land cover data. See: http://edc.usgs.gov/glis/hyper/guide/1_250_lulc
IGDS	MicroStation's Interactive Graphic Design Software (IGDS) is a CAD export format.
IGES	Initial Graphics Exchange Standard (IGES) is a neutral format for CAD/CAM data (*.iges, *.igs).
MIF	MapInfo's Map Interchange File (MIF) stores graphic data in (*.mif) and tabular data in (*.mid) files. Import MIFs in ArcToolbox, Conversion Tools, Import to Shapefile. For more information on the MIF format, see: http://www.mapinfo.com/community/free/library/interchange_file.pdf
MOSS	US Department of Interior's Mapping Overlay Statistical System (MOSS), implemented by the BLM in 1977. The exchange files. mif, dpf, dpw
S-57	International Maritime Organisation format, defined by the International Hydrographic Organisation Special Publication 57 (hence the name). A hierarchical collection of oceanographic features.
SDTS	US Geological Survey's Spatial Data Transfer Standard (STDS). Note that only point type data can be imported with an ArcView license. Import STDS using ArcToolbox, Conversion Tools, Import to Coverage, SDTS.Point to Coverage.
SLF	USF National Mapping and Imagery Agency's Standard Linear Format (SLF).
TIGER	US Bureau of Census's Topologically Integrated Geographic Encoding and Referencing system (TIGER/Line). See: http://www.census.gov/geo/www/tiger/index.html

Data models and structures

CHAPTER 3

Coordinate systems, projections, and GPS

3.1 Location, location, location...

Location is *the* essential feature of maps in general, and geographic information systems in particular. Humans have mapped geographic phenomena for tens of thousands of years, and numerous ways to locate geographic features have been developed. One of these is to simply name a place. *Place names* are commonly used to reference locations, such as Timbuktu, San Francisco, and Meade's Ranch. But place names do not always remain constant through time, so trying to locate Constantinople on a World Atlas now would likely produce much frustration, unless you knew its more current name of Istanbul. (Why the name change? "...that's nobody's business but the Turks!") Moreover, the spatial resolution of places names varies greatly — picture the area covered by the following place names: Asia, Nepal, Mt. Everest, and the summit of Mt. Everest. Another method to locate places are postal addresses, which are used across the globe to locate residences and businesses. They, of course, work remarkably well for the delivery of mail, but they are problematic for other uses, such as identifying the response location during an emergency call (i.e. 9-1-1). Also, natural features such as mountains, rivers, and prairies cannot be addressed well. (We will return to postal addressing and geocoding later in this chapter.)

As a result, we have devised ways to more systematically locate geographic features to reference any location on the globe with fine detail. The globe has been a particularly useful construct because mapping on them entails minimal distortion. Distance, direction, shape, area, and proximity can be measured accurately. Locations on a globe are defined by a *geographical coordinate system*, namely latitude and longitude. Latitude and longitude are actually angular measurements using spherical polar coordinates. But globes are bulky and are not very functional for mapping detailed features, and distance and area computations on a globe are more complex because they require spherical geometry. Because of these impracticalities, projections were developed to transform spherical coordinates to planar (Cartesian) coordinates, to create what is called a *projected coordinate system*.

3.2 Scale

Geographic features are typically reduced in size to enable them to be represented and displayed on a globe or map. The amount of reduction is called the map scale. There are four common ways of expressing map scale, which are described in detail below. But it is important to understand that discussing scale in this way is very much an artifact of historical and current reliance on paper maps and the inherent limitations of them. Because much digital data are still derived from paper maps, the concepts of scale, resolution, and detection remain important for digital GIS, however.

The *scale* of a map is the ratio of a distance on a map to a distance on the earth. Globes are scale models of the earth. A baseball-sized (3.5") globe would be at a scale of 1:125,000,000, while a 24" globe would be at 1:20,000,000 scale. To draw a typical US highway map (1:1,000,000) would require a 41' diameter globe, while a 1,750' diameter globe would be required to map at a scale of 1:24,000 (USGS 7.5' Topographic map). On a paper map, if the length of a city block is 1 cm and on the ground it is 1 km (100,000 cm), then the map scale is 1:100,000. Notice that map scale is unitless.

Geographers (and occasionally others) are trained to refer to maps as "large" or "small" scale maps. So-called large-scale maps have relatively large ratios, such as 1:50,000, whereas small-scale maps have relatively smaller ratios, such as 1:1,000,000. Unfortunately—at least for the geographers—other disciplines and the general public tend to refer to the scale of maps in the opposite way. That is, to the broader public, large-scale maps depict broad spatial extents (e.g., 1:1,000,000, while small-scale maps show smaller extents (e.g., 1:50,000). To reduce potential confusion when discussing map scale, the terms *fine-scale* (i.e. 1:50,000) and *broad-scale* (1:1,000,000) are preferred.

A second way to describe scale is simply to use words, such as "1 inch equals 1 mile" (which corresponds to 1:63,360). A third and more common way to describe scale is to use a representative fraction, such as 1:24,000. This is expressed as a true ratio and defines scale precisely. A final method to describe scale is to use a graphic scale. A conventional way to show a graphic scale is in the form of a line drawn on a map that contains subdivisions of units appropriate to the scale of the map. Although this method is not as mathematically precise, it has the advantage that the scale changes size in proportion to changes in map size. That is, if you make a reduced (or enlarged) photocopy of a map, the graphic scale also is reduced and thus is still accurate, whereas the representative fraction scale (based on the original map) for the photocopied map is incorrect.

The ability to resolve features on a map depends largely on the scale of the map. Because the finest mark on a paper that can be readily reproduced is typically 0.5 mm, then the *resolution*, or ability to distinguish individual parts of a geographic object, is equal to the map scale times 0.5 mm.[1] For example, if you had a 1:24,000 scale map, the smallest feature you can represent on it is 12 meters (see Table 3.1). And to *detect* a feature requires twice the resolution, so the smallest object that can be detected on a 1:24,000 scale map is 24 m wide. It is important to know the scale of the map you are working with and to understand the associated resolution and detection levels. For one thing, determining polygons that have areas smaller than the area of the smallest detectable size feature will help you understand what features can be represented (and to set a benchmark limit to define spurious polygons).

TABLE 3.1. Sample resolution, detection, and area amounts assuming the minimum line on a map is 0.5 mm.

Scale	Resolution	Detection	Area
1:10,000	5 m	10 m	100 m^2
1:24,000	12 m	24 m	576 m^2
1:50,000	25 m	50 m	2,500 m^2
1:100,000	50 m	100 m	10,000 m^2
1:250,000	125 m	250 m	62,500 m^2
1:1,000,000	500 m	1,000 m	1,000,000 m^2

Another important concept for computer-based mapping is the precision with which spatial coordinates are stored. For example, if someone provides you with latitude and longitude coordinates that are specified to the nearest second, then what is the precision of the location

---

1.   Tobler, W. 1988. Resolution, resampling, and all that. In: *Building databases for Global Science*, Mounsey, H. (ed.) Taylor and Francis. Pgs 129-137.

that was specified? Assuming 111,195 m per degree of latitude (at the equator), then specifying location to the nearest second is precise to within ± 30.8 m (Table 3.2).

TABLE 3.2. Precision of latitude and longitude measurements.

Precision	Distance (m)
Degree	111,195
Minute	1,853
Second	30.8
Decimal degree (d.d)	11,119.5
Decimal degree (d.dd)	1,111.9
Decimal degree (d.ddd)	111.1
Decimal degree (d.dddd)	11.1
Decimal degree (d.ddddd)	1.1

Another related concept is the idea of the *minimum mapping unit* (MMU). The MMU is a measure of the detail (resolution) of which discrete features are represented—features on a map must be at least as large as the MMU. For example, the standard MMU for mapping land cover polygons for the USGS National Gap Program is 100 ha—smaller patches of land cover are not typically mapped. The MMU concept, however, needs to also include the shape of features in addition to area. Linear-shaped patches such as riparian areas alongside a stream are often quite large in area (and greater than the MMU), but are often not mapped because they are long and thin.[2]

3.2.1 Scale in a digital world

As was discussed earlier, traditional concepts about scale are rooted in the paper map (or analog representation), which imposes some limitations when using GIS because geographic features can now be represented and analyzed digitally. Scale in a digital world has some important differences.[3] First, with digital data, the idea of a representative fraction is no longer a definitive characteristic. That is, there is no longer a requirement for the trade-off between geographic coverage (a.k.a. spatial extent) and the resolution (or grain) of a map. Instead, it is theoretically possible to create an electronic dataset that has all 1:24,000 quads for the US (all 53,911 of them) tiled together into a single, seamless (and very large) dataset that would cover roughly four international-size soccer fields. In this case, the resolution or grain of the data would be based on 1:24,000 scale, but the coverage would be for the whole US. So, describing this map as a national-scale map would belie the detail of features. Second, it is

2. Theobald, D.M. 2000. Correcting linear and perimeter measurement errors in raster-based data. *Cartography and Geographic Information Science* 27(2): 111-116.
3. Quattrochi, D.A. and M.F. Goodchild (eds.). 1996. *Scale in Remote Sensing and GIS*. Boca Raton, Florida: Lewis Publishers.

possible for geographic features to be represented in a way (e.g., through object-oriented data structures like the geodatabase) so that the feature changes depending on the context of the display or analysis. For example, it would be best to use point features to represent cities if you are computing a city-to-city mileage table for a gazetteer (e.g., to determine the number of miles from Santa Fe to Denver). However, it would be best to represent cities as areal features if you wanted to estimate the amount of urban land cover, and perhaps how that has changed (i.e. the city that has sprawled most: Atlanta? Los Angeles?) in the past decade. In these examples the domain of the question (the whole US) has not changed, but the feature abstraction (point vs. area) has changed. Representing geographic features as objects offers the ability to address this complexity during display as well as analysis. Third, the detail with which features can be represented on paper maps is constant throughout the map. However, often the sampling resolution of collection varies from location to location, and digital maps can fully represent this variability. For example, census blocks (a subdivision of the more familiar census tract) are the fundamental unit for counting population in the US and for possible rearrangement of political districts. Blocks vary widely in size depending mostly on housing density — they can be as small as a city block in an urban area, as large as a whole neighborhood in a suburban areas, or encompass tens of thousands of acres in rural areas. The sampling intensity varies tremendously, but this is not typically taken into account during analysis. As more and more datasets are created digitally and rely less and less on paper maps, the differences between digital and paper scale will become paramount. An important "take home" message of this discussion is that because extent and grain are independent properties of a digital map, one needs to specify both the spatial extent (broad or local) and grain (coarse or fine) when describing a map.

3.3 Geographic coordinate systems

Thinking of the Earth as a sphere is convenient, and provides the basis for the idea of a globe. On a sphere, geographical coordinates are typically portrayed by drawing a systematic grid of latitude and longitudinal lines, called a *graticule*. A graticule is a set of meridians and parallels that represent the locations of latitude and longitude. Because the Earth rotates, the rotational axis forms a useful reference point. A *parallel* is a line on the Earth's surface formed by the intersection of a plane that is normal (perpendicular) to the rotational axis, or a line drawn through both poles. The *equator* is a parallel that intersects the center of the sphere, and so is found at 0° latitude. Parallels are identified by their latitude. A *meridian* is a line on the Earth formed

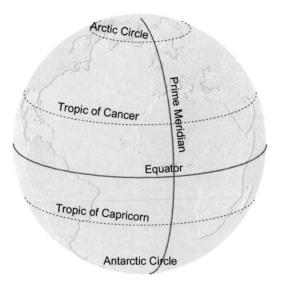

by the intersection of a plane passing through both poles. Meridians and parallels intersect at right angles on a globe. Because there is no natural reference point for meridians, the starting point for longitude, or *prime meridian* (0° longitude), has been arbitrarily defined to pass through the Royal Observatory in Greenwich, England.[4] As a result, the eastern hemisphere runs from east of this line through the International Date Line at 180°, while the western hemisphere lies to the west of the prime meridian. Geographic locations are then described in terms of degrees, minutes (there are 60 minutes in a degree), and seconds (there are 60 seconds in a minute) away from the prime meridian (east or west longitude) and from the equator (north or south latitude). To more easily represent geographic coordinates in a computer, degrees, minutes, and seconds are converted to decimal degrees, with the western hemisphere in negative longitude and the southern hemisphere in negative latitude. Typically meridian and parallel lines are drawn at 30° to form a graticule for world projections, but can be smaller for maps that cover a smaller area (finer-scale maps).

---

4. Why in Greenwich, England? Actually, numerous countries developed maps with their own prime meridians: France on Paris, US on Washington, D.C., and Brazil on Rio de Janeiro. In 1884, delegates from 25 nations convened in Washington at the International Meridian Conference, where it was decided that the world standard was to be in England, largely because England was the world naval power at this time.

3.3.1 Spheroids and datums

Well, the idea that the Earth is a perfect sphere is nice and makes the mathematics easier, but it turns out (pun intended) that the Earth's shape is not a perfect sphere. Rather, it bulges slightly at the equator due to the force of rotation, which is called an oblate spheroid. Ellipsoids are used to represent the oblate spheroid, with the amount of flattening defined as the reduction of the minor axis relative to the major axis. Also, there are some other irregularities in the shape due to the geological composition of the Earth's surface that are important for projections when high precision is required. So, cartographers and surveyors have developed a number of *spheroids* to more accurately approximate the true shape of the Earth. Different spheriods have been developed to fit a particular region of the Earth.

Spheroids are used to parameterize a coordinate system called a *datum* – a set of control points. A datum defines the position of a spheriod (usually) in relation to the center of the Earth and establishes a reference frame for measuring locations on the surface. Different representations of the spheroid result in different datums such as NAD27 (North American Datum 1927), NAD83 (North American Datum 1983), and WGS84 (World Geodetic System of 1984). The NAD27 uses the Clarke1866 spheroid, and the origin of the datum is a location called Meades Ranch, Kansas. Since 1927, a number of technologies have enabled more accurate measurements, so the NAD83 was created. It uses the GRS1980 spheroid, and its origin is the Earth's center of mass. The corrections to NAD27 caused shifts in North America as much as 500 feet. Because the GRS1980 spheroid is very similar to the WGS1984 spheroid, NAD1983 data are compatible with GPS data that are collected using the WGS1984 datum. Currently, the HARN (High Accuracy Reference Network) effort is re-adjusting the NAD1983 datum to a yet higher level of accuracy. There are also *vertical datums*, such as the North American Vertical Datum of 1988 (NAVD88).

TABLE 3.3. Common datums used in North America.

Datum	Description
North American Datum 1927 (NAD1927)	NAD1927 used the Clarke 1866 spheroid and yielded adjusted lat/longs for roughly 26,000 survey stations
North American Datum 1983 (NAD1983)	NAD1983 used the GRS80 ellipsoid (which is Earth-centered) and yielded adjusted lat/longs for roughly 250,000 survey stations
World Geodetic System of 1984 (WGS84)	Developed by the US Department of Defense, it has been updated by satellite measurements and uses the WGS84 ellipsoid.

3.3.1.1 Geographic transformations

When you are projecting data into a coordinate system based on a different spheroid, you will also have to specify the *geographic transformation* to convert between datums. For example, if you are converting between NAD27 and NAD83 datums, then typically you will use the NADCON conversion method that is based on the National Geodetic Survey's CONUS grid that specifies the transformations for the contiguous 48 states and results in sub-meter accuracy.

3.4 The Global Positioning System (GPS)

The *Global Positioning System* (GPS) is a satellite-based system that provides locational information anytime, anywhere (or roughly so). The GPS was developed by the US Department of Defense for military and civilian use. GPS works basically by having a number of satellites each broadcasting its status and location on a precise schedule. A GPS receiver picks up a signal, and determines the range (or distance) by computing the time delay between the scheduled and the actual arrival of signals. Signals from multiple satellites are required to fix a location on the surface of the earth. Prior to May 2000, the accuracy of GPS was degraded by "selective availability" scrambling.

There are three components to the system: the satellite constellation, the ground control network, and user equipment. The *satellite constellation* is based on a constellation of NAVSTAR satellites placed into orbit about 26,600 km from the center of the Earth (see right, source US Dept. of Defense). The first GPS satellite was launched in 1978 and the full constellation of 24 active satellites (plus spares) was acheived in 1994. The satellites are scheduled so that at least 4 are "visible" anytime, anywhere, but most locations are likely to have 6 to 8 satellites available. There are 6 orbit planes with a 55° inclination, each containing 4 to 5 satellites. Each satellite makes roughly two revolutions per day (one-half of a sidereal day or 11 hours 58 minutes).

The *control network* maintains the system through five monitoring stations and a master control station at Schriever Air Force Base near Colorado Springs, Colorado. These stations correct orbit and clock errors.

The *user component* consists of individuals with one or more GPS receivers. A receiver collects measurements simultaneously from at least four satellites to solve for three dimensions of position (latitude, longitude, and altitude), measured in WGS84 datum.[5]

---

5. Obtaining precise altitude estimates is problemmatic though, because of real-world distortions in the shape of the Earth -- see: Fraczek, W. 2003. Mean seal level, GPS, and the Geoid. ArcUser (July-September).

One of the main determinants of the precision of measurement is the satellite geometry, or the arrangement of satellites that are used to fix a location. The higher they are in the sky, the lower the precision, so satellites lower in the sky provide a better measurement (but their signals are more likely to be disrupted!). This makes using a GPS problemmatic in landscapes with canyons and thick forests (e.g., Figure 3.1).

FIGURE 3.1. Hmmm, does this thing work? Waiting for a fourth satellite in a rainforest in Nicaragua.

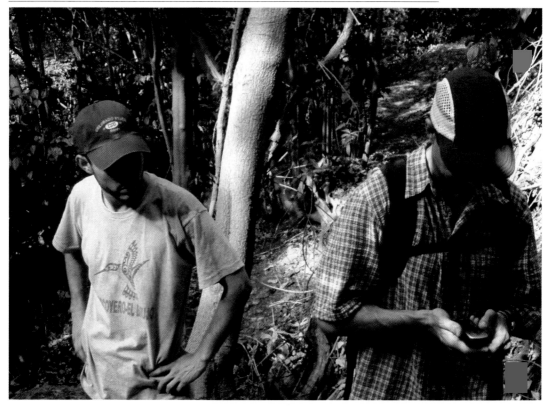

The most common measurement of precision is called *Positional Dilution of Precision* (PDOP). The higher the PDOP, the poorer the measurement. Generally, a PDOP value from 1-3 is considered very good, 4-5 good, 6 fair, >6 poor. Typical accuracies are between 10 to 30 meters.

Three techniques are commonly used to improve the accuracy of GPS measurements. A simple method involves collecting many position fixes (for 10-30 minutes) while remaining at the same location and then the fixes are averaged to attain a location. A second method is to use *differential correction* that employs two receivers -- one receiver is established as a base station with a precise known location. The differences between the field-roving unit and the base station (see Figure 3.2) can be computed and used to correct the field-roving positions, providing sub-meter to centimeter (survey-grade) accuracy. Post-processing of GPS positions can also be done (but is of limited usefulness when precise navigation in the field is required).[6] A third method is to conduct real-time differential correction using the Wide Area Augmentation System (WAAS). WAAS is based on a network of ground reference stations that compute a differential correction, which is then transmitted to a geo-stationary satellite. The correction signal is then broadcast back to the surface of the Earth, where WAAS-enabled GPS devices can correct signals in real-time. This results in errors that are less than 7 meters 95% of the time.

FIGURE 3.2. Setting up a base-station for differential correction west of Fort Collins, Colorado.

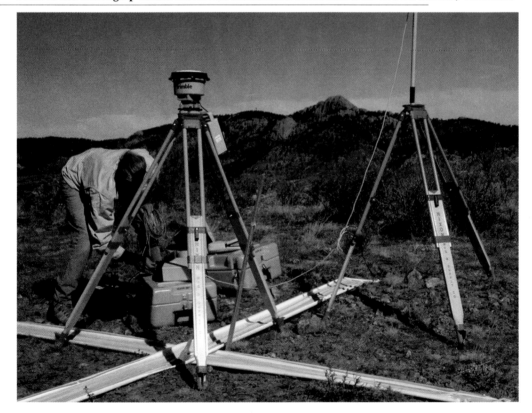

---

6. Post-processing correction files can be obtained online from: www.ngs.noaa.gov/OPUS

3.5 Projected coordinate systems

Projections are a systematic rendering of geographic coordinates, and allow a sphere to be transformed to a planar surface with Cartesian coordinates. One important reason to project geographic coordinates is that degrees of latitude and longitude do not have a standard length -- that is distance and area on the surface of the Earth decline systematically as you move towards the poles away from the equator. As a result, distances (if they involve any east-west orientation) and area are systematically biased. The greater the range of latitude values, and the further the latitudes are away from the equator, the more distortion is involved[7] (Table 3.4).

TABLE 3.4. Change in east-west distance as a function of latitude.

Latitude(+/-)	Proportion	Distance (km) of 1° of longitude
0°	1.000	111.32
10°	0.985	109.63
20°	0.940	104.61
30°	0.866	96.41
40°	0.766	85.28
50°	0.643	71.56
60°	0.500	55.66
70°	0.342	38.07
80°	0.174	19.33

3.5.1 Properties and characteristics

All projections have distortions in distance, direction, shape, area, or proximity. Most projections are the result of some useful compromise in one or more of these properties. *Conformality* means "correct form or shape." Conformal projections show the shapes of small features correctly (large features may have some distortion). The latitude-longitude graticule intersects at right angles in conformal projections.

Equal-area projections have the property that a unit area is equivalent in any location. So, a coin placed on one part of a map covers exactly the same area as any other part of the map. Scale changes that occur in one direction must be offset by changes in the opposite direction, and so this compensation causes some distortion, such as compaction or elongation of features. Lines

---

7. These are rough approximations, more detailed estimates depend on the spheroid assumed.

of latitude and longitude do not intersect at right angles. A map cannot be simultaneously conformal and equal area.

Equi-distant projections have the property that distance from one point to others, but not all points to all other points, can be measured accurately. The most common equi-distant projection is the azimuthal equidistant projection.

Equi-azimuthal projections preserve angles (or direction), where the azimuth is defined by the angle formed at the starting point of a straight line in relation to a meridian.

All projections have discontinuities, where the globe needs to be "torn" along an edge. Most commonly for world projections this is done at the poles and at 180° longitude.

3.5.2 Projection types

A useful way to categorize map projections and to understand their patterns of distortion is to understand projection surfaces and projection light sources.

3.5.2.1 Geometric

There are three geometric projection surfaces: the plane, cylinder, and cone (Figure 3.3). Typical planar projections work by simply laying a plane on top of the globe, touching at only one point. Conceptually, cylindrical projections work by wrapping a piece of paper around the globe, then unrolling it to make a map. Conical projections work by making a "hat" (cone) and placing it on the globe. The cylinder and cone then can be "developed" or unrolled to make a planar surface. Notice that both the cone and cylinder touch (or are tangent to) the globe along a line, rather than just at a single point.

FIGURE 3.3. Different geometric projections: planar (polar orthographic — top left); conical (Albers equal area — top right); and cylindrical (Mercator — bottom).

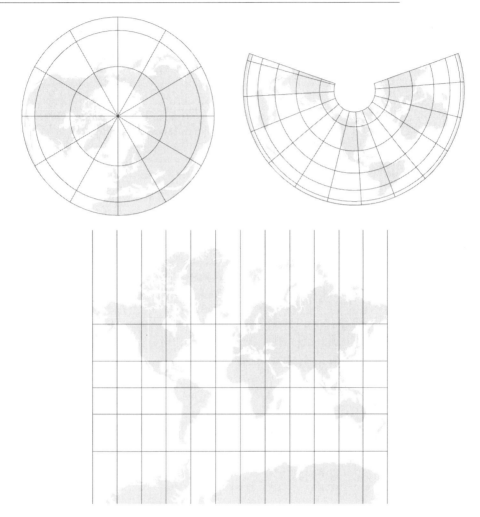

Projection characteristics can be classified by the *light source location*. Again, there are three: gnomonic, stereographic, and orthographic. A *gnomonic* light source is located at the center of the globe. This means that any *great circle* – the shortest distance between two points on a globe – is a straight line on a gnomonic projection.

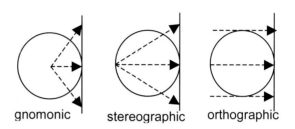

gnomonic   stereographic   orthographic

Gnomonic projections are typically used for aviation. The light source for *stereographic* projections is located at the antipode (the point exactly opposite the point of tangency of the projection surface). This light source typically creates conformal projections. The light source for *orthographic* projections is at infinity. True direction can be measured with orthographic projections.

There are three orientations of projection surfaces: normal (or regular), transverse, or oblique. The *normal* orientation for planar projections is at the pole, for cylindrical projections it is tangent along the equator, and for conical projections it is tangent along a parallel (line of latitude) with its apex over a pole. The *transverse* orientation occurs when tangency is changed by 90 degrees, so that a plane is tangent at the equator, a cylinder is tangent along a meridian (line of longitude), and the apex of a cone is above the equator. *Oblique* orientations lie in other locations besides the normal or transverse orientations.

Projection surfaces can be *tangent,* so their surfaces touche the globe at a point or along a line, or *secant,* when the surface intersects and passes through the globe. The secant case of projections is frequently used to minimize overall distortion when displaying continental-scale data. For example, the Albers Equal-Area projection is commonly used when displaying data for the coterminous United States. The secant case of this projection uses two standard parallels, typically at 29°30' and 45°30' latitude. In this projection, features that are between the standard parallels are reduced slightly, while above and below the standard parallels features are enlarged slightly. Distortion is minimal for features right at the standard parallels, while distortion is greatest at 37° and below 29°30' and above 45°30'. However, distortion is minimized for all features in the US compared to if a single standard parallel were used (tangent case).

3.5.2.2 Mathematical
Projections can also be defined by some mathematical formula. For instance, the Mercator projection (which is based on a normal, cylindrical geometric surface) is defined as:

$$x = R(\lambda \angle \lambda_o)$$

$$y = R(\ln(\tan((\pi/4) + (\phi/2))))$$

where R is defined as the radius of the sphere at the scale of the map, λ is longitude east of Greenwich, λ_0 is longitude east of Greenwich of the central meridian or of the origin of the rectangular coordinates, and ϕ is north latitude. There are many other mathematically based projections.[8]

3.5.3 Distortion patterns

Because all projections have distortion, it is important to understand how the geometry of the projection leads to minimal distortion in one location and maximal distortion in others. Understanding these distortion patterns will help you choose a proper projection.

In the tangent case, distortion is minimal at the point of tangency and increases with increasing distance from the tangent (see Figure 3.4). In the secant case, there is minimal distortion at the line of tangency, and distortion increases at locations toward the center of the map away from the line of tangency. Also, distortion increases at locations away from the line of tangency toward the edges of the map. This pattern holds true for planar, cylindrical, and conical surfaces.

FIGURE 3.4. Distortion patterns on planar surfaces.[9] Higher levels of distortion are shown by darker shades.

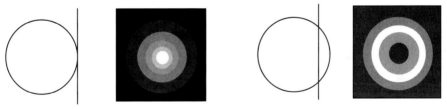

tangent   secant

In the 19th century, a French cartographer named Tissot devised a way to show distortion in both shape and size. His method, known as Tissot's indicatrix, simply plots circles at different locations of a projection. On conformal projections, the circles stay circles everywhere, while on equal area projections, they stay the same size.

8. Snyder, J.P. 1984. *Map projections used by the U.S. Geological Survey.* Geological Survey Bulletin 1532. US Government Printing Office, Washington, D.C.

9. Adapted from Muehrcke, P.C. and J.O. Muehrcke. 1992. *Map Use: Reading, analysis, and interpretation.* Madison, Wisconsin: JP Publications.

3.5.4 Selecting a projection

If you are making a fairly detailed map, for example of a city, or if the requirement for accuracy is minimal, then perhaps you need not worry too much about what projection you are using. However, if you are either making a map of a regional to continental to global scale *or* are interested in precise shape, area and/or distance measurements, then you should choose a projection carefully. For many applications or study areas, there is already a standard projection, such as the State Plane Coordinate System for county and city governments, or UTM for state governments.

There are limitations to accuracy even when using a projection, and understanding the limitations is critical. There are three factors to consider when selecting a projection: *latitude of area*, *extent*, and *theme*. For low-latitude areas (near the equator), use a cylindrical projection with normal aspect. For mid-latitude areas use a conical projection, and for polar regions use an azimuthal planar projection. If the extent of the area you are mapping is fairly broad in the east-west extent (e.g., the US), then a conical projection should probably be used, but if it is long in the north-south extent (e.g., Africa), then a transverse-case cylindrical projection should be used. If you are making a thematic map that compares different values in different locations, then typically you will use an equal-area projection.

3.5.5 Commonly used projections

ArcGIS supports a wide variety of projections. The available coordinate systems are organized by geographic region (e.g., polar, continental, world).[10] Some of the most widely used world projections are: Plate Caree, Robinson, and Sinusoidal (Figure 3.5). The Plate Caree is a cylindrical projection, creating a grid of equal rectangles. The polar regions are less distorted in area compared to Mercator. Robinson is a pseudo-cylindrical projection developed by Arthur Robinson (a.k.a. the "Dean of American Cartography") and used since 1988 by the National Geographic Society. Sinusoidal is also a pseudo-cylindrical projection, and the meridians are based on *sine* functions. In the US, two of the most commonly used projections are UTM and State Plane Coordinate System.

10. The ArcGIS desktop documentation provides a comprehensive list of coordinate systems that are supported. In ArcGIS Desktop help, go to the Contents tab, **Map projections** -> **Supported map projections** -> **List of supported map projections**.

FIGURE 3.5. A few common world projections (from top to bottom): Plate Carree, Robinson, and sinusoidal.

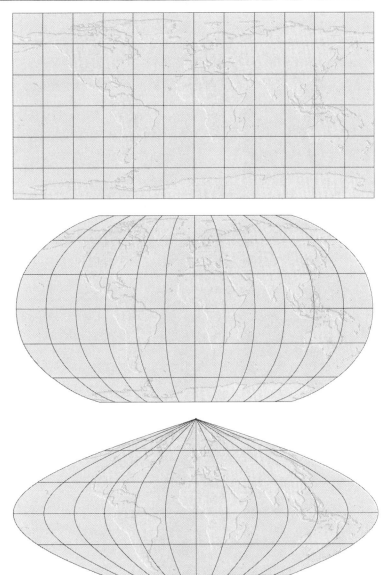

3.5.5.1 UTM

UTM stands for Universal Transverse Mercator grid. This projection extends a flat grid from 80°N to 80°S. There are 60 zones, starting at 180° longitude and wrapping around the earth (Figures 3.6). Each zone is 6° longitude wide, with an additional 0.5° of overlap on each side. This makes it possible to have a maximum error of 1 per 2,500 in each zone.[11] The x coordinate within each zone starts at a false *easting* located 500,000 m west of the center of the zone. The y coordinate starts at a false *northing* located at the equator for the northern hemisphere and 10,000,000 m south of the equator in the southern hemisphere. Thus, to correctly specify a UTM coordinate, you need to specify the easting, northing, zone, and hemisphere (e.g., 100,000 m E; 3,700,00 m N; Zone 13, northern hemisphere). The coordinates are in meters.

3.5.5.2 *State Plane Coordinate System*

The State Plane Coordinate System (SPCS) is used for local areas (usually for counties or cities) and has a maximum error of 1 part in 10,000.[12] Each state is divided into a number of zones (up to five) (see Figures 3.7 and 3.8). For zones with a greater north-south extent, a UTM projection is used. For zones with a greater east-west extent, the Lambert Conformal Conic is used. SPCS usually uses coordinates expressed in feet. The false origin is placed usually 2,000,000 feet to the west of the center of the zone, and some arbitrary but consistent distance south of the zone.

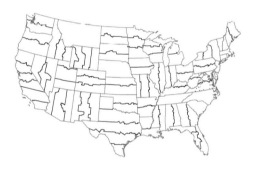

11. Muehrcke, P.C. and J.O. Muehrcke. 1992. *Map Use: Reading, analysis, and interpretation*. Madison, Wisconsin: JP Publications.

12. See an excellent discussion of these errors for Oregon: http://gisweb.iservices.state.or.us/coord/project/gpl.html

FIGURE 3.6. UTM Zones in North America.

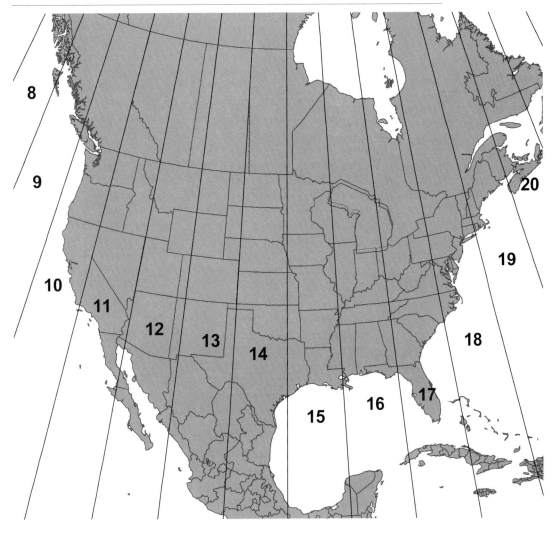

FIGURE 3.7. State Plane Coordinate System zones for the western US.

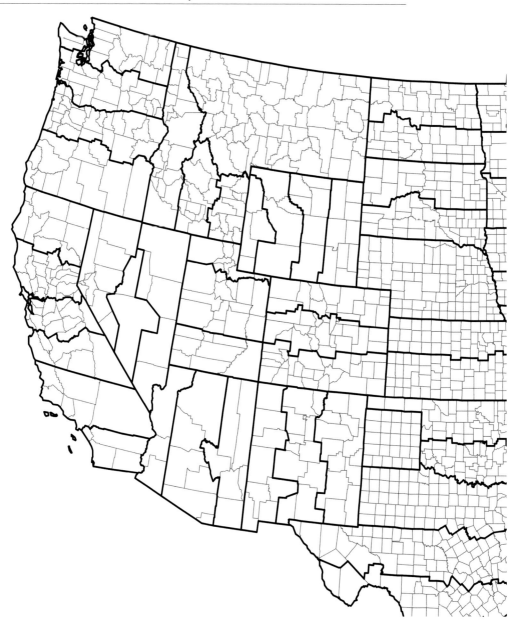

FIGURE 3.8. State Plane Coordinate System zones for the eastern US.

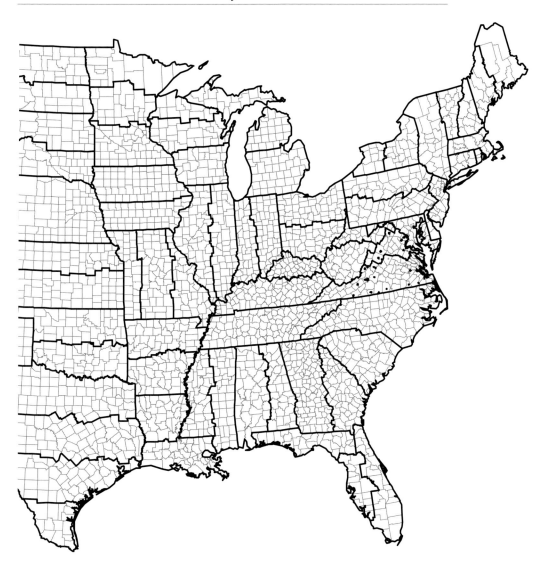

3.6 Changing coordinate systems

In order for ArcGIS to display layers so that they align properly, the coordinate systems for a dataset must be specified. Because geographic datasets often are stored in different coordinate systems, you will likely want to change coordinates to a different projection system at some point, and so another critical function of GIS software is the ability to manipulate coordinate systems. There are two ways to manipulate coordinate systems in ArcGIS so that data align properly. The first is to change the coordinates permanently through projecting the actual coordinates of the data. That is, if a dataset's coordinates were in latitude/longitude (so that its values ranged from + or -180° and + or -90°), you could create a new dataset with its data in a different coordinate system, for example in the Mercator projection (which uses planar coordinates in meters). The second way is to change the coordinates temporarily by "on-the-fly" projection to a different coordinate system defined by the data frame in ArcMap. In order for both the permanent and temporary projection to work, ArcGIS needs to be able to determine the coordinate system of a dataset, which it does by looking for a projection definition file.

3.6.1 Projection definition file

One of the most important pieces of meta-data for a dataset is its projection. Typically, the coordinate system parameters for a dataset are described in a *projection definition file*, in addition to any meta-data files. If the dataset is in the geographic coordinate system, then the datum (based on a spheroid) is specified and the coordinates are in decimal degrees of latitude and longitude. If the dataset is specified in a projected coordinate system, then, in addition to the geographic coordinate system parameters, the projected parameters

are provided, including: datum, spheroid, units (e.g., meters, feet, etc.), projection name, and any parameters specific to that projection. For example, the zone would be specified for the UTM projection, while an Albers Equal Area would have the central meridian, central parallel, and standard parallels specified. Coverages and GRIDs have their projection definition in a file that is stored in the coverage folder, called prj.adj (which is a specially formatted text file). Shapefiles store the definition as a *.prj file and geodatabases store it in its database. You can easily access the coordinate system information for a given layer through the Source tab of a Layer's property dialog.

It is likely that you will need to create or modify a projection definition file, especially for shapefiles.[13] Note that creating or modifying a projection definition file does *not* change the actual values of the spatial coordinates. In ArcGIS, you access this file principally through ArcCatalog, but also through ArcToolbox and ArcMap. In ArcCatalog, the coordinate system parameters of a shapefile can be viewed and edited. In the next dialog, you can select the coordinate system from a predefined list, import it from another existing definition file, or define a new coordinate system.

Creating a coordinate system definition file

1. In *ArcToolbox*, open **Data Management Tools**, then open **Projections and Transformations**, then **Raster.**[a]

2. Double-click on the **Define Projection** tool.

3. Note that a **Batch Define** tool is provided in the Samples tools to create definition files for more than one dataset at a time.

-- or --

1. In *ArcCatalog*, navigate to location of dataset and right-click on dataset and select **Properties**.

2. Select **Fields** tab.

3. Select **Shape** field, then click on ellipses button ("...").

4. Click on **Select** button, fill in information, then click **OK**.

---

a. At v9.1 this tool can operate on both feature and raster, but is under the raster toolset for some (unknown) reason.

---

13. Until the release of the Projection Utility for ArcView v3.2, shapefiles did not support projection definition files (*.prj).

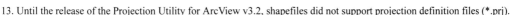

In ArcMap, a projection definition file can be viewed, but not edited, through the Source tab in the Layer's Properties dialog. Note that at the ArcView level, you cannot create or modify projection definition files for coverages or GRIDs.

3.6.2 *Permanent projection*

To create a new dataset with its spatial data in a different coordinate system, you will need to project the data (sometimes called "reprojecting"). This is done in ArcGIS using the *Project tool* found in ArcToolbox. First, locate the source dataset(s) that you want to project. Second, specify the new dataset's name. Third, select the new coordinate system (or modify an existing one to create a custom projection). Note that the Project Wizard requires that the source dataset must have a valid projection definition file first. At the ArcView level, coverages and GRIDs cannot be projected, only shapefiles and geodatasets.

Projecting a dataset

1. In *ArcToolbox*, open the Data Management Tools -> Projections and Transformations -> Feature.

2. Double-click on the Project tool to open the dialog. Also note that there is a *Batch Project* tool available.

3. Navigate to the location of the dataset to be projected.

4. Specify an output location by clicking on the folder button (or type in the file and pathname directly).

5. Click on the Output Coordinate System button.

6. Specify a Geographic Transformation if needed.

7. Click OK.

3.6.3 Temporary, on the fly, projection

A dataset can also be displayed in a different projection than its defined projection through *on the fly* projection. When you add a dataset to a data frame, ArcMap recognizes the coordinate system of the first dataset added (whether it is a geographic or projected coordinate system) and sets the data frame's coordinate system to its coordinate system. (Note that you can also later change the data frame's coordinate system.) All subsequent datasets are displayed using the data frame's coordinate system. If a dataset's coordinate system does not match the data frame's, then ArcGIS automatically projects the data on the fly.

On-the-fly projection works by referencing a dataset's geographic coordinate system (that's why *all* projection definition files are needed), "back" projecting the native coordinates to geographic coordinates, and then "forward" projecting them as specified by the data frame's parameters. As a result, on-the-fly projection is most efficient when all the layers share the same geographic coordinate system. You will be warned if layers in a map have different geographic coordinate systems (see

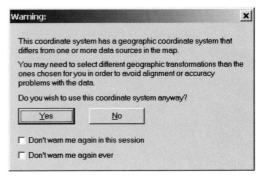

above right). For most situations where broad areas of the Earth are being displayed (countries, states, etc.), the small differences in datums will not result in much difference in display or analysis. But, if your analysis has to be very precise or you are working in a very small area (e.g., city, parcel, etc.), then you should be sure that the datums match.

The advantage of on-the-fly projection is that, as long as your datasets have projection definition files associated with them, you can easily display datasets that are in different coordinate systems without much hassle. The downside is that the display time slows slightly when on-the-fly projection is needed. Also, on-the-fly projection is not as mathematically accurate.

Raster data are also on-the-fly projected during display. This works reasonably well for simply looking at patterns, but the on-the-fly projection for raster data is approximate. Because a low-order transformation is used, some distortion can be introduced. It is recommended when using these data in analyses to either make sure the data frame projection is set to be the same as the raster data set of interest, or that you permanently project the raster data using the Project tool—but this requires ArcEditor or ArcInfo level functionality.

CHAPTER 4 — *Visualization of spatial data*

Visualization of spatial data

4.1 Overview

Cartographers have been making maps for a long time and have developed a rich body of work on the art and science of making maps.[1] We can draw from this work a number of cartographic principles and rules of thumb that should be used to create a useful map. With the advent of computer-cartography and GIS, many cartographers have cautioned about the "democratization" that advanced computer technologies and software (such as ArcGIS) have enabled, providing neophytes who know little about cartography the power to create authentic maps. Because maps are a powerful way to communicate information, many fear that improper, or perhaps misleading, maps will be created through this enabling technology. While this perspective may be considered to be grumbling by the old guard, it is wise to heed their caution and learn from their knowledge and experience. And remember never to underestimate the power of a non-GIS-based map to convey critical information (e.g., Figure 4.1).

---

1. Probably the most widely used text book is by Arthur Robinson and others. Robinson, A.H., P.C. Muehrcke, AJ. Kimmerling, S.C. Gupti, and J.L. Morrison. 1995. *Elements of Cartography* (6th Ed.). New York: John Wiley & Sons.

FIGURE 4.1. A white-board map of the boundaries of Chocoyero-El Brujo National Park, Nicaragua.

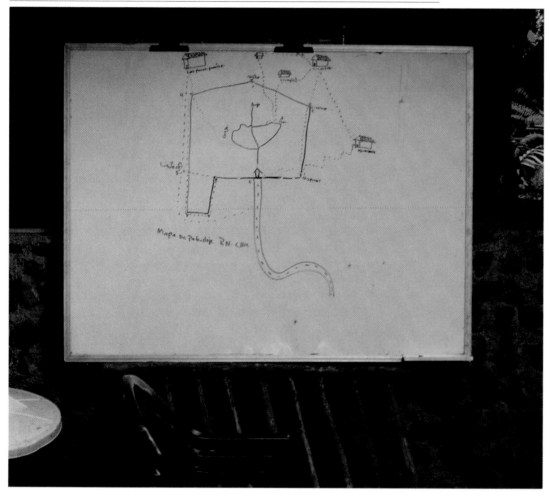

Part of this perspective can be explained by considering the roles of the map creator and reader in the long-established "map as communication" paradigm. In the past, maps were created primarily to communicate some geographic pattern to a map reader. The goal for map communication was to create a single map that displayed the "proper" geographic pattern because the map reader is essentially passive (again, an artifact of paper-based maps). This has led to the suggestion that the map maker has three responsibilities: a) to be fair to the data; b) to be clear to the map reader; and c) to anticipate ways in which a third person may be affected by a *foreseeable* misinterpretation of a map.[2] To be sure, many (perhaps most?) maps are still created and consumed in this fashion.

More recently, there has been a slight paradigm shift, known as analytical cartography[3], that emphasizes the creation of maps that can be easily explored and analyzed. The goal in map analysis is to create a map that can be easily analyzed, because the map reader can query and explore the data behind the map.[4] Thus, the consumers of a map are no longer passive (indeed some would suggest they have a responsibility to be inquisitive), and so map exploration is best described as an iterative process:[5] *frame* the question, *understand* the data, *choose* a display or analytical method, *examine* the results, and *revise* the question and start again.

This chapter describes how to create maps in ArcGIS from both a communication and an exploratory perspective. Again, much of the experience gained and rules of thumb developed in the context of cartographic display are still relevant, and some of the more important ones are described below. Also, MacEachren's primer on map symbolization and design is a very helpful, accessible guide to these principles.[6] But there are also some exciting opportunities for dynamic, "live" maps that transcend the limitations of paper and fully utilize the possibilities provided by digital technology. To this end, a *visualization framework*[7] can help set the broader context of the different roles of maps in GIS, as well as additional possibilities for visualizing spatial data beyond the traditional paper map (Table 4.1). Although the framework is typically conceived of as a linear sequence, in reality it is a cyclic and dynamic process. First, geographic data is *explored*. Traditionally, numerous maps would be created to examine the geographic distribution, but with GIS, additional opportunities are available to explore the data, especially through interactive queries. Second, maps are occasionally used to *confirm* an assumption or hypothesis about the geographic phenomena. Perhaps more often, maps are used to generate hypotheses, and more rigorous statistical methods and spatial analysis are used to confirm a hypothesized pattern. Third, geographic data can be *synthesized*, to distill the patterns found, not only in a single map but through analysis of multiple layers of geographic information. Fourth, GIS are used to present geographic information. Again, the traditional

2. See: Gersmehl, P.J. 1985. The data, the reader, and the innocent bystander -- a parable for map users. *Professional Geographer* 37(3): 329-334.
3. Waldo Tobler, Professor Emeritus at University of California, Santa Barbara, is widely regarded as the father of analytical cartography.
4. See: Muehrcke, P.C. 1981. Whatever happened to geographic cartography? *The Professional Geographer* 33(4): 397-405.
5. For example, see the analysis process described in: Mitchell, A. 1999. *The ESRI guide to GIS Analysis*. ESRI Press.
6. MacEachren, A.M. 1994. *Some truth with maps: A primer on symbolization and design*. Association of American Geographers, Washington, D.C. 129 pgs.
7. This framework is very loosely based on MacEachren's framework for the role of maps.

format of this is a paper-based map, but increasingly their are opportunities for other types of digital presentations, such as animations and fly-throughs.

TABLE 4.1. Visualization framework using GIS.

Visual thinking		Visual communication	
Exploration			
	Confirmation		
		Synthesis	
			Presentation

4.2 Thematic mapping

There are a wide variety of *thematic map* types that have been developed to portray the attributes of geographic features. The map type to use depends on the purpose of the map—what geographical aspect are you trying to visualize? For example, the locations of important bird areas can be shown within the spatial context of ecological regions. It also depends on the type of attribute data that is being displayed. Recall the discussion in Chapter 2 about attribute data types: qualitative (nominal) or quantitative (ordinal, interval, cyclic, ratio). Table 4.2 provides an overview of the mapping methods provided in ArcMap, organized by feature types. The map type is defined through the Symbology tab of the Layer Properties dialog (see graphics below). After the various types of maps are described, a detailed discussion about graphic symbology is provided.

TABLE 4.2. How different featured and data types are displayed using ArcMap map methods. (N=nominal, O=ordinal, I=interval, C=cyclic, R=ratio).

ArcMap method	Point	Line	Area	Raster
Feature (shows location)	N, O, I, C, R	N, O, I, C, R	N, O, I, C, R	
Categories - unique values	N	N	N	N

TABLE 4.2. How different featured and data types are displayed using ArcMap map methods. (N=nominal, O=ordinal, I=interval, C=cyclic, R=ratio).

ArcMap method	Point	Line	Area	Raster
Quantities				
- graduated color	O, I, C, R	O, I, C, R	O, I, C, R[a]	O, I, C, R
- graduated symbols	O, I, C, R	O, I, C, R	O, I, C, R	
- proportional symbols	O, I, C, R	O, I, C, R	O, I, C, R	
- dot			O, I, C, R	
Charts				
- Pie	R	R	R	
- Bar/Column	R	R	R	
- Stacked	R	R	R	
Multiple				
- Quantity by category	R	R	R	

a. These are also known as choropleth maps when the data are normalized.

4.2.1 Features map type

The *features map* type simply displays the location of features using a single symbol — no attribute value is displayed. This can be valuable because it emphasizes the geographic distribution of features. For example, the capital cities are shown by blue stars, and they can be seen to be highly clustered in the New England region (due to the small size of states) and in some places in the west as well (e.g., Denver, CO and Cheyenne, WY; Sacramento, CA and Carson City, NV). The US Interstate system is shown by the red lines, and again

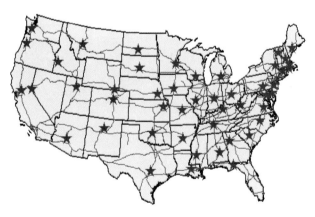

there is a higher density in the East, Midwest, and southern California. It is also interesting to note the Interstate 27 "spur" in northern Texas, dropping down from Interstate 40 to Lubbock and the Interstate 390 spur in western New York, terminating at the village of Bath. By comparing the location of a capital within its respective state, the geographic representativeness appears to be highly skewed in a number of states (especially Florida, Nevada, and Wyoming).

A specialized features map type is an isoline map that displays the values of a continuous phenomenon. An *isoline* connects points of equal value, and this map is commonly used to show the distribution of continuous surfaces, not by changing their symbology, but simply through their location in relation to other isolines. For example, contour lines are isolines that map locations of equal elevation (Figure 4.2).

FIGURE 4.2. Isohyets, or lines of equal precipitation, in Colorado (center) and Utah (left) demonstrate the strong relation between precipitation and topography, including the rain shadow effect of the Rockies (shown by the two large polygons of lower precipitation to the east of the Front Range, interrupted by the Palmer Divide).

4.2.2 Categories map type

The *Categories map* type is typically used to portray nominal data, such as land use classes or vegetation types—based on *unique values* of an attribute. Features with unique values are drawn with a different color or symbol. This type of map shows the geographic distribution of features, but also differentiates them by an attribute. It also shows visually how many are in a category compared to others. For example, the states (right) are grouped into different divisions, each displayed with a unique color. Also, most

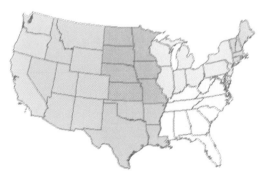

locational and road maps are this type, simply showing the difference in roads (e.g., interstate,

state highways, secondary, local roads, etc.). For raster datasets, nominal data can also be portrayed using the unique values option. Note that the unique values can be drawn from the values found in one field or multiple fields (up to three). This second option allows features to be differentiated based on their unique combination of two or three attributes.

This is an effective method for displaying nominal data, but humans have difficulty distinguishing between color hues when there are more than ten or so classes (and ideally around seven). Therefore, it is recommended to combine classes to create groups of values or categories to reduce the number of classes. With more than a dozen classes, this legend type is occasionally used to distinguish locations, but the resulting map is too visually complex to be useful for examining categories. Typically, when using a unique value classification, similar colors will be used for related categories. For instance, for urban classes (residential, commercial) use shades of red, or for forest classes (ponderosa pine, Douglas fir, etc.) use shades of green. In addition, classes can be grouped manually.

Grouping classes in a legend

1. In _ArcMap_, right-click on a layer and select **Properties**.

2. Select the **Symbology** tab.

3. Select **Categories** and then **Unique Values,** then specify the **Value** field, then click on **Add All Values.**

4. Select the classes to be grouped (using shift-click and/or ctrl-click).

5. Right-click and select **Group values.**

6. Click **OK**.

4.2.3 Quantities map type

The _Quantities map_ type displays quantitative attribute data, such as daily maximum temperature, the population change in the past decade in the US, the Nielsen rating for NBC's television show at 7:00 p.m. on Thursdays, the annual sales generated in a territory, or the number of acres of habitat for an endangered species. There are four different display methods for quantitative data: _graduated color, graduated symbol, proportional symbol_, and _dot density_. Which type should you use? The main consideration is the type of attribute data that is to be mapped (i.e. whether it is ordinal, interval, cyclic, or ratio). For line and areal data, also consider whether the geographic features that will be portrayed with some attribute value vary in size or length. For example, an attribute might contain ratio values that represent a count or raw amount (e.g., the population per state in 2000). It might also contain ratio values that represent densities (e.g., population density per state in 2000) — this is called a ratio (because it is normalized by some denominator). When geographic features are fairly uniform, then mapping raw counts or amounts is reasonable. However, when geographic features vary (especially the size of areal features), then you should portray the data as densities, not raw counts — cartographers call these _choropleth_ maps. The reason is that raw counts are highly correlated with the area of a feature — the larger a state, the more likely it is to have more people than a small state. So, large counties, like San Bernadino, CA, stand out disproportionately (Figure 4.3). Also, choropleth maps are typically used when the polygons (e.g. counties) are determined independently of the phenomenon. Raw count data should be converted to ratio or density data by _normalizing_ them with another attribute (e.g., area of a state or total US population).

In order to better understand the various situations in which particular map types are used for displaying quantitative data (which are discussed in detail below), a short discussion about classifying data is warranted.

FIGURE 4.3. A comparison of raw values and normalized display of population by county in 2000. Note that when geographic features vary in size, it is recommended to portray data as normalized values (right).

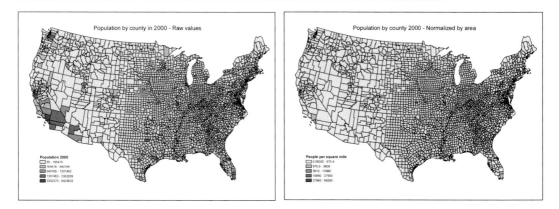

4.2.3.1 Classification

A *classification* is a method that groups similar features based on an attribute value into a smaller set of groups or classes by assigning the same symbol to each member of the class. This helps to simplify the visual complexity of a map, making the map easier to read and understand. First, select the number of classes, which typically should be between 3 and 10. Why 3 to 10? The smaller the number of classes, the more simplified a map will be and greater within-group variation, but using fewer than three classes causes vast generalizations that are rarely helpful. The larger the number of classes, the closer the attribute values can be portrayed and the within-group variation decreases. But, because humans are limited in our ability to differentiate shades of gray and colors and because too many classes make a map complex, the cartographic rule of thumb is to use somewhere between 3 to 10 classes.[8] Note that even this first, fairly arbitrary decision, can result in maps that are quite different.[9]

There are five standard classification schemes that are available in ArcMap. The standard classifications are: *defined interval, equal interval, natural breaks, quantiles,* and *standard deviation.* A sixth classification is called *manual,* where the class limits can be adjusted to create your own classification.

The *equal interval* method divides the full range of attribute values into equally sized sub-ranges, then the features are classified based on those sub-ranges (Figure 4.4). Equal-interval

---

8.   Dent, B. 1985. *Principles of thematic map design.* Addison-Wesley Publishing.

9.   Indeed, some have offered a cynical view of mapping, for example: "One of the trickiest ways to misrepresent statistical data is by means of a map. A map introduces a fine bag of variables in which facts can be concealed and relationships distorted." From Huff, D. 1954. *How to Lie with Statistics.* W.W. Norton.

legends are also fairly intuitive to map readers. A closely-related method is the *defined interval* method, which divides the full range of attribute values into equally sized sub-ranges that are based on a specified interval size. Rather than specifying the number of classes and calculating the resulting interval, the interval is set and the number of classes is calculated.

FIGURE 4.4. Equal-interval classification.

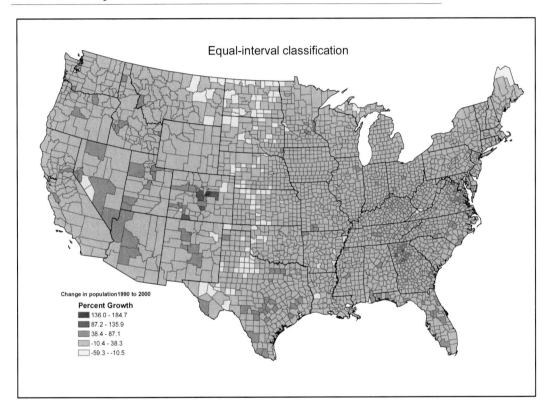

The *natural breaks* method identifies breakpoints between classes to form groups that are internally homogeneous while assuring heterogeneity among classes (Figure 4.5). This method uses a statistical formula that minimizes the sum of the variance within each of the classes, often called Jenks optimization.[10] This is the default classification. Because the legend values change with each distribution and therefore with each map, beware when comparing maps

10. The primary reference for Jenks optimization procedure is: Jenks, G.F. and M.R. Coulson, 1963. Class intervals for statistical maps. *International Yearbook of Cartography* 3:119-134. Also see: Fisher, W.D. 1958. *On grouping for maximum homogeneity.* American Statistical Association Journal 53: 789-798.

depicting similar, but different data. The differences you observe might simply be artifacts of the class ranges, rather than differences in the data themselves. For example, do not use this classification type when comparing data between years, because the class ranges will change depending on the data, making inter-year comparisons very difficult.

FIGURE 4.5. Natural breaks classification.

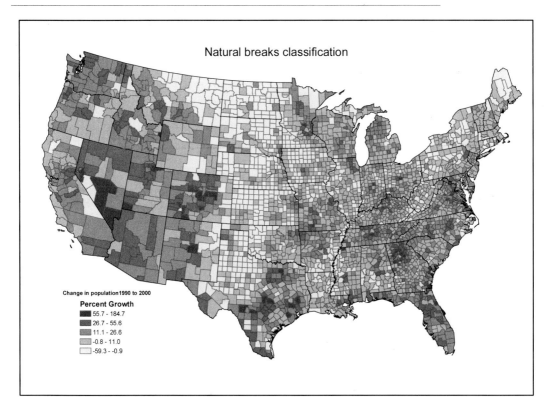

The *quantiles* method identifies breakpoints between classes so that each class contains approximately the same number of features (Figure 4.6). If the number of classes is five, then the data is broken into quantiles. If the number of classes is four, then it results in quartiles. This method is well suited for data that is linearly (or uniformly) distributed.

FIGURE 4.6. Quintile classification method.

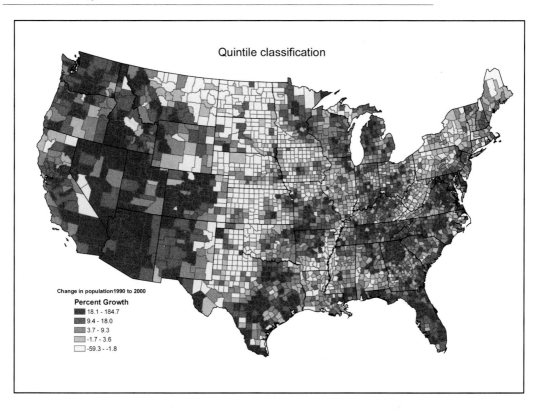

The *standard deviation* method finds the mean value and then places class breaks above and below the mean at intervals of either one-fourth, one-half, or one standard deviation until all the data values are contained within the classes (Figure 4.7). This classification should be used only when the data approximate a normal distribution.

FIGURE 4.7. Standard deviation classification method.

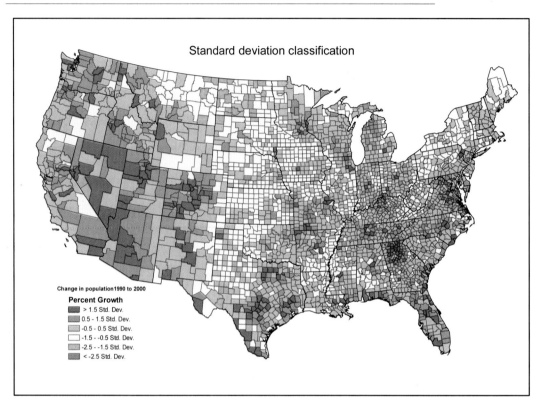

To summarize, there is no "correct" way to classify data, no one "right" map. Changing the number of classes or the class ranges through different classification schemes creates maps that emphasize different aspects about the distribution of an attribute (as the figures above demonstrate). A useful exercise is to understand the distribution of attribute data to see if they are overly skewed, lumped, bi-model, or perhaps have outliers that will bias statistics. It is important to explicitly consider the goal for making a map—different goals require different strategies. A different approach will be taken if the goal is to communicate some known distribution rather than to explore geographic data to notice possibly unexpected distributions.

Occasionally, there will be some additional guidance—perhaps the classification needs to conform to specific criteria or to some standard format. For instance, there may be a specific threshold value that is either mandated in a regulation or has simply emerged as a useful comparative value (e.g., greater than 50% cover, slopes greater than 25%, etc.) As a result, ArcGIS also allows the classification to be customized by editing class values directly to change the breaks between classes. This is accomplished through interacting with a histogram of the attribute values (Figure 4.8).[11] For example, often data is classified in comparison to some statistical average—here we'll map the county population growth rates as compared to the national average.

FIGURE 4.8. Classification dialog illustrating manual setting of classes.

> *Displaying a histogram*
> 1. In *ArcMap*, right-click on a layer and select **Properties**.
> 2. Select the **Symbology** tab.
> 3. Click **Classify....**

At the top of the Classification dialog, change the classification method to "manual." Note the *classification statistics* in the top right corner showing count, minimum, maximum, sum, mean,

---

11. This is a big improvement over ArcView v3.2, which provided no easy means of viewing the distribution.

median[12], and standard deviation of the attribute values. In the lower part of the dialog is the histogram, with the data aligned from minimum to maximum values. The number of histogram columns or bins shown in the graph can be adjusted by changing the value in the "Columns" box. To the right of the histogram are the *break values* that specify the class limits. In the break values list, the first class of the US population growth rates runs from the minimum value to the first break value—in this case 0 (so the first class ranges from -59.2530 up to and including 0). The next value is 9.0992, the average percentage growth per county from 1990 to 2000 (this is slightly less than 1% annually). The next values represent twice, five times, and ten times the national average (Figure 4.9). The last break value is also the maximum value of 184.7—which is over 20 times the national average (Douglas County, Colorado)! The break values can also be specified by click-dragging on the vertical lines in the graph that separate classes. Note also that specific features can be excluded from being displayed by clicking the Exclusion... button and entering the desired value. This feature is useful when some particular feature(s) should be removed temporarily from the list of features.

_____

12. New with v9.1.

FIGURE 4.9. Manual classification method comparing growth rates to national average.

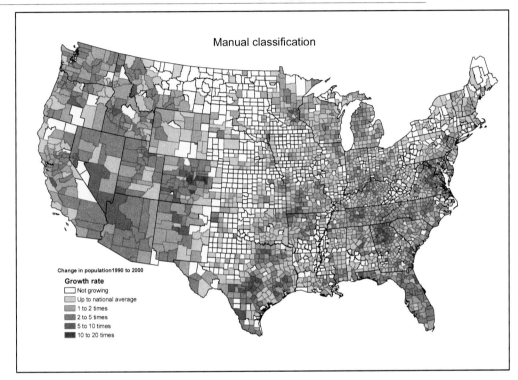

4.2.3.2 *Graduated color*

A common method of displaying quantitative attribute data is to vary the color of features according to an attribute value. Population density and growth rates (at right) are typically portrayed in this fashion.[13] This method works for point, line, and areal geographic features (and raster data as well). The cartographic rule of thumb that applies here is the *greater* the attribute value, the *darker* (more intense) the color value. In this way, features with higher values are visually dominant.

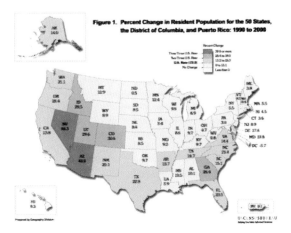

When depicting ratio data, it is best to use *monochromatic* color ramps, where darker color values correspond to higher values in your data. If the phenomenon being depicted naturally has a division, has both negative and positive values, or if you want to show areas above or below an average, then *dichromatic* ramps are useful. For example, if you are portraying temperature, then use a dichromatic ramp with blue symbols depicting values lower than freezing and red for values higher than freezing. Otherwise, avoid using dichromatic ramps, especially for data with no natural separation in the distribution. There are a number of other "specialty" color ramps available, such as for elevation, sea floor elevation, and land cover, which are available by clicking on the **Color Ramp** drop-down list.

Another type of isoline map is called a *shaded isoline* map. Often, the interior areas of an isoline map are shaded so that colors represent an attribute value. A common example of this is a weather map showing temperature, or perhaps precipitation amounts (Figure 4.10).

---

13. Source: US Census Bureau, 2002.

FIGURE 4.10. In contrast with the map in Figure 4.2, a shaded isoline map shows areas of equal value—in this case precipitation in Colorado (center) and Utah (left). Notice the dry, interior deserts in Utah and Arizona, the wet "islands" in blue, and the rain shadow effect of the Rockies (this time distinguished by color differences in the two large polygons of lower precipitation to the east of the Front Range).

For raster datasets, quantitative data can be displayed using the *classified* option, which is essentially the same as the graduated color option for feature data. In this case, the number in the value attribute table is displayed with a color. For example, the mountain ranges of the world can be seen by the yellow-red-brown values (above right).[14] The only aspect of a raster cell that can

---

14. This shows world topography, stored as a MrSID image using GTOPO30.

be controlled is the interior color—the outline color or fill pattern of a raster cell cannot be changed. Raster data can also be displayed using the *stretched* classification type, which stretches values along a color ramp. This is used mostly for adjusting images and photographs.

4.2.3.3 Graduated and proportional symbols

Another way to symbolize quantitative data is to keep the color and symbol constant, but vary the size of a symbol in relation to the attribute value. Typically, point feature data, such as population of cities, are portrayed in this fashion (right), though this method can also used for linear features (e.g., different stream orders). In ArcGIS, graduated symbols for areal features are portrayed by placing a marker symbol in the center of the polygon. A *cartogram* is another type of graduated symbol method that varies the size of the polygon features, but this type of map is not a standard feature of ArcGIS.[15]

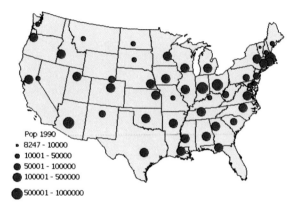

Pop 1990
- 8247 - 10000
- 10001 - 50000
- 50001 - 100000
- 100001 - 500000
- 500001 - 1000000

The difference between *graduated symbols* and *proportional symbols* is that, for graduated symbols, the values are grouped into a few, discrete classes. In contrast, for proportional symbols, the values are considered to be continuous and no discrete classes are formed, so the size of the symbol reflects the actual data value.

---

15. Discontinuous cartograms can be easily created, however, by scaling the area of polygons in relation to the attribute value. A classic paper on cartograms is: Olson, J.M. 1976. Noncontiguous Area Cartograms. *The Professional Geographer* 28(4): 317-380. Also see: Jackel, C.B. 1997. Using ArcView to create contiguous and non-contiguous area cartograms. *Cartography and Geographic Information Systems* 24(2): 101-109.

Layer Properties

General | Source | Selection | Display | Symbology | Fields | Definition Query | Labels | Joins & Relates |

Show:

Features
Categories
Quantities
    Graduated colors
    Graduated symbols
    Proportional symbols
Charts
Multiple Attributes

Draw quantities using symbol size to show relative values.   Import...

Fields
Value: POP1990
Normalization: <NONE>

Classification
Manual
Classes: 5   Classify...

Symbol Size from: 4   to: 18

Sym...	Range	Label
•	8247 - 10000	8247 - 10000
●	10001 - 50000	10001 - 50000
●	50001 - 100000	50001 - 100000
●	100001 - 500000	100001 - 500000
●	500001 - 1000000	500001 - 1000000

Template
●

☐ Show class ranges using feature values

Rotation...

OK   Cancel   Apply

4.2.3.4 *Dot density*

A *dot density* map displays quantitative data values for polygon features only by adjusting the density of dots in relation to the value of an attribute. Each dot represents a specific number that can be set, and the more dots in an area, the higher the value. However, you will need to trade off the number of dots, which is controlled by the attribute value and the *dot value* setting that specifies the value represented by a single dot, and the *dot size*, or the point size of a dot. Dots are distributed randomly throughout a defined area specified by a polygon, and because of this random component, this type of map

"fuzzies up" the location of features, so that the exact location of a geographic feature cannot be discerned. For example, the number of acres placed into the US Conservation or Wetland Reserve Program is shown (above right), but not the precise location of leases.[16] Several variables can be displayed at once by selecting multiple attributes that use a distinct color to portray the dots and a transparent background.

Dot maps are fairly intuitive to most map readers, but they can be very misleading as well. Beware of maps that use this type of legend, especially when showing population density, because the human eye naturally infers pattern, even if none exists. For example, although population in Nevada (Figure 4.11) is highly clustered around Las Vegas, the randomly located points within the state give the impression of a fairly homogenous distribution, even though only about 10% of Nevada is private land. A powerful feature provided in ArcGIS to address this issue to some extent is the ability to force dots to be either included in or excluded from areas defined by a *mask* layer (that must be a polygon type). This is a type of *dasymetric* mapping.[17]

16. Source: US Department of Agriculture, Natural Resource Conservation Service.

17. This technique was first developed to map population density in Cape Cod: Wright, J.K. 1936. A method of mapping densities of population. *Geographical Review* 26: 103-110. Also see: Eicher, C.L. and C.A. Brewer. 2001. Dasymetric mapping and areal interpolation: Implementation and evaluation. *Cartography and Geographic Information Science* 28(2): 125-138; and Theobald, D.M. 2001. Land use dynamics beyond the American urban fringe. *Geographical Review* 91(3): 544-564.

FIGURE 4.11. Population in California, Nevada, and Utah using dot density mapping. Notice that lakes were used to exclude dots from being located there randomly.

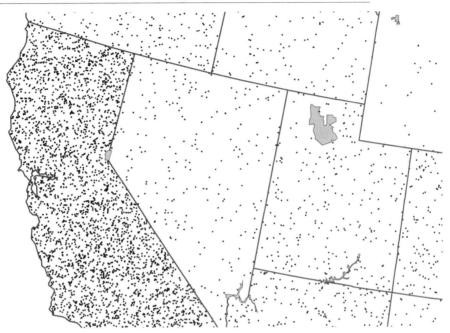

4.2.4 Charts

Charts are used to display the values of multiple attributes of a feature. For example, the metropolitan and non-metropolitan percent change in population can be compared by region (right). In ArcMap, pie, bar, and stacked charts can be created. *Pie charts* are useful for showing proportions or ratios. *Bar charts* are useful for comparing amounts of related values (see right[18]), and to show trends over time. *Stacked bar charts* are useful for comparisons and relative relationships.

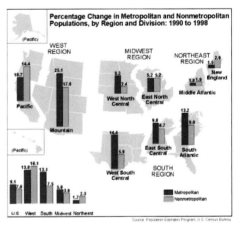

18. Source: US Census Bureau.

4.2.5 Multiple attributes map type

This type of map, also known as a *multi-variate* map, displays two or more attributes simultaneously on the same map, including a combination of categorical and quantitative data. Point and line features are commonly portrayed using multi-variate maps. For example, the size of marker symbol could show population, while the color could show the proportion of that population that is of Hispanic origin. There is a variety of combinations of maps, but you must be cautious when displaying multi-variate data because the map may become overly complex and hard to read.

4.2.6 Symbology

Depicting distributions of geographic phenomena rely on our well-developed ability to visualize and comprehend spatial patterns. Graphic primitives, such as color, symbol size, and arrangement, can be used to portray spatial patterns. One of the most comprehensive efforts to create a typology of graphic variables was Bertin's classic study: *Semiology of Graphics*.[19] The

---

19. Bertin, J. 1983. *Semiology of graphics: Diagrams, networks, maps.* Madison, Wisconsin: University of Wisconsin Press.

graphic primitives he identified, with more recent extensions,[20] include the following: location in space (x,y,z), size, shape, color, texture, orientation, arrangement, and focus. These are the building blocks of symbols that are used to depict geographic phenomena on maps.

Obviously, mapping the *location* of geographic features allows one to distinguish their geographic distribution and their interrelationships. Changing symbol *size* is particularly effective because sizes are easily differentiated by human perception. Larger sizes are intuitively associated with higher attribute values, but nominal values should not be portrayed by different sized symbols. *Shape* is well suited to represent different nominal values. Human perception is sensitive to different shapes, but there is essentially no intuitive ordering to different shapes.

Color *hue* is what most people associate with the word "color." Technically, hue is defined by a color's wavelength. Remember "ROYGBIV" from high school physics class? Those hues can be seen (right, the *Color Selector* dialog) as: red, orange, yellow, green, blue, indigo, violet. Changes in hue are well suited for depicting nominal data. However, a common mistake is to use hue to map quantitative data because we quickly are overwhelmed with maintaining a sense of order with hues.

Color *saturation* is the purity or brilliance of a hue. Technically, saturation is the range of wavelengths—a narrow range is perceived as a pure hue, while a wide range of wavelengths results in a cloudier color. Saturation is well suited to represent numerical values.

Color *value* is the variation in lightness or darkness of a color, which ranges from 0 to 100%. High color values are light (i.e. white) while low color values are dark (i.e. black). Because color value clearly has an order, variations in color value are useful for depicting quantitative data, although we have a limited ability to distinguish color value (up to 10 or so) and grey tones (about 7 or so). Two hue-value combinations are useful for ordinal data: yellow through green to blue or violet and yellow through orange to red. The Hue Saturation Value (HSV) color model (as depicted in the Color Selector dialog above) compensates better for the non-linear changes in human color perception, as

compared to the RGB color model (red, green, blue).[21] The color model of the Color Selector

---

20. DiBiase, D., J.B. Krygier, C. Reeves, A.M. MacEachren, and A. Brenner. 1991. *An Elementary Approach to Cartographic Animation.* Penn State University, University Park, PA.

can also be changed to the RGB or CMYK (cyan, magenta, yellow, black) models that are used by printers and photographers as well, using the arrow button at the top-right.

Texture describes the spatial pattern of geographic features (see right). Changes in texture are best used to symbolize areal features. Different textures can be applied to features using the different fill patterns available, as well as through dot density mapping.

Orientation of a symbol can be used to depict either nominal or quantitative data. It is most often used in combination with texture to create fill patterns (see right). A really good use of orientation is to describe cyclic data (particularly aspect) by rotating a point symbol or marker, to show wind direction for example. *Arrangement* is also an aspect of pattern, and so it is most useful to depict areal features. *Focus* describes the clarity of a symbol, and is ideally suited to depict uncertainty or accuracy.

But what symbology should be used to depict a feature in ArcMap? Symbology in ArcMap is set in the *Symbology tab* of the Layer Properties dialog, as has been shown in the discussion of different classification types above. Note that the symbol can be adjusted through the *Symbol Selector* dialog, and there is a unique dialog for points, lines, and polygons. *Marker* symbols are used for point features, and the symbol shape, size, angle, fill color, and outline color can be changed. There are four types of markers: simple (fast-drawing based on "glyph" patterns); character (based on TrueType font), arrow, and picture (that uses a bitmap or enhanced metafile graphic). There are many, many existing marker symbols that are available by clicking on the **More Symbols**... button (and additional ones can be loaded from files as well). Note that the color can also be transparent (no color). There are five types of line symbols: simple (fast-drawing, one-pixel lines with predefined pattern); cartographic (straight lines with template patterns); hash (these use hachures and template patterns); marker (use marker

---

21. The RGB (red, green, blue) color model is particularly popular in for color video monitors. The intensity of color lies along the axis of 0, 0, 0 (black) to 100, 100, 100 (white), when all RGB values are equal. One of the problems with RBG is that linear changes in RGB values do not correspond to linear changes in color perception—for example, the human eye is less sensitive to changes in blue (see Bonham-Carter 1996). One alternative model is the HSV, which uses the same intensity as RGB. *Hue* refers to the angle in a plane normal to the intensity axis, while *saturation* is the radius from the intensity axis. Also see: Shih, T.Y., 1995. The reversibility of six geometric color spaces. *Photogrammetric Engineering & Remote Sensing* 61(10): 1223-1232.

decorations); and picture (a continuous tiling of a bitmap or an enhanced metafile graphic).[22]
For area features, there are five types of *fill symbols*: simple (fast-drawing fill with optional
outline); gradient (linear, rectangular, or circular color ramp fills); line (hatched lines at any
angle, separation and offset); marker (marker symbols drawn randomly or ordered); and
picture (continuous tiling of a bitmap or an enhanced metafile graphic).[23] You can also bring
up the *Color Selector* dialog and the *Symbol Property Editor* dialog (these dialogs are shown on
the two previous pages).

---

22. There are some very powerful combinations here, including a symbology method to virtually "dissolve" boundaries between
same-value features. See: ArcGIS Desktop Help, ArcMap, Symbolizing your data, Working with advanced symbolization.

23. There is a lot more to symbols in ArcMap than can be adequately covered here. Please see ArcGIS Desktop help, type "symbols, marker," "symbols, line," or "symbols, fill" in the Help Index.

4.2.6.1 Layer files

After a geographic dataset has been added and the layer has been symbolized and classified in ArcMap, the settings of how to display the data can be saved to a *layer file* (*.lyr). A layer file exists outside of the map document on disk, and in it are all the settings that specify the way the features are symbolized and the classification applied.[24] These layer files can be added to a map document, just like an existing dataset. Also, the symbology can be imported from an existing layer file and applied to a target dataset by clicking on the Import... button in the Symbology tab of the Layer Properties dialog of the target layer. Importing existing layer files is a useful way to save time and hassle so that existing legends can be applied to a new layer. Unfortunately, at v8.2 layer files cannot be imported to affect the symbology of GRID files. A work around is to create a copy of the layer, then replace the dataset the layer file points to. This is accomplished through the Source tab of the Layer Properties by clicking on the Set Data Source button.[25] Layer files are used in ArcGIS, essentially replacing ArcView v3.x legend files (*.avl). However, *.avl legend files created in ArcView v3.x can be imported into ArcGIS and subsequently saved as a layer file.[26]

Note that a layer file simply points to the dataset it is based on, but does not store the actual data itself. So, if you would like to share a layer with someone, you need to provide both the dataset and the layer file. There are two ways that ArcGIS stores that pathname to the datasets in a layer file. The default method is to use the *absolute* or *full pathname* (e.g., c:\esri\data\usa\counties.shp). This requires that those who wish to use the layer file have the data on their computers using the same folder structure.

---

24. Layer files also typically save the selected features as well—though you can change this in the Selection Options dialog.
25. ArcGIS Technical Article #18240.
26. Support for importing legend files for GRID data is not supported yet at ArcGIS v8.2.

Datasets can also be referenced using *relative* pathnames (e.g, \usa\counties.shp). Because relative paths do not contain drive names, data can be moved more easily between computers.

Changing absolute or relative pathnames

1. In *ArcMap*, click File ->Map Properties....

2. Click on the Data Source Options... button.

3. Click the radio button to set Store full path names or Store relative path names.

4. Click OK.

When a layer in ArcMap references data that does not exist at the specified location on a computer, ArcMap flags the layer using a red exclamation point next to the layer's name in the table of contents. This is called a *broken link*. Links can be broken when a dataset is moved, renamed, or deleted, or if it is inaccessible for some other reason such as a downed database connection. Broken links can be repaired either one at a time, or for multiple layers.[27] Note that the data source for a layer can be changed even when the link is not broken. Indeed this is a useful technique to apply a particular legend onto a different or updated dataset.

Repairing broken links

One layer at a time:

1. In *ArcMap*, right-click on the layer with a broken link and select Properties.

2. Select the Source tab.

3. Click on the Set Data Source... button and navigate to find the desired dataset, then click OK.

Multiple layers:

1. In *ArcMap*, right-click on a layer with a broken link and select Data->Set Data Source....

2. Navigate to find the desired dataset, then click OK. (ArcMap looks for other layers in the same folder).

---

27. A broken link is roughly parallel to the dreaded project repair process (i.e. Where is file....?) in ArcView v3.x. The ability to repair multiple broken links at once, however, is a big step forward.

4.2.6.2 *Advanced symbology*

There are numerous advanced methods for customizing symbology. One of the more useful tools is to specify the *transparency* of a

layer.[28] In this way, features can be displayed that allow underlying features to be viewed as well. Transparency, which ranges from 0 to 100% transparent, can be specified in three different ways. The same transparency for all features in an individual layer can be set through the layer properties or through the Effects tool (above). The transparency can also vary by feature, as specified in a field (values in percent) in a layer's attribute table. Note that the *brightness* and *contrast* can also be set—for raster layers only. Another useful technique is to use a polygon feature layer to define an area to virtually clip the map to. That is, you can display an irregular portion to "clip" a map to (e.g., a couple of counties), and exclude the other areas, without having to permanently clip your layers. This is done through the data frame properties.

---

28. In ArcView v3.x, this concept of transparency only worked for GRID data, but now it applies to all layers (including feature types).

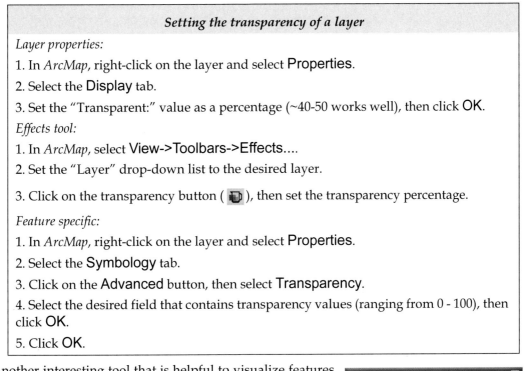

Setting the transparency of a layer

Layer properties:

1. In *ArcMap*, right-click on the layer and select Properties.

2. Select the Display tab.

3. Set the "Transparent:" value as a percentage (~40-50 works well), then click OK.

Effects tool:

1. In *ArcMap*, select View->Toolbars->Effects....

2. Set the "Layer" drop-down list to the desired layer.

3. Click on the transparency button (   ), then set the transparency percentage.

Feature specific:

1. In *ArcMap*, right-click on the layer and select Properties.

2. Select the Symbology tab.

3. Click on the Advanced button, then select Transparency.

4. Select the desired field that contains transparency values (ranging from 0 - 100), then click OK.

5. Click OK.

Another interesting tool that is helpful to visualize features below a polygon or raster layer is called the *Swipe* tool. This tool is found on the Effects toolbar (the button on the far right).

Whether a layer is displayed at a given scale or not can be controlled by setting a layer's *scale range* on the General tab of the Layer Properties dialog. You can set both the minimum and maximum thresholds, so that when the data frame is outside the minimum to maximum range, the layer is not drawn (even if you have the display checked in the TOC). This feature is useful when you want to prohibit users from zooming in too far and making decisions that the data may not support. Or it can be used to show layers with different representations of the same geographic features. These layers can also be combined into a *group layer* and then the scale range for the group layer can be set. For example, at a coarse scale, cities would be displayed as points, but at a finer scale, a different layer representing cities as polygons could be displayed.

Custom color ramps can be created for quantitative maps. Set the top and bottom (and any intermediate) color symbols, and then ramp colors (using right-click). If you wish to save this customized color ramp, right-click on the color ramp drop-down arrow and select "Save." Note that the names of color ramps can be displayed instead of the color ramp graphic (again, right-click on drop-down arrow).

4.2.7 Styles

Styles are used to describe how maps are drawn, including symbol properties, label specifications, color schemes, legend and scale bar characteristics, and the location and the appearance of other cartographic elements. Styles help you to manage a familiar "look-and-feel" of a map, so that standard symbols, colors, and patterns can be maintained. In ArcMap, styles are accessed through the Style Manager dialog by clicking Tools->Styles->Style Manager....

4.3 Landform maps

In addition to thematic mapping that was described above, a second common form of mapping is to depict landforms. For many centuries cartographers have developed clever ways to portray the Earth's surface, or topography. Early explorers used symbols and hatch marks to delineate mountain ranges and canyons. These techniques reached their pinnacle in Erwin Raisz' work of landforms, which shows land features in intricate detail.[29]

---

29. See: Raisz, E. 1962. *Principles of Cartography*. McGraw-Hill. Also see: http://www.mercatormag.com/article.php3?i=66.

FIGURE 4.12. The beautiful landforms of sand dunes in Death Valley National Park.

Probably the most important type of map developed to portray terrain are maps that use contour lines (or their below sea level counterparts, *bathymetric contours* or *isobaths*) (Figure 4.13). This type of map, of course, has been well utilized in the USGS Topographic map series.

FIGURE 4.13. Contour lines (lines of equal elevation) in Colorado and Utah depicting 1000 m intervals.

An early innovation of computer cartography and GIS was a series of alternative methods to depict landforms from an *oblique perspective,* in contrast to the *orthographic perspective* (essentially looking straight down on a surface). An oblique perspective typically allows map readers to more readily understand spatial relationships between features because the landscape appears much as it does when looking out of the window of an airplane. An oblique perspective requires three inputs: the zenith angle (the angle measured from a horizontal, which ranges from 0° to 90°), the viewing azimuth, which specifies which direction you are looking (0° to 360°), and the viewing distance (how distant the observer is from the surface). One of the first innovations was to create *fishnet* or *wire-frame* diagrams to depict terrain using vector graphics (e.g., the SYMVU program).

The next major advance in landform visualization was the development of *hillshade* maps, which is an approach that models the hypothetical illumination of a surface (Figure 4.14). Hillshade maps can be created using the Spatial Analyst, 3D Analyst, and Geostatistical Analyst extensions, and are discussed in detail in Chapter 7. A further innovation that has taken full advantage of powerful computer graphics is to represent features in three dimensions, from which surfaces, terrain, and whole landscapes can be visualized and analyzed. This is what the ArcScene and 3D Analyst extensions allow you to do.

FIGURE 4.14. Hillshade map showing the dramatic relief of the Rocky Mountains around the Roaring Fork Valley, home to Aspen, Colorado.

4.4 Labeling maps

In addition to portraying geographic features using symbology, you may want to label features simply with their names. A *label* is some descriptive text that is associated with a feature. If labels are to be added to only a few features, then perhaps it makes sense to add them manually. This can be accomplished by creating a text graphic, placing it near the feature to label, and then typing in the desired description. The *Labelling toolbar* (above) provides easy access to the Label Manager dialog and a variety of ways to prioritize and weight labels for each layer.

Four types of labels are available. First, simple text that follows a straight line (usually horizontal, but it can be rotated) can be entered using the *New Text* tool. Second, text can be added so that it follows a curved line using the *splined text* tool, for example, when labeling a winding river. Third, features can be labeled with one of their attributes by clicking on a feature with the *label* tool. Fourth, text can be added in a callout box using the *callout* tool.

Labeling features

1. In the Draw toolbar, select one of the four text tools: *New Text, New Splined Text, Label*, or *Callout*.

New Text: **A**

2. Click at a location and enter the text label in the properties dialog. Click OK.

New Splined Text: ⚘

2. Click to add vertices that follow a curving feature and double-click to end the line, then type in the dialog.

Label: ⌧

2. Set the field to label features from the Labels Tab of the Properties dialog.

3. Click on a feature.

Callout: ⌷

2. Click at a location, then type text into the dialog.

New polygon text: ⌧

2. Click the vertices of a simple polygon (double-click to close), then type desired text into the dialog.

New rectangle text: ⌧

2. Click and drag a rectangle, then type desired text into the dialog.

New circle text: ⌬

2. Click and drag a circle, then type desired text into the dialog.

4.4.1 Dynamic labels

If many or all of the features on a map are to be labeled, then it makes sense to automatically label a layer with what are called *dynamic labels*. To do this, select Label Features from the

---

context menu of a layer. You can specify the attribute that will be used to label in the Labels tab of the Layer Properties dialog. Note that if an attribute value is changed, the label for that feature changes as well. Also, all features can be labeled the same way, or differently by groups (again specified by selecting an attribute). Labels can be turned off by selecting Label Features again. The placement of labels can be controlled, because sometimes in a location dense with features, labels may overlap or conflict. One of the options is to set labels with a priority value.

4.4.2 Annotation

To provide more control over label placement, labels can be converted to *annotation*. Annotation labels can be worked with independently, so the location or font size can be adjusted. Note that other graphic features (points, lines, circles, etc.) can become annotation as well. Annotation (text and graphics) is stored with the map document, or alternatively as a feature type in a geodatabase. One advantage of storing annotation in a geodatabase is that *feature-linked annotation* can be created, which creates a strong linkage between an annotation and its feature. This means that if a feature is moved, then the annotation moves as well. (Note that this functionality requires the ArcEditor or ArcInfo level.)

4.5 Graphs

In addition to maps, geographic data can be visualized using a *graph*, which portrays information about geographic features in a slightly different way than a map. A graph typically aligns attribute values against two dimensions (sometimes three). Often, graphs are used to present summary information that has been gleaned from a spatial analysis (Figure 4.15). Graphs are dynamically linked to their source tables so they are updated as the selection of records (and features) changes. There are a number of different types of graphs available, including the option of overlaying lines on bars (Table 4.3).[30]

---

30. These graphs are quite powerful, and are a big improvement on the graphs that are provided with ArcView v3.x.

FIGURE 4.15. An example of a graph showing summary statistics for major land cover types in Colorado. Note that the graph properties can be modified by right-clicking in the graph title bar.

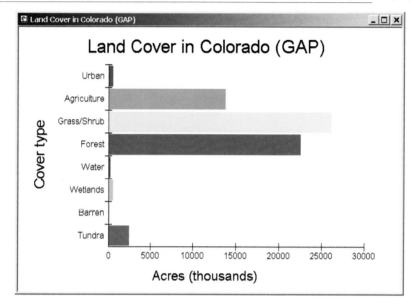

Creating a graph

1. In *ArcMap,* select Tools->Graphs->Create.... to open the Graph Wizard.

2. Select the type of graph.

3. Specify the layer and select the attribute values to graph.

4. Specify the look of the graph.

5. Click Finish.

TABLE 4.3. Available graph types in ArcGIS.

Type	Description	Picture	3D?
Area	Like a line graph, but shades between lines emphasizes quantities. Useful for showing the relationship of several attributes over time.		Y
Bar and column	Consists of two or more parallel bars, each represents an attribute value. Useful to compare amounts between different attributes or trends over time.		
Bubble	Like a scatter graph, but the size of the symbol (bubble) indicates the values of a third attribute.		
High-low-close	Chart a range of values in Cartesian space. Range is shown by vertical bar, and the high, low, and close shown by horizontal crossbars.		
Line	Shows trends in a value along a continuous scale using one or more lines or sequences of symbols drawn on a Cartesian grid. They can be used to display rising and falling trends among several variables.		Y
Pie	Shows the relationship of proportions or between parts and the whole.		Y
Polar	Similar to a line graph, but uses a polar grid where the line relates values to angles.		
Scatter	Plots points based on link attribute values to the x and y axis. These are useful for examining the relationship or correlation between two variables.		Y

Specify the data the graph will be displaying by selecting the records (or fields for most graph types) that will be linked to the x and y axes. Here you can also choose to have the graph change according to the selected set of records, or show all the records all the time.

Finally, specify the appearance by setting the title and labeling the axes. There are a number of additional, advanced features as well, accessed through the **Advanced Options...** button. You can specify titles; modify axis tick, color, and labels; set the fonts for the text; change the markers and symbology; add statistical lines (e.g., min, max, mean, etc.); fit trend lines (e.g,. linear, power, log, etc.) and add a second y-axis[31] by using an *overlay graph*; add error bars (e.g., standard

deviation or standard error); and set the style of the background. Graphs can be added to the layout view, managed through the *Graph Manager* dialog, and accessed through Tools--

---

31. Only available on the area, column, high-low-close, and scatter graph types.

>Graphs.... They can also be exported to a graphic file by selecting Export... from the graph's context menu (*.bmp, *.jpg, *.png, *.wmf, *).

4.6 Map layout

Numerous books have been written about map design and composition, so the approach here is to mention a couple of cartographic rules of thumb, to introduce you to some of the tools that ArcMap provides and to provide references for additional information where appropriate. Maps are composed in the layout view of ArcMap. A layout can have multiple data frames in it to show different views or maps (Figure 4.16).[32] Also, various elements can be added to the layout to provide additional information needed to make a comprehensive, stand-alone map. The typical elements that are found on a map, in addition to the map itself, include: a map title, legend, map scale, north arrow, projection information, and source statement. These elements can be added to a layout view through the Insert menu.

---

32. This may seem limiting compared to ArcView v3.x's ability to have multiple layouts in a project. However, because ArcMap allows layers to be copied in one map document and pasted into another, maps can be best organized by using individual map documents (*.mxd)—rather than packing them into one file (e.g., in an *.apr file)—and still be able to copy layers between map documents.

The *map title* needs to describe, through a short phrase, the essence of the map — what is trying to be conveyed to the reader. Some description of the source data that were used to produce the map, the date of the data, and the map projection should be provided as well. A *neatline* can be added to frame or organize map elements. These elements can be placed on the map using a *text* graphic. The *legend* explains the symbols that are found on the map. A *north arrow* shows the orientation of the map. The *scale bar* shows the amount of detail (or generalization) displayed on the map through a graphic, and the *scale text* portrays the same information, but using words (e.g., "1 inch equals 1 mile"). Finally, other pictures or images can be added as well, for example to incorporate a company logo. A *graticule*, which provides a grid of spatial coordinates on top of the map, can be added to a data frame through its Properties dialog.

4.6.1 *Templates*

ArcMap provides the ability to create a map template. *Templates* are used to standardize layouts so that map series can be easily created and to provide a jump-start to create comprehensive maps. A number of templates are provided with ArcGIS as well, and templates can be shared within and between organizations. Map templates are actually a special type of map document (*.mxt), and so existing template files can be opened by selecting File->Open..., then modify the "Files of Type:" drop-down list to templates. Templates can be saved in the same fashion (File->Save as...). Templates also store the state and configuration of the user interface, such as whether additional toolbars are being used, or whether they are "docked" or not. Also, custom tools are stored in templates.

FIGURE 4.16. Example map layout of the Democratic Republic of Congo.[33]

4.7 Exporting and printing

There are a number of ways a map can be exported to output maps, shown in the data view or layout view, onto different media. First, a map can be exported to a graphic format that can be incorporated into a digital document (e.g., Portable Document Format). Second, it can be printed directly or from one of the exported formats (e.g., Encapsulated PostScript). Third, interactive maps can be created that are web-browser compatible.

TABLE 4.4. Types of maps and their media.

	Media	Advantages	Disadvantages
Map Document	ArcGIS	Full display, query, analysis Hyperlinks, map tips	
Internet Map	ArcIMS	Full dynamic browsing	
Interactive map	ArcPublisher & ArcReader		
Image map	DHTML	Fast, very stable, very portable, low technology investment	
PDF	Adobe Reader	Standard format	Cannot query specific features, information content low
Graphics format	E.g., Enhanced Metafile	Can resize without distortion	
Paper		Easy to read	Expensive

Maps created in ArcMap can be exported to a number of different graphic files[34] — the choice of which method is best depends on a couple of factors. First, does your map contain raster layers, or just feature layers? Feature layers can be exported to what is called vector graphic format, which keeps the features intact and allows the graphic to be resized with little distortion. Second, large-format maps can create very large graphic files (i.e. megabytes to gigabytes in size). As a result, some graphic formats use compression, but it is important to understand whether the compression technique is lossy or lossless. A *lossy* compression technique results in smaller file sizes, but can result in slightly degraded image quality — notably JPEGs. A *lossless* technique compresses files but does not result in image degradation (e.g., GIFs and PNGs). A number of export options are available (Table 4.5).

---

33. Source: from ArcGIS Sample maps, DemocraticRepublicOfCongo.mxd.
34. Compared to ArcView v3.x, the exporting capabilities are much improved, and the application is much more stable.

Also note that a world file can be generated for all graphic file types. A *world file* is an additional file that contains infromation to tell other software where the image is located in the world -- that is, it stores spatial coordinates (but not projection information). The file will have the same name as the image file, with the file extension based on the first and last letters of the image's file extension, plus "w" (e.g., *.tif --> *.tfw). This option is only available when exporting in the Data view.

TABLE 4.5. Graphic formats available when exporting ArcMap data and layout views.

Format (*ArcPress)	Type	Transparency support	World file?
Adobe Illustrator	vector and raster		No
Bitmap	raster		Yes
Computer Graphics Metafile			No
Encapsulated PostScript	vector and raster	yes	No
EMF (Windows Enhanced Metafile)	vector and raster		No
JPEG	raster, lossy compression		Yes
PDF (Adobe's Portable Document Format)	vector and raster	yes	No
PNG*	raster	yes	Yes
SVG (Scalable Vector Graphics)	vector and raster		No
TIFF	raster	yes	Yes

Adobe Illustrator Format (*.ai) — This is a useful format for post-processing maps in Adobe Illustrator (v6.0 and above is supported). Not only does it export maps at 720 dpi, it exports colors in CMYK and preserves most layers from ArcMap, including annotation, labels, and data frame graphics.

Bitmap (*.bmp) — This is a native Windows graphic format, but it can handle only raster images, though it does resize very well. The color depth can also be specified: use 24-bit for maps with color gradients and fills, 8-bit for plain color, and 1-bit for black and white maps. A background color and header file (*.bpw) can be exported to georeference the image (only available with data view).

Computer Graphics Metafile (*.cgm) — This format is a standard in the oil and gas industry. The best resolution choice is 300 dpi.

Encapsulated PostScript (*.eps) — This is the most commonly used format for high-end cartography and printing, and it can handle both feature and raster data. A resolution of 300 dpi produces a good quality graphic, and fonts can be downloaded as well.

Enhanced metafiles (*.emf) — This is a native Windows graphic format that can handle both vector and raster graphics. A nice feature of this format is that these files can be resized without much distortion inside another document (e.g., Microsoft® Word, Microsoft® Powerpoint, Adobe Acrobat PDF, etc.). A resolution of 300 dpi produces a good quality graphic.

Joint Photographic Experts Group (*.jpg) — This is a format for raster graphics, and because it utilizes compression, it has been a favorite for web graphics. However, this format uses a lossy compression technique, and because lines and text in particular become fuzzy, it is recommended to be used only for printing images (like an aerial photograph).[35] Reasonable quality images can be created using 72 or 96 dpi and medium to medium-high quality settings. A progressive JPEQ displays as a series of scans as the file downloads (useful for the Web). Selecting **Clip** removes the white margin of the map (when you are in layout view).

Portable Document Format (*.pdf) — This format is robust and works well across computer platforms, and handles both raster and vector graphics well. A resolution of 300 dpi produces a good quality graphic, and you can also choose to download any fonts used.

Portable Network Graphics (*.png) — This a very useful format as it uses a lossless compression technique and it improves on the older *.gif format by supporting 24-bit color. Use 72 or 96 dpi for web graphics. It also supports transparency (use 24-bit color).

Scalable Vector Graphics (*.svg) — This is an XML-based file format designed for viewing graphics over the Web, and is the standard vector Web format. It is rescalable.

Tagged Image File Format (*.tif) — This format is very robust for handling raster images, and because it works well across computer platforms (e.g., Windows, Mac, UNIX), it is often the format of choice. The background color and a header file (*.tfw) can be exported to georeference the image (only available with data view). If you have the *ArcPress* extension, then a number of additional options are available. ArcPress is a PostScript-based raster image processor that converts maps into high-resolution bitmaps for high-quality printing. When ArcPress is used to print, first the map is exported to an Enhanced Metafile, which is then converted to Encapsulated Postscript. Then, the EPS file is rasterized into a printer-specific bitmap image. The advantage is that the printer does not need to process the image, making it print faster, and making it more robust for really big graphic files. ArcPress is especially useful to print maps with large raster data sets and transparent or complex symbology.

---

35. In the past, this was one of the old standards, but there are much better alternatives available.

> ### *Exporting a map*
>
> 1. In *ArcMap*, select **File->Export Map...**, then choose the format from the dialog.
>
> 2. Navigate to the desired location and specify the filename.
>
> 3. Set the "Save as type:" drop-down list to the desired format.
>
> 4. Modify the options as necessary.
>
> 5. Click **Export**.

4.7.1 Creating interactive maps

An interactive map allows users to query and manipulate the display of a map, either stand-alone on a computer or through the World Wide Web.[36] There are a number of methods to create interactive maps.

4.7.1.1 DHTML

A common format of interactive maps uses Dynamic HTML, particularly an *imagemap*, that allows users to click at a location to bring up specific text or images (Figure 4.17), and to move their cursor to a feature (a "mouse-over") to display text information. Also, clicking at a specific location on a map triggers something, typically a new hyperlink or perhaps a zoomed-in image. ArcGIS does not provide a method to create imagemaps directly, but a number of third-party extensions have been developed that do this.[37]

---

36. For example, see: Peterson, M. 1995. Interactive and animated cartography. Prentice Hall. 257 pgs.; Kraak, M.J. and A. Brown. 2001. Web Cartography. Taylor & Francis. 213 pgs.

37. For example, Alta4's ImageMapper: http://www.alta4.com/eng/products_e/im/im8/

FIGURE 4.17. An example image map allowing users to click at a location and bring up additional information, as well as providing mouse-over information as a "map tip."[38]

4.7.1.2 ArcPublisher

A new type of interactive map can be produced by ESRI's *ArcPublisher* extension, and read by a free plug-in called *ArcReader*. This type of map does not contain the data itself—rather it simply points to data elsewhere on the computer (or Internet). This is a powerful method to create very simple, intuitive interfaces for the general public to gain access to current data.

4.7.1.3 Internet Map Service

A slightly more powerful way to serve maps over the Internet is called *Internet mapping*. This generally requires specialized software (e.g., ArcIMS) to serve data over the Internet (Figures 4.18 and 4.19). One of the main advantages of this method is that it allows users to be able to zoom and pan to their areas of interest, rather than preparing set levels of zoom. It is perhaps most useful when data is updated on a frequent basis (e.g., daily).

---

38. http://www.swegis.com/english/software/imagemapper/samples/im2/dom/index.html

FIGURE 4.18. An example Internet Map Service application—the GeoMac Wildland Fire Support system. Here the perimeter (as of August 15, 2002) of the largest fire in Oregon's history is displayed.[39]

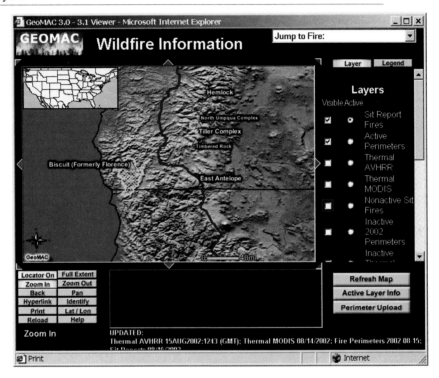

39. http://geomac.usgs.gov/

FIGURE 4.19. An example Internet Map Service application showing the Colorado Ownership, Management, and Protection spatial database displayed in the Colorado Division of Wildlife's Natural Diversity Information Source (www.ndis.nrel.colostate.edu).

Querying a map

5.1 Overview

One of the critical differences between an electronic map displayed in GIS and a paper map is the ability to access or query the data "behind" the map. Queries about map features can be accomplished in two ways. Attribute (*aspatial*) queries utilize attribute data to query a database. For example, a query could find which counties in the US have greater than 100,000 people. *Spatial* queries utilize spatially explicit data and relationships between spatial features. An example of a spatial query would be to identify all counties that have an interstate highway passing through them.

5.1.1 Selection method

Queries can be used to identify and distinguish certain features with desired attributes from the rest of the features of a dataset. The features that are found to match the query specifications are termed *selected* or the *selected set* (examples are shown in Table 5.1). The selection of features is often talked about in terms of sets, based on Boolean logic operations: AND, OR, NOT, and XOR (Table 5.2).

Basically, these methods instruct ArcMap either to disregard the currently selected set of features (i.e. create new), or to recognize the current selection and add to it, remove from it, or select from it. The most commonly used (and by default) selection method is *create a new selection,* which does not recognize the selected set of features before the new query is applied. Another method is to *add to current selection,* which adds those features selected by the new query to the current selected set. You can also *remove from current selection,* which removes features selected in the new query from those that were already selected. Finally, *select from current selection* respects the current selection and returns only those already-selected features that meet the new criteria.

Selection of features has changed slightly in v9 to make it consistent with the geoprocessing framework. Previous versions did not differentiate between the situation where zero features were selected and where no selection set existed (a selection has to be made to in order for a selection set to exist). This enabled functions in the past to assume that "no selection is the same as all the features selected." Now, with v9, these states are differentiated. If you query a feature dataset and the selection criteria results in zero features being selected, then the next Geoprocessing operation will use 0 features (instead of all that would have occurred pre-v9).

TABLE 5.1. Examples of applying different selection methods on a table with 5 features. The current selected set (A) is used by selection query (B) to obtain a resulting selection. C denotes the set of all features.

Method	Current selection	Selection query	Resulting selection	Boolean set
Create a new selection	1, 2, 3, 4, 5	1, 2, 3	1, 2, 3	B
	1, 2	1, 2, 3	1, 2, 3	
Add to current selection	1, 2, 3, 4, 5	1, 2, 3	1, 2, 3, 4, 5	A OR B
	1, 2, 3	3, 4	1, 2, 3, 4	
Remove from current selection	1, 2, 3, 4, 5	1, 2, 3	4, 5	A NOT B
	1	2, 3	1	
Select from current selection	1, 2, 3, 4, 5	1, 2, 3	1, 2, 3	A AND B
	1, 2, 3	2, 4, 5	2	
Select all	1, 2, 3, 4, 5	1, 2, 3, 4, 5	1, 2, 3, 4, 5	C
	1, 2	1, 2, 3, 4, 5	1, 2, 3, 4, 5	
Switch selection	1, 2, 3, 4, 5	-	-	C NOT A
	1, 2, 3	-	4, 5	
	1, 3, 5	-	2, 4	

5.2 Where is…? Where are...?

There are two methods to locate a feature through its attributes: through the **Find** dialog and through the **Select By Attributes** dialog.[1] Which to use? Find is best used for fairly simple queries, while Query Builder provides the ability to develop more complicated queries involving several attributes and even compound Boolean logic.

5.2.1 Find

You can quickly find features in ArcMap through the *Find* dialog.[2] For example, where is the US zip code 90210 anyway? By default, *Find* searches through string and numerical fields in all *visible layers* in ArcMap, finding matches to the input search string. Matched records are listed at the bottom of the dialog, and by right-clicking on the value, you can flash the feature(s) on the map, zoom to the feature(s), and even set the spatial extent that contains the features as a bookmark. You can list all the attributes of that feature (like Identify), and you can also select the features by clicking on them — selected features on the map are shown by a highlighted color (default is cyan).

```
 Find                                                        ? x

Features | Route Locations | Addresses |                    Find

Find:     90210                                        ▼      Stop

In layers: <Visible layers>                            ▼    New Search

      ☑ Find features that are similar to or contain the search string
                                                             ◉
Search: ⦿ All fields

        ○ In fields   FID                        ▼

        ○ Each layer's primary display field                Cancel

Right-click a row to show context menu.

Value          Layer               Field
90210          Zip Code Points     ENC_ZIP
90210          Zip Code Points     ZIP
90210          Zip Code Points     ENC_ZIP
90210          Zip Code Areas      ZIP

4 objects found.
```

Querying using Find

1. In *ArcMap*, click **Edit->Find…** (or click on the Find button 🔍).

2. Fill out the "Find:" string and other parameters.

3. Click **Find**.

---

1. In ArcView v3.x, this was called the Query Builder dialog.
2. Note that ArcCatalog's Search feature finds whether a dataset is within some geographic region that you specify.

There are a number of options to modify the way Find works. First, the layers that are to be searched can be specified to find values in: all visible layers (default), selectable layers, all layers (in data frame), all layers in all data frames, and individual layers by name. Second, you can match strings that are similar to the search string (default, like a wildcard search), or exactly the search string (case-sensitive as well). Third, all fields can be searched, a specific field you choose, or just the field that is used to display a layer's labels (the *display field*). Also note that the search string is automatically recorded and available for subsequent searches.

5.2.2 *Select by attributes (SQL)*

Another way to accomplish this type of query is to specify a query string or expression using Structured Query Language (SQL) in the **Select By Attributes** dialog. A proper SQL query is formed by a threesome of field, operand, and value, which must be separated by spaces.[3] There are five steps (start at the top and end at the bottom) to use this powerful dialog. (Note, the Select by Attributes dialog has been improved with v9.1 (shown at right[4]). First, select the layer you want to query (only those layers in a data frame are listed). The list of fields in the selected layer's attribute table is updated automatically (and notice there is plenty of room for long field names). Note that you can limit the entries in this list to only "selectable" layers (set in Selection -> Set Selectable Layers...). Second, select one of the four selection methods -- default is a new selection.[5] Third, specify a query

---

3. Expressions must be in the form: <field> <operand> <value>, while compound expressions can be formed as well: <field> <operand> <value> {AND|OR|NOT} <field> <operand> <value>

expression in the expression text box. One way to do this is to simply type in an expression. A faster and easier way is to form the query expression interactively -- this way you will not need to recall the syntax! Double-click on the desired field to add the quote-delimited field name to the expression text box. Click on one of the operand buttons (=, <>, >, >=, <, <=, Like, or Is). To get the unique values associated with a given field, click on the "Get Unique Values" button. Then, double-click on the desired value(s). Fourth, decide if you want to save your expression for later (this is a good habit to form!). Fifth, press OK. Viola!

For example, our earlier query for the Beverly Hills zip code 90210 will look like this:

"ZIP" = '90210'

---

4. The *Query Wizard* button in v8 of the dialog has gone away.
5. In v9.1 the default method can be specified by....

Note that fields must be delimited by double-quotes ("", no spaces!), strings must be delimited by single quotes, and numbers cannot have delimeters—for shapefiles (dBASE) and coverages (INFO) (Table 5.2).[6] Numerical values have no delimeters (and you cannot use comma delimeters for thousands, millions, etc.). There are a number of operands available: = (equals), < (less than), > (greater than), <= (less than or equal to), >= (greater than or equal to), and <> (not equal to). There cannot be a space between the <=, >=, or <> characters (e.g., **"Field" >= 23** is valid, while **"Field" > = 23** is invalid (because of the space between the > and =). Use parentheses if you need to change the assumed left-to-right evaluation order .

6. This can be slightly confusing for ArcView v3.x users because fields were delimited by square brackets and strings by double-quotes.

> ### *Querying using Select by Attributes*
>
> 1. In *ArcMap*, click **Selection->Select by Attributes….**
> 2. Select the desired *layer*.
> 3. Select the desired selection method.
> 4. Create the query expression by typing the expression in or clicking on the desired *field*, the appropriate operand (action), and the value.
> 5. Save your expression to an expression file (for later use and documentation).
> 6. Click **OK**.

TABLE 5.2. Summary of SQL idiosyncrasies

Dataset	Field delimiter	Case sensitive	Wildcard
Shapefile (dBASE)	"AREA"	Y	_ , %
Coverage (INFO)	"AREA"	Y	_ , %
Geodatabase (ACCESS)	[AREA]	N	?, *
SDE	AREA		

Some additional examples are as follows (assuming shapefile and coverage databases):

("area" >1500) ' do not enclose values in quotes

("pop2000" < "pop1990") ' finds all counties with declining population

("area" * 0.000247105 <= 25) ' can include calculations—convert area in m to acres

("pop1990" / "area" <=25) ' can include fields in calculations

("state_name" = 'colorado') ' strings are single-quoted

("county_name" LIKE 'rio%') ' use % as a multiple character wildcard

("owner_name" LIKE '_aul') ' use an "_" (underscore, not hyphen) as a single character wildcard, gets Saul and Paul

("county_name" >= 'r') ' select counties with names beginning with R to Z

Compound queries can be created that use the Boolean logic operators: AND (both criteria must be true), OR (either criteria must be true), and NOT (exclude). Compound queries query values from multiple fields (Table 5.3).

("area" > 1500) and ("garage" > 3) ' complex query can use AND, OR, NOT

TABLE 5.3. Compound statements using Boolean AND, OR, and NOT. The table below describes the possible combinations of conditional statements (T = TRUE, F = FALSE). Both statements must be true when using the AND operator, and either statement can be true when using the OR operator.

A	B	A AND B	A OR B	NOT A	NOT B
T	T	T	T	F	F
T	F	F	T	F	T
F	T	F	T	T	F
F	F	F	F	T	T

5.2.2.1 Advanced SQL

Note that there are a number of additional SQL operators that can be used in the Select by Attribute dialog, in addition to =, >, >=, etc. These include: ASC, BY, CURRENT_DATE, DATE, DESC, FROM, IN, IS, LIKE, LOWER, NULL, ORDER, SELECT, TRUNC, UPPER, and WHERE.[7] For example:

"DATE" < DATE '1999-12-25' ' select records before Christmas 1999

"STATE" IN ('Alabama', 'Alaska', 'California', 'Florida') 'true if one of these in list

"STATE" IS NULL ' find records where no values has been entered yet

"STATE" LIKE 'New%' ' gets New Hampshire, New Jersey, New Mexico, New York

NOT "STATE" = 'California') 'finds all states but California

LOWER("STATE") = 'colorado' 'only in Access and SDE - converts text to lower case

UPPER("STATE") = 'COLORADO' 'only in Access and SDE - converts text to upper case.

There are a number of advanced options available through the *Select By Attributes* dialog. One of the most important of these is that query strings can be saved to and loaded from an *expression file* (*.exp). This is useful to save the query to help document your work. To use this, first create a query string, then save it to an expression file.[8] Unfortunately, only one query can

7. Descriptions of these can be found in Visual Basic help, which can be accessed through **Tools -> Macros -> Visual Basic Editor**. Then, select **Visual Basic Language Reference -> Functions**.

be saved at a time per file — make sure the filename captures what the expression does. The most recent query is also left in the dialog.

5.2.3 Definition query

By default, all features of a layer are displayed and queried. In certain situations, however, it is useful to restrict a layer to a subset of its features temporarily and query from that subset. For example, you may only care about major rivers instead of all rivers contained in a layer. Instead of creating a separate dataset, you can temporarily remove the unwanted features by applying a *definition query*. An advantage of temporarily subsetting a layer is that if the dataset is updated or modified, changes will be automatically reflected in the layer the next time the map document is opened. Using a subset of the data also speeds up the drawing speed and any analytical operations on a layer. Definition queries are specified through the Definition Query tab in the Layer Properties dialog (using the same interface as the Select by Attributes).

Setting the Definition Query

1. In *ArcMap*, right-click on the layer and select Properties.

2. Select the Definition Query tab.

3. Click on the Query Builder... button.

4. Create a query using the Select by Attributes dialog, then click OK.

5. Click OK.

---

8. By saving these in a central place—either within a folder that contains your project documents, or a globally-available location—a "library" of expressions can be created.

5.3 What is here?

5.3.1 *Identify*

To query a particular location, use the

Identify tool ⓘ. Clicking with this tool on a feature in a layer brings up the Identify Results dialog that displays the attribute values for the feature. In contrast to queries that select features, the Identify tool does not change the selected set. Also note that you can specify which layers will be searched: *visible layers* (those that are displayed or drawn in the view portion of ArcMap), *selectable layers, all layers, top-most layer*, and each layer in the data frame by name. Each value can be copied (right-click) so they can be transferred more easily.

In a similar fashion to Identify, the primary attribute of a feature can be easily displayed using *map tips*. The display value for the feature at the location of the cursor is updated as the cursor is moved across the map. Note that more than one layer can have map tips on, and that map tips also works on raster datasets.

Turning map tips on

1. In *ArcMap*, right-click on the layer and select Properties.

2. Select the Display tab.

3. Check the Show Map Tips box.

4. Click on the Fields tab to set the primary display field.

5. Click OK.

5.3.2 *Interactive selection*

Features can be selected using the cursor, and then the selected set can be examined in the attribute table. To query a layer through *interactive selection,* use the *Select Features* tool(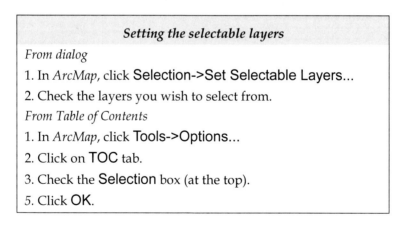). First, you need to specify which layers to select features from, and that is typically accomplished through the *Selectable Layers* dialog. One common source of confusion is that as layers are added to a data frame, they are automatically made selectable, so features from many layers may get selected by default. An additional, and useful, way to view the selectable layers is to add the **Selection** tab in the table of contents so that the selectable layers can be displayed in the Table of Contents. To display the number of selected features for a single layer, click on the layer name and the status bar will display "*n* features selected", where n is the number of selected features. Note that the number of features selected is displayed in the status bar in the lower-left part of the ArcMap window.[9]

Setting the selectable layers

From dialog

1. In *ArcMap,* click **Selection->Set Selectable Layers...**

2. Check the layers you wish to select from.

From Table of Contents

1. In *ArcMap,* click **Tools->Options...**

2. Click on **TOC** tab.

3. Check the **Selection** box (at the top).

5. Click **OK**.

---

9. In v8.3 and v9, when the "Number of features selected:" is displayed, the number of selected features for all layers is summed and the total is displayed.

Features can also be *deselected*, or removed from the selected set by shift-clicking, and *switch selection*, which reverses the selected features. Note that interactive selection actually selects all the features within a *selection tolerance*, that is, those features that are found within a radius of a specified number of pixels (three by default).[10]

Interactively changing the selected set

To add to the selected set

1. In *ArcMap*, check the layers you desire from the *Selectable Layers* dialog.

2. Select the *Select Features* tool( ).

3. Select the first feature, then shift-select subsequent features.

To switch selection

1. In *ArcMap*, right-click on the layer and select **Selection->Switch Selection**.

2. Select the **Display** tab.

To modify selection tolerance

1. In *ArcMap*, click **Selection->Options...**

2. Set the **Selection tolerance** (in pixels).

3. Click **OK**.

---

10. Note that the point-in-polygon algorithm is likely not used here, because the selection can be an area (as specified by the selection tolerance).

5.4 How big?

One way to determine the area of a feature is to use the *Identify* tool to get the value of the area field in a polygon coverage theme. You will need to know what units represent this value, which are usually based on the projection. Many times, however, there is not an area field in the attribute table (though you can create one). In this case, you can visualize the size of certain features on a theme by placing a graphic in the data view and resizing it through the Properties dialog, using the "Size and Position" property. For instance, if you want to see how features on the map compare to a 100 km radius circle (above right), you could add a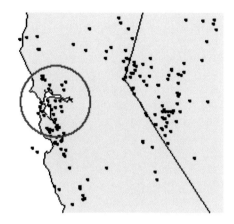
circle and change the radius value. This is useful when trying to visualize features that are within a certain distance or how large features are compared to a benchmark (e.g., an acre, hectare, soccer field, city block). One caution: it is recommended to calculate length and area only on projected views because distance is greatly distorted as a function of increasing latitude with geographic coordinates (or spherical distance and area calculations are needed).

5.5 How far?

You can determine the distance between features by using the

Measure tool 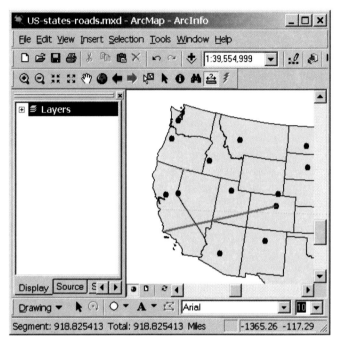. After selecting the tool, click on the map at the start of a feature, then click at the end of the feature you are measuring. You can also measure a complex feature by using a number of line segments to approximate a curvilinear feature. Both the segment length and total length (of all segments) are displayed in the status bar in the units defined in the General tab of the data frame's Properties dialog. For example, the as-the-crow-flies distance between Denver, Colorado and Santa Barbara, California is 918 miles. The display units can be changed through the properties (General tab) of the data frame.

5.6 What features are near another feature?

Another powerful method of selecting features of a layer is through their
spatial relationships with another
layer(s). ArcMap allows you to select
features of a layer based on their relationship to features of another layer
using the *Select by Location* dialog.
With this spatial query method, problems that involve issues of proximity,
adjacency, and containment can be
addressed. For example, what cities
and towns in the western US are
located within the forest fringe
(above, right)? This type of operation
requires that you specify *target* and *filter* layers. The *target* layer is the layer
that contains the features you want to
select (e.g., towns and cities—black

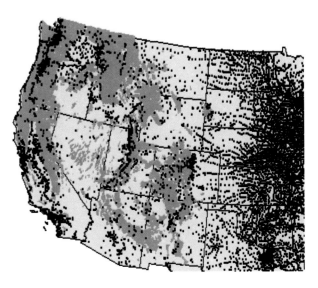

dots). The *filter* layer contains the selected features that you want to use as a filter (e.g., forest
land cover—in green). Note that you can specify multiple target layers.

> ### *Querying using Select by location*
>
> 1. In *ArcMap*, click **Selection->Select by location...**) to bring
> up the dialog.
>
> 2. Specify the type of selection in the "I want to:" drop-down
> list.
>
> 3. Check the box next to each *target* layer you want to select
> from.
>
> 4. Set the spatial relation type (e.g., intersect).
>
> 5. Set the filter layer you want to select features in relation to.
>
> 6. Click **Apply**.

5.6.1 Spatial relation types

ArcMap provides eleven ways to relate features from one layer to another. Recall from the discussion of spatial relations in Chapter 1, that there were topological, directional, and proximal relationships. ArcMap provides methods for both topological and proximal relationships. To spice up what can be a rather dry topic, I will use the analogy of a pizza in a box to explain spatial relation types: not just any pizza, but a circular pizza,[11] perfectly cut into at least four slices so that all touch at the center point. Sounds delicious so far, but one slice has anchovies on it (yuk!).

5.6.1.1 Equivalent

The *are identical to* method is used to test whether two or more features (of the same feature type) are spatially equivalent. This means that for two slices of pizza to be the same, they must be the same size, shape, and be placed directly on top of one another. They also must have the same number of vertices and the vertices must be in the same location. So, in a topologic sense, there are no two pieces that are equivalent in the pizza.

5.6.1.2 Partially equivalent

To test whether two or more features are partially equivalent (meaning that they overlap one another or cross one another), the *intersect* method is used typically. Polygon features intersect if they overlap, if they share a line segment, or even if they share a point. This means that a given slice of pizza intersects all other slices (at the center), even though it does not overlap any other slice. The *are crossed by the outline of* method is similar, but a feature is only selected if the area of overlap (two polygons) or length (line/line, line/polygon) is greater than 0. Shared segments or vertices do not count: no slice of pizza is adjacent to any other. The *have their center in*

---

11. If the analogy of spaghetti worked so well when talking about topology and data structures, why not pizza?

method requires that not only the area of overlap (or length) exceeds 0, but a feature's center[12] is within the polygon feature as well.

5.6.1.3 Contained

The *are completely within* method requires a feature to be contained in another so that all of the overlapping areas (or length) are within the polygon, and they cannot share any boundary segments or points. A slice of a pizza is completely within the box if it does not touch an edge. The *are contained by* method also requires all of the area (length) to be overlapping, but the features can touch at a point or share a line segment. So, a slice is contained by the box even if it touches the edge. The reverse methods are: *completely contain* and *contain* (but the slices cannot contain the pizza box — completely or otherwise).

5.6.1.4 Adjacency

Adjacency occurs when two features share a common boundary or meet at a point. The *share a line segment* method means that a given slice has two and only two adjacent slices — the slices on either side of a given slice. The *touch the boundary of* method means that two features are adjacent when they share even a single point, so that all slices are adjacent to a given slice (because of the center point).

5.6.1.5 Separate

Features that are separate or disjoint cannot overlap or touch (not even a single vertex). This means, for many people, that the anchovy slice must not overlap or even touch any other slice for it to be edible.

5.6.1.6 Proximal

The *are within a distance of* method selects features near or adjacent that are within a specified distance. This means that for some extreme folks, the anchovy slice must not be in the same room, lest the remaining piece be rendered inedible.

5.6.2 Buffered selections

A useful feature in the Select by Location dialog is the *apply a buffer to the features of* option. This applies a buffer of a specified distance from the features in the filter layer.

5.6.3 Examples of common selections

A common need in locational queries is to select point features that are near a linear feature (*point near line*). For example, to select locations that occur within 25 m of a river, set the linear

---

12. A feature's center is not its centroid, the centroid is the center of mass, and can fall outside for convex polygons, whereas the center is always guaranteed to fall within the polygon.

feature (e.g., rivers) to be the *filter* layer, and then select point features using *are within a distance of* 25 m.

Often the points that are found within polygon features are needed (*point in polygon*). For example, to determine the number of people who are potentially at risk from forest fires, the points (e.g., towns and cities) that *intersect* the forested area (polygon layer) could be selected. The features from the filter layer (the forest polygon) could also be buffered (e.g., by two miles) to extend the notion of the forest fringe, so potentially some locations are at risk outside of the forested area.

You can also select linear features that pass through or intersect polygonal features (*line in polygon*). For example, you could select administration units (e.g., counties), using *intersect* or *are crossed by the outline of*, that have interstates running through them. You might also select wilderness areas that have roads running directly on their borders using *share a line segment with*.

Linear features that occur within certain polygonal features can also be selected (polygon on line). For example, you could select stretches of streams and rivers in the western US that occur on public land. By using the *intersects* method, you would find any stream that even touched public land, for example if the stream formed the boundary of public land. By using the *have their center in* method, you would likely find the large stretches or rivers within public land. If you used the *are completely within* method, then the entire river stretch would need to be on public land.

5.6.4 *What is adjacent?*

A simple way to determine features that are spatially adjacent (a.k.a. *first-order neighbors*) to a particular feature is to select them interactively using the *Select Features* tool. However, interactively selecting features can be a time-consuming and error prone process for complex themes. So, how can adjacent features be found in a more automated process? Although many people assume that because shapefiles do not maintain topology (i.e. a file depicting neighborhood relations) that adjacent features cannot be selected. However, adjacent features *can* be selected in ArcMap, but the same dataset must be represented by two different layers in order to trick the Select by Location dialog.

> ### *Finding adjacent neighbors*
>
> 1. In *ArcMap*, right-click on desired layer and select Copy.
>
> 2. Right-click on the *data frame,* then select Paste layer.
>
> 3. Bring up the Select by Location dialog, the box next to each *target* layer you want to select from.
>
> 4. Set the spatial relation type (e.g., intersect).
>
> 5. Set the filter layer you want to select features in relation to.
>
> 6. Click Apply.

To do this, first make a copy of the layer in the data frame so that two layers depict the same dataset (select Copy from the layer's context menu, then Paste layer from the data frame's context menu). Then, set the relation type to *intersect*, and choose the layer and the copy of the layer for the layer selections.

Querying a map

CHAPTER 6

Creating and editing feature data

6.1 Overview

There are numerous ways to edit existing datasets or create new ones in ArcGIS, and in this chapter these techniques are discussed in detail. There are two issues of particular importance in this chapter that provide the context for these methods. The first issue is to understand the trade-offs involved with creating new spatial data vs. dynamically subsetting or joining data. The second issue is that of editing to create and/or maintain map topology. Although ArcMap does not automatically check topology, the tools *are* provided that allow for the creation and maintenance of topologically valid (planar enforced) datasets. Also presented in this chapter are methods to edit attribute data in tables.

6.2 Creating a new dataset

Frequently, a new dataset will need to be created from scratch. The process of defining the type of feature and attributes needed is accomplished through ArcCatalog, and then new features are created through ArcMap. Another common way to create a new dataset is through some selection (either all or some features) of an existing dataset, and then individual features are edited. Occasionally, features themselves do not need to be modified, rather simply a selection of features from an existing dataset is needed. In this case, either a new dataset can be created, or a dataset can be dynamically subsetted.

6.2.1 Creating a new dataset

New shapefiles, geodatabases, and coverages[1] are created in ArcCatalog, and the properties cannot be modified after a new dataset is created. The properties that need to be specified for a shapefile include its name, the type of features it will contain (point[2], polyline, polygon), whether it also stores *m* values (measured values) at each vertex (used for routes), whether it stores *z* values (elevation) at each vertex, and the coordinate system. After the dataset is created, then the attributes can be specified through the layer's properties (right).

For geodatabases, the process is similar, but slightly more complicated because of the numerous feature datasets, classes, and relationships that can be specified.[3] Recall that only personal geodatabases can be created with ArcView-level functionality.

---

1. Coverages cannot be created with ArcView-level functionality, but shapefiles and simple geodatabases can be created.
2. A multi-point feature type can also be created.
3. See ArcGIS Help -> Geodatabases -> Introduction to Geodatabases -> Creating your database.

Creating a new shapefile dataset

1. In ArcCatalog, navigate to a desired folder (remember it should not have non-alphanumeric characters).

2. Select File -> New -> Shapefile. If this is greyed-out or not available, be sure that you do not have a dataset already selected.

3. Specify the name of the shapefile (again, use only alphanumeric and the underscore characters).

4. Select the feature type.

5. Click on the Edit... button to specify the coordinate system.

6. Check the *m value* and/or the *z value* check-boxes, as desired.

7. Click OK.

8. Find the newly-created shapefile and right-click, then select Properties.

9. Add a new field by clicking in the Field Name column in the space below the last existing field, and type in a field name.

10. Specify the field type by clicking in the Data Type column and selecting the desired type.

Creating a new geodatabase dataset

1. In ArcCatalog, navigate to a desired folder (remember it should not have non-alphanumeric characters).

2. Select **File -> New -> Personal Geodatabase**. If this is greyed-out or not available, be sure that you do not have a dataset already selected.

3. Specify the name of the geodatabase (again, use only alphanumeric and the underscore characters).

New feature dataset

4. Right-click on the geodatabase and select **New -> Feature dataset...** Name it, then click **OK**.

New feature class

5. Right-click on the geodatabase and select **New -> Feature class...** Name it, then click **Next**.

6. Specify the configuration keyword, then click Next.

7. Click on the **Shape** field name, then specify the feature type by clicking on **Geometry Type.**

8. To add other attribute fields, click in the **Field Name** column in the space below the last existing field, and type in a field name.

9. Specify the field type by clicking in the **Data Type** column and selecting the desired type.

10. When finished adding fields, click **Finish**.

6.2.2 *Converting a dataset*

There are a number of reasons to convert a dataset from one format to another, including: to create a new dataset containing a subset of the original dataset; to create a dataset in a different coordinate system; to speed up display time (e.g., using shapefiles); and to standardize format with other users. One common method available in ArcMap (ArcView-level) is to export a dataset to a shapefile.

Exporting a dataset to a shapefile

1. In ArcMap, right-click on layer to export and select **Data -> Export Data...**

2. Select the features to export: all, selected, or in view extent.

3. Choose whether to use the layer or data frame's coordinate system.

4. Click on the folder icon to navigate to a desired location, and select the output format.

5. Click **OK**.

6.2.3 Sub-setting a dataset

If the features themselves do not need to be modified, then a new dataset can be created that is simply a subset of the original dataset. In addition, there are methods to dynamically subset a dataset, and there are important trade offs to understand when choosing which method to use. To subset a dataset, a definition query is applied. Definition queries are specified through the Definition Query tab in the Layer Properties dialog (described in detail in Chapter 5).

Sub-setting a dataset in current extent

1. In *ArcMap*, select **Tools -> Options...**

2. Select the **TOC** tab, and check the box to show the Selection tab. Click OK.

3. Click on Selection tab in the Table of Contents.

4. Select only the features in the current extent using the Select features tool.

5. Right-click on desired layer and select **Create Layer from Selected Features**. Note that the new layer trimmed to the current extent is automatically added to the map document.

TABLE 6.1. Advantages and disadvantages associated with permanent or dynamic subsetting of a dataset.

Data type	Function	Advantages	Disadvantages
Spatial	Definition query	Subsets features, both visibly in the layer and in attribute table Less confusing Updates to layer automatic	For large layers, possible long query times when opening map document
	Convert	Smaller datasets Can edit individual features	Updates to parent layer not automatic
Table	Relate/Join	Less storage Updates automatic	Cannot edit the related table
	Export joined file	Smaller file size Can edit joined field values	Not automatically updated

6.3 Topology revisited

As was discussed in Chapter 2, topology plays a central role in GIS. Planar topology has been employed traditionally in GIS through the use of topological data structures, chiefly for two reasons. First, explicit depiction of neighborhood relationships allows advanced spatial analysis to be conducted on a set of geographical features. Second, topology provides a rigorous method to clean up spatial data that have been created during digitizing and editing to identify artifacts that result during the creation of spatial data. The traditional *modus operandi* of creating digital spatial data has been to digitize a map by following the borders of features, crossing from one to another without respect to the feature. This so-called *spaghetti digitizing* developed historically because computers and display technology were too slow to conduct any real-time checking of the input geometry, so topology was employed to post-process digitized data to ensure topological consistency. This provides a practical means to build large spatial datasets in a rigorous manner. As a result, a whole GIS lexicon has formed over the process of digitizing, editing, and building topology.

To illustrate how spaghetti digitizing works and why topology is needed, imagine that the boundaries of four rural residential blocks are being digitized from an aerial photo in order to create areal units for census-related activities (Figure 6.1). First, the boundary is digitized by starting at one corner, then intermediate vertices are placed along the roads[4], going around the

---

4. Single vertices are specified by clicking on a location. You can also set ArcMap to *stream digitize* to automatically capture points as you move the cursor across the screen, through the General tab of the Editor Options dialog.

perimeter of the blocks and ending back at the starting point. Second, the three lines that separate the blocks are digitized. Next, labels are added to uniquely identify each polygon. Finally, the data are ready to be post-processed to remove spurious artifacts.

FIGURE 6.1. "Spaghetti" digitizing of four polygons: 1) outer boundary is digitized (upper left); 2) three bisecting lines are digitized (upper right); 3) clean up overshoots and undershoots (lower left); 4) add ID labels (lower right).

Recall that a polyline (or chain) has a node at the start and end point, with a series of segments called arcs. By definition the starting and ending point of a polygon must be at the same location, but in practice it is virtually impossible to click exactly at the location of the starting point when digitizing. If the start and end nodes do not touch, the polygon is not closed (called an *undershoot),* resulting in a polygon that has multiple labels associated with it (Figure 6.2).

So, to ensure that polygons close and polylines intersect, start and end vertices are purposefully placed such that the polyline crosses another line and the small fragment that extends beyond the intersection to the end node is called an *overshoot*. As a result, spaghetti digitizing creates numerous *dangling nodes*, both of the overshoot and undershoot variety, that need to be cleaned up.

FIGURE 6.2. Common artifacts created during spaghetti digitizing and "cleaning and building" of topology.

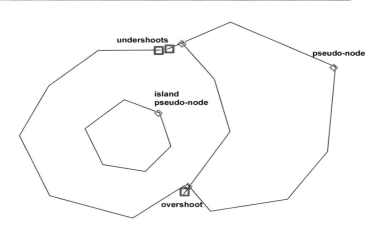

The "clean and build" process enforces planar topology by identifying all the line intersections. If two lines intersect, but not at the location of two nodes (the start or end point of one line and the start or end point of a second line), then the line(s) is cut into two lines forming nodes at the intersection. The next step is to automatically identify and remove dangling nodes, which requires that a *dangle length* be defined such that overshoots that are less than the dangle length are removed. Here we are stuck with a problem reminiscent of one that Goldilocks faced—the "just right" problem, solved best by trial-and-error. That is, the dangle length must not be too large such that undershoots that represent parts of a polygon boundary are removed, nor should it be too small so that overshoots are left remaining. Also, a *fuzzy tolerance* must be defined, such that if two vertices are within a given distance, they will be snapped together. In this way lines that have been *double digitized* are cleaned up, but if the fuzzy tolerance is too large, then real features can be simplified and possibly removed altogether. This is especially problematic when editing maps with a large extent, because the default tolerance is typically set to a fraction of the spatial extent (e.g., 1/10,000). Further compounding the difficulty of clearly identifying dangling nodes is that there are a number of real-life features that are legitimate dangling nodes. For example, roads often stop abruptly a short distance from an intersection, often in cul-de-sacs. Occasionally, when only two polylines touch, a feature called a *pseudo-node* is created. These are typically artifacts of the digitizing process where two individual lines were digitized, and are generally not needed. Some pseudo-nodes are needed, however, such as *island pseudo-nodes* that are required to create an island polygon.

6.4 Feature-oriented editing

Although it remains important to understand how topology is used to post-process spaghetti-digitized data, currently the tools exist to digitize from a feature-oriented perspective.[5] This approach to digitizing and editing spatial data also ensures a planar-enforced map, but does not require post-processing and thus artifacts such as overshoots and undershoots do not need to be cleaned up! To illustrate the difference between spaghetti and *feature-oriented digitizing*, let us return to our example of digitizing the boundaries of four residential blocks from an aerial photo (Figure 6.3).

The feature-oriented approach creates one feature at a time and for polygon features, relies on three main editing tools provided in ArcGIS: *create new feature, auto complete polygon*, and *cut polygon features*. These tools ensure that adjacent polygons share boundaries—which means that planar topology is enforced (this is called *topological association* in ArcMap) to prevent overlaps. First, a new polygon can be created by digitizing individual vertices and then double-clicking within the snap distance of the starting point to close the polygon. Second, adjacent polygons can be created using the auto complete tool by beginning at one corner and digitizing the three edges of the second block, ensuring that the two adjacent polygons share boundaries. Third, a single large polygon can be "cut" into multiple smaller polygons. The resulting four polygons have topology without clean and build operations, nor arc-node features.

Topology is fully implemented in Geodatabases in ArcGIS v8.3.[6] It is important to note that the approach to topology in Geodatabases reflects this feature-oriented perspective and is a significant departure from topology as implemented in the past. There are two main differences in this new approach to map topology. First, rather than storing topological relationships explicitly in data files (i.e., like coverages do), Geodatabase topology stores the rules, ranks, and cluster tolerance that are applied to check topology on-the-fly, rather than as a final editing process (i.e. as in CLEAN and BUILD with ArcInfo v7). Second, topological

---

5.   ArcView v3.x provides these tools as well. Actually, as early as 1987 a GIS system was designed to approach digitzing from this perspective: White, D., J. Corson-Rikert, and M. Maizel. 1987. "WYSIWYG" map digitizing: Real time geometric correction and topological encoding. *Proceedings from Auto-Carto 8*: 739-743.

6.   For a helpful introduction to topology at v8.3, see: Childs, C. 2003. ArcGIS topology for ArcView users. *ArcUser* (July-September): 48-49.

relationships can be examined not only between features within a dataset (e.g., a vegetation layer), but also between datasets (e.g., a vegetation layer and a road layer). This is a powerful addition that enables coincident geometry between datasets.

FIGURE 6.3. Feature-centric digitizing of four polygons: 1) create new, closed polygon (upper left); 2) add adjacent polygon using the "auto-complete" tool (upper right and lower left); 3) "cut" polygon into two polygons (lower left) to create the four polygons that are planar-enforced (lower right). Note that no post-processing is needed.

6.5 Feature editing basics

When editing spatial data in ArcMap, there are a couple of important ways to control how the editing tools work. A primary means is the snapping environment that specifies whether Arc-Map recognizes existing features that are found either in the same layer that is being edited or in a different layer. Editing is accomplished through the Edit toolbar after an edit session is established.

6.5.1 Starting an edit session

After a dataset has been added as a layer to ArcMap, an edit session can be started. To edit layers, the Editor Toolbar must be added to the ArcMap interface (or already available). Only one collection of datasets can be added at a time from the currently active data frame. When you start an edit session, ArcMap will notify you if there are multiple datasets available in your ArcMap document, and then you will need to choose one. Once an edit session is established, all the changes made are placed into a temporary buffer. These changes are not made permanent until the edits are saved, and adding, moving, deleting features can be incrementally undone (ctrl-Z).

FIGURE 6.4. Editor toolbars in ArcMap showing v8.2 and v8.3. Notice that the Shared Edit tool (second from right in v8.2, above) has been removed in v8.3 (below) and placed on the Topology toolbar.

When you begin editing, you'll need to think about the "3Ts" of the editor toolbar: *target, task,* and *tool*. First, think about the *target*—what dataset do you want to edit? Second, what is the edit task? There are a dozen or so different tasks available that are used to create or modify features.[7] Third, which tool will be used to accomplish the task? The sketch ( ) and edit ( )

---

7. At v8.3, tasks are grouped in the Editor toolbar into create, modify, and topology tasks.

tools are the main tools you will use, but there may be other tools available depending on the task. Basically, a tool is used to perform some task on a particular target.

Starting an edit session

1. In ArcMap, add the Editor Toolbar by selecting View -> Toolbars -> Editor.

2. From the Editor Toolbar, select Editor -> Start Editing.

3. If multiple datasets are in ArcMap, select the desired one to edit.

Note that editing datasets with a large amount of data may be fairly slow, so to speed things up a bit you have the option to create an *edit cache* to store in memory all the features found within a user-defined extent.

6.5.2 Snapping environment

One of the principal ways to ensure that features line up, connect, or directly abut another feature when you are creating or editing features is through the use of *snapping*. Snapping allows newly created or modified features to coincide with existing features within the same layer or from different layers. The snapping environment controls how features relate to one another.

The *snapping tolerance* specifies the distance within which a feature is snapped to another feature, or the pointer is snapped to another location. The snapping tolerance is typically defined in terms of map units, but can also be specified by the number of screen pixels. Graphically, the snapping tolerance is shown by a circle around the pointer. If the pointer is within the snapping tolerance, then the circle snaps to the location; otherwise, the circle stays centered on the pointer. The *snapping properties* specify the part of a feature that the snapping responds to. That is, snapping can respond to all vertices, the edge, and/or the

Snapping Environment			×
Layer	Vertex	Edge	End
snapping-parks	☑	☐	☐
counties	☑	☐	☐

☐ Perpendicular to sketch
☐ Edit sketch edges
☐ Edit sketch vertices

endpoints of a feature. These properties can be set independently for each layer listed in the *Snapping Environment* dialog, and the priority follows the order of the listing of the layers.

Setting the snapping environment

1. From the Editor toolbar, select Snapping...

2. Check the boxes for the feature parts for each layer.

3. Prioritize the snapping order if needed by click-dragging on a layer name.

4. To change the snapping tolerance, from the Editor toolbar select Options..., then the General tab.

6.6 Common editing tasks

6.6.1 *Adding new features*

Typically, new features are drawn or digitized in relation to existing features. *Heads-up digitizing* is a method that is commonly used, which describes digitizing when looking at the monitor and occurs when other spatial data, usually an image, is used as a base map. This contrasts with *paper-map digitizing*, which employs a paper map mounted to a digitizing tablet. Another method of digitizing is used, though less frequently, when a description of the geometry of the feature is known. This is typically from descriptions of metes and bounds or coordinate geometry, for example from a surveyor or from a land plat map.

To illustrate how creating new features occurs using the heads-up digitizing method, let's digitize some geographic features from an aerial photograph (right). The location of buildings may be digitized as points that mark the location of each building. Trails are typically digitized as lines (also called *polylines*), which are represented by a start point, a series of intermediate points or vertices, and an end point. In *point mode digitizing*, vertices are established at a location (by clicking on it), and you are actually sampling a real-world feature by approximating it with line segments. Another method, though perhaps less common, is *stream mode digitizing*, where points are established at defined intervals along a feature as

the cursor is moved across the map. Typically, lines should not be self-intersecting (Figure 6.5). Areal features such as parking lots or vegetation patches would be digitized as *polygons*, where the starting point and ending point of a line are the same. Care must be taken when creating polygons so that non-valid polygons (so called *weird polygons*) are not created (Figure 6.5).

Note that ArcMap provides a number of digitizing options through the Sketch tool's context menu (right-click), for example, to remove the last vertex digitized. Also, a number of digitizing methods are available that utilize "CAD-like" editing methods. For example, a vertex can be established by providing an *absolute x,y* location by typing in the x and y coordinates, or through providing *relative x,y* coordinates from the last vertex. A vertex can also be located by providing an *angle* and *length* from a known location. *Parametric* and *tangent* curves can also be created.[8]

---

8. See ArcGIS Help -> Editing in ArcMap --> Creating new features --> Creating features from other features.

FIGURE 6.5. Common digitizing problems: A self-intersecting line (left) is a polyline that crosses itself. A self-intersecting polygon (right), also known as a "weird polygon," crosses itself with no vertices at the boundary intersection(s).

Note that there are a number of techniques available to help ensure that data are planar enforced. One common method is simply to set the snapping environment so that new vertices snap to existing vertices in a layer that is being edited. In this way new polylines and polygons can directly connect to adjacent features. Polylines should touch one another only at the end points (Figure 6.6).

FIGURE 6.6. Polylines should connect or touch one another only at the ends of lines (right), rather than at the mid-point of lines (left).

Creating a new feature.

1. Establish an edit session and set the desired *target layer.*

2. Select the Sketch tool.

3. Set the task to: **Create New Feature.**

4. Digitize the location(s):

Points

Single-click on the desired location (double-click to end for lines and polygons).

Lines

Click at the beginning of a line, then click on intermediate vertices, then double-click at the endpoint.

Polygons

Click at the beginning of the polygon, then click on intermediate vertices, then double-click on the start point to snap the polygon closed.

5. Click on the Attribute button (🞖) to enter attributes through the Attribute dialog.

6. Save edits.

Also, when digitizing a new polygon adjacent to an existing one, to make sure the boundaries match you must create vertices that duplicate every vertex and only the vertices from the existing polygon. Because this can be both tedious and fraught with error, ArcMap has a powerful task called *Auto Complete Polygon*, which allows a new polygon feature to be digitized such that it automatically shares the boundaries of existing features. After setting the snapping environment on, start at the vertex where the new feature starts from an existing feature (see point 1, right)—which is called the *common vertex*
(like a node), then digitize the new points that form the new polygon (2, 3, 4). Then close the polygon back on the vertex of an existing polygon (5).

6.6.2 *Splitting a feature*

Occasionally, an existing polyline or polygon feature needs to be split or cut into two or more features. Because you are cutting a particular feature(s), then you'll need to first select the feature to be cut into pieces. This can be accomplished for line features using the Split tool (✎). Note that if you want to split the line at a particular vertex, then set the snapping environment appropriately. A second way to split a line is to specify the location by defining a distance or percentage from the starting (forward) or ending (reverse) point. For polygon features, use the *Cut Polygon Features* task. Polygons can also be split to cut out an *island polygon* or *doughnut* from the parent polygon by drawing a line that closes on itself (an interior polygon) but does not cross the boundary of the polygon that is being cut. To test whether a polygon is an island polygon or is simply overlapping on top of another polygon, click on the island with the Identify tool—if only one record was found, then it is an island polygon. Note that ArcMap automatically updates the length (for polylines) or area (for polygons) field for geodatabases only—but not for shapefiles.

Splitting features

Polylines

1. Select the target polyline layer.

2. Select the feature to cut using the Edit tool.

3. Select the Split tool (✏), then click on the line at the location to split the line. To split the line via a distance or percentage, select Editor->Split..., then use the Split dialog.

4. Save edits when finished.

Polygons

1. Select the target polygon layer.

2. Select feature(s) to cut using the Edit tool.

3. Set the task to: Cut Polygon Features.

4. Draw the "cut" line by beginning and ending the split line at a boundary vertex, on the boundary line, or outside the polygon boundary. Double-click to end the line.

5. Save edits when finished.

6.6.3 Deleting features

Once an edit session has been established, features can be easily deleted by first selecting the features to be deleted, then by simply pressing the Delete key. Recall that a deletion can be undone using ctrl-Z.

6.6.4 Modifying features

Existing features often need to be modified to add, delete, or move vertices, for example. Note that ArcMap provides a *Shared Edit* tool (➤), which is similar to the *Edit* tool (▶), but allows features to be modified that maintain shared boundaries. At v8.3 of ArcGIS, the Shared Edit tool was moved from the Editor toolbar to the *Topology Edit Tool* (▨)located in the Topology toolbar. A number of common ways to modify features is summarized in Table 6.2. Two principle "tasks" allow you to modify features. The first task is *Modify Feature*, which allows you to work directly on vertices. A second task is *Reshape Feature*, which operates on a sketch that is drawn on top of the existing feature. This second method is useful when editing a complicated shape, and where knowing the "old" location of a line is helpful.

There are also a number of methods to affect how two nearby, adjacent, or overlapping features *from the same layer* interact (Figure 6.7): merge, union, intersect, or clip. Features can be *merged* or *unioned* so that two or more features from the same layer become one feature. Typically, adjacent features such as two polygons (either sharing a common boundary or overlapping) are merged into a single feature. However, *disjoint features* (features that are not spatially connected) can also be merged together into a single, but *multi-part*, feature. Multi-part features can also be created during digitizing by creating individual parts, then grouping parts by "finishing the sketch."[9] The constituent parts of a multi-part feature can be obtained by *exploding* a multi-part feature. For example, if you had a single feature (polygon) that represented the Hawaiian Islands and needed the individual islands, the so-called explode method could be used. This functionality is available through the *Multi to Single Part* tool in the Features toolset (in Data Management). Also, all adjacent features in a layer that have the same attribute value can be merged so that their shared boundary is *dissolved*. Dissolving a layer is accomplished using the *Dissolve* tool in the Generalization toolset (Data Management toolbox), which is covered in depth in Chapter 7. Like merge, features can be *unioned*, but the union command combines features from *different layers* into a single new feature in the target layer. This method allows features from other layers to be easily incorporated into the target layer.

FIGURE 6.7. Common editing procedures with two or more features. These include merge or union (left, center-left, and center), intersect (center-right), and clip (right).

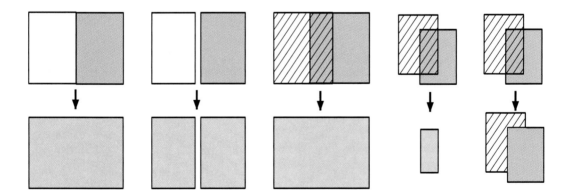

When two features from the same layer overlap, the *intersection* (left) can be found or a feature can be clipped from the other (right). With intersection, note that the original features remain and a new feature that represents the intersection is added. Alternatively, when two features

9. See ArcMap help: Editing in ArcMap -> Creating new features -> Creating lines and polygons.

overlap, one feature can be used to subtract or *clip* the other feature. The top polygon gets subtracted from the bottom polygon, so the overlap portion of the bottom polygon is clipped, while the top polygon remains unchanged. Note that the feature that is being used to clip can also be *buffered* by a specified distance (in map units).

TABLE 6.2. Summary of step-by-step methods for common modification editing tasks.

Method	Tool	Task	Step by step
Clipping features	Edit	Modify features	1. Select two features that overlap. 2. Select **Editor -> Clip...**.
Deleting a vertex	Edit	Modify features	1. Select feature. 2. Right-click on a vertex, select **Delete Vertex**.
Flipping polylines	Edit	Modify features	1. Select polylines to flip. 2. Right-click, select **Flip**.
Inserting a vertex	Edit	Modify features	1. Select feature. 2. Right-click on line segment, select **Insert Vertex**.
Intersecting overlapping features	Edit	Modify feature	1. Select two features that overlap. 2. Select **Editor -> Intersect**.
Merging features	Edit	Modify feature	1. Select two or more features to merge. 2. Select **Editor -> Merge**.
Moving a shared boundary	Shared Edit	Reshape Feature	1. Click on the common boundary between two polygons (it will turn orange). 2. Click and drag the line to a new location.
Moving a shared node	Shared Edit	Reshape Feature	1. Click on the node location where two or more polygons come together (an orange dot should appear). 2. Click and drag the node to new location.
Moving a shared vertex	Shared Edit	Modify feature	1. Click on the common boundary between two polygons (or common vertex between two polylines). 2. Click on a vertex and drag to new location.

TABLE 6.2. Summary of step-by-step methods for common modification editing tasks.

Method	Tool	Task	Step by step
Moving a vertex	Edit	Modify features	1. Select feature.
			2. Move cursor over vertex to move, then left-click and drag to new location. Or, right-click and select **Move To** to specify a new x,y coordinate location. Or, right-click and select **Move** to specify distance and direction to move.
Unioning features from different layers	Edit	Modify features	1. Select a feature from the target layer.
			2. Select a feature from another layer.
			3. Select **Editor -> Union**.

6.6.5 Removing an overlap

An *overlap* occurs when a feature overlaps another feature, where two features are coincident and the area of overlap for polygons and length of overlap for polylines is greater than 0. Although sometimes it is valid and useful to have overlapping features, typically these are considered to be errors in planar topology created during digitizing or editing. Typically overlaps are removed by simply clipping one of the features from the other(s).

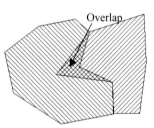

6.6.6 Removing a sliver polygon

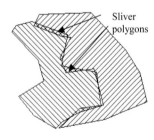

Sliver polygons are small, usually narrow, and almost always unwanted polygons. Two processes typically create these artifacts. The first is that a sliver polygon is an artifact of digitizing boundaries of two adjacent polygons where the vertices are not snapped together.[10] Sliver polygons are characterized by high perimeter-to-area ratios. The paradox of sliver polygons is that in trying to more precisely digitize two boundaries, more, albeit smaller, sliver polygons are created.[11] Sliver polygons are also created occasionally when overlaying two layers whose features are roughly coincident in some locations. For example, if a layer of soil boundaries was overlaid (e.g., unioned) on top of a layer of vegetation polygons,

---

10. DeMers, M. 1997. *Fundamentals for Geographic Information Systems*. New York: John Wiley & Sons.
11. Goodchild, M.F. 1978. Statistical aspects of the polygon overlay problem. In: *Harvard papers on geographic information systems*, vol 6, Ed. G. Dutton. Reading, MA: Addison-Wesley.

then because the ecotones, or edges, of vegetation polygons sometimes follow the boundaries of a sharp change in soil type, sliver polygons along this ecotone may be created. The challenge of sliver polygons is not merely in their ubiquity, but lies more in the difficulty of deciding whether a small polygon is an artifact and should be removed or is simply just a small polygon that should be retained. As a result, sliver polygons are the bane of GIS.

It is important to identify and remove these sliver polygons. When you are displaying maps at fine scales, sliver polygons can make your boundaries look poor. Probably more importantly though, computing statistics on an attribute table of a theme that contains slivers may introduce errors because of the additional polygons. For example, if you want to compute the average population in your state by county, and you have 5 sliver polygons in addition to the 20 "legitimate" polygons representing counties, you will be significantly underestimating the average value (because you will be dividing by 25 instead of 20). So, take care and screen maps by both visually inspecting them for sliver polygons (but these can be hard to see) and by comparing the number of records (polygons) in the attribute table to the number you would expect.

To remove a single sliver polygon, simply union or merge the sliver polygon with an adjacent polygon. Although you can select for sliver polygons by building a query that tests for polygon size and/or perimeter length, unfortunately there is not an easy way in ArcMap to eliminate many sliver polygons at once. However, the *Eliminate tool* in ArcToolbox[12] can be used to merge selected polygons that have the longest common boundary between them, or the polygon with the largest area.

Another type of sliver polygon is created when joining a number of map tiles together. If neighboring features on the border of a tile do not join perfectly, *merge slivers* are created (see right). These are more problematic to remove, because an operation such as eliminate does not reliably remove these artifacts. However, there is a specialized method to join or *append* map tiles together (also called *mapjoin*). This method is available through the *Append wizard* in ArcToolbox.[13] Note that appending datasets enforces planar topology and typically assumes that features from adjacent layers typically do not overlap. A

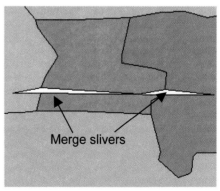

Merge slivers

similar method is to *Merge* layers using the Merge tool in the General toolset (Data Management toolbox), which is usually used to combine layers with the same feature type representing features that are adjacent and do not overlap. However, Merge does not enforce

12. Not available at ArcView functionality level.
13. Also not available in ArcView functionality level.

topology, and so features at the edge can overlap, or merge slivers can be created accidentally as well.

6.6.7 Patching a gap

A *gap* is a hole in a polygon layer where no feature exists, but it is surrounded by polygons. Gaps are occasionally created (usually accidentally) through editing in a non-topological fashion, or when a layer is created from a selection of another layer. Probably the easiest way to patch a gap, if the gap is fairly small and simple, is to simply create a new polygon ensuring the vertices snap to the surrounding polygon vertices. For large, complex-shaped gaps, this might not be feasible, however, and so a more robust method is needed. A process likened to patching a hole in a bike tire works reasonably well (Figure 6.8).

FIGURE 6.8. Graphical depiction of steps in patching a gap polygon (see step-by-step instructions below). To patch a gap (left), place a "patch" polygon over the gap (left-center). Then select a polygon that overlaps the patch (center), and clip the patch (right-center). Repeat with all other polygons that surround the gap to create a new polygon that fills the gap (right).

Patching a gap
1. Create a new polygon "patch" over the gap.
2. Select an original polygon that intersects the patch polygon.
3. Select Editor -> Clip, use a buffer distance of 0 and check "Discard the area that intersects." Click OK.
4. Repeat steps 2 and 3 using another original polygon, working around the gap.
5. Save edits when finished.

6.6.8 Integration

Another editing method available (before v8.3) in ArcMap is *integration*, which essentially snaps vertices together that are within a certain distance as specified by a *cluster tolerance*. This is a potentially powerful method to remove a number of common artifacts, such as overlaps, gaps, sliver polygons, and merge slivers. It works by searching through the features in a layer, and determines if two vertices are within the cluster tolerance. If two or more vertices are within the tolerance, then a single vertex replaces them approximately midway between the original vertices (Figure 6.9). The cluster tolerance is specified in map units, and because it searches from two (or more) nearby vertices, the tolerance needs to be set at half the required distance. For example, if you want to integrate vertices that are 100 units or less away, then use a cluster tolerance of 50. Again, we are faced with the Goldilocks problem: you must be careful to choose a "just right" tolerance that cleans up unwanted artifacts, but does not overly simplify features by removing needed vertices (including nearby vertices on the same feature).

FIGURE 6.9. Integrating a layer to remove artifacts and assisting in creating a dataset that conforms to planar topology. The original two polygons have a gap with vertices separated by 100 units and an overlap with vertices separated by 50 units (left). Also notice the small peninsula at the bottom of the right polygon with vertices separated by 75 units. A cluster tolerance of 25 removes the overlap (upper right). Increasing the tolerance to 35 does not clean up the gap, but removes the peninsula (lower right). A tolerance of 50 units is needed to clean up both the gap and overlap, but again has removed the peninsula (lower right).

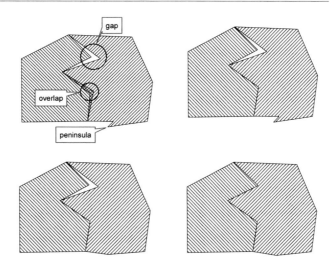

> ### *Integrating a layer*
>
> 1. Specify an edit session.
>
> 2. Specify the cluster tolerance by selecting **Editor -> Options**. Select the Topology tab and specify the tolerance (in 50% map units).
>
> 3. Select **Editor -> Integrate**.
>
> 4. Save edits when finished.

6.6.9 Changing feature order

Features are drawn in the order they appear in the attribute table. Occasionally you may want to re-order features so they draw in a different order. Why? For shapefiles that contain features that overlap, you may want the smaller features to draw on top of the bigger features, or perhaps to have features draw over others based on some attribute value. Perhaps this could also be used for visualization by drawing features from bottom to top, or from the center out, or randomly. Remember that it is simply a convention that features are typically drawn from left to right, top to bottom! Permanently re-ordering features in a layer requires utilizing some VBA code, however.

6.7 Map topology

Beginning with version 8.3, map topology has been fully implemented in ArcGIS. A map topology can be imposed on simple geometric features during an ArcMap edit session. Features can be from either a shapefile or geodatabase dataset. There are generally two steps where topology comes into play. The first is when you are editing features by reshaping or moving features. The second is termed *validation* and is used to exam-

---

ine whether a dataset or set of datasets conform to the specified topology rules. Note that validation can only be done using Geodatabase topology, available with an ArcInfo license.

Defining a map topology

1. From the Editor toolbar menu, select More Editing Tools -> Topology. This adds the Topology toolbar.

2. From the Editor toolbar menu, select Start Editing.

3. Select the source dataset to be edited on the Editor toolbar.

4. From the *Topology* toolbar, click the Map Topology button (🗃).

5. Check the feature classes that will take part in the map topology.

6.7.1 Topology rules

The types of topology rules allowed are based on spatial relation types (see section 5.6.1) between the geometric primitives (points, lines, polygons) that make up features. There are a number of types of geometry that are used when editing a topology, including edges, nodes, pseudo-nodes, and vertices. *Edges* are line segments that define polyline features or polygons. *Nodes* are the ending points of an edge. *Pseudo-nodes* are the end points that occur at the intersection of two (and only two) edges. *Vertices* are the non-end point *x,y* locations that define the geometry of an edge. When features have intersecting (adjacent) or overlapping (partially-equivalent) features, the edges and nodes that comprise these parts are termed *shared*. Topology edit tools allow you to move vertices, nodes, or whole edges of shared features, thus maintaining planar topology.

There are a variety of rules that can be imposed on Geodatabases (Table 6.3). Rules define the possible (allowed) spatial relationships between features within a dataset or between datasets.

TABLE 6.3. Topology rules between feature types in a Geodatabase.

Feature(s) types	Rule	Example uses	Possible fixes
Polygon	**Must not overlap** - polygon interiors must not overlap, though polygons can be disconnected or share edges or vertices. This is used to enforce planar topology.	Ensure that administrative boundaries (e.g., counties, states, etc.) are mutually exclusive	Reshape a polygon to move vertices of one to another (use snapping) Subtract one polygon from the other Merge two polygons into a single polygon
Polygon	**Must not have gaps** - there cannot be voids between polygon interiors, though polygons can share edges or vertices. This is used to ensure that polygons are completely space-filling and tesselate the whole study area.	Ensure there are no gaps between land ownership parcels or vegetation polygons	Reshape a polygon to move vertices to snap to the nearest polygon Create a new polygon that fills the void
Polygon - polygon	**Must not overlap with** - the interior polygons of one feature class must not overlap with those of another feature class	Ensure that features from two layers are mutually-exclusive, such as lakes and soil types	Reshape a polygon to move vertices to snap to the nearest polygon Subtract a polygon from another
Polygon - polygon	**Must be covered by feature class of** - a polygon in one feature class must cover polygons in a second feature class	Ensure that hierarchical relationships are maintained (e.g., states are completely covered by counties)	Subtract one polygon from the other Create a new polygon that fills the void
Polygon - polygon	**Must cover each other** - polygons in one feature class must share all of its area with polygons of another class	Ensure that hierarchical relationships are maintained (e.g., nested watersheds)	Subtract one polygon from the other
Polygon - polygon	**Must be covered by** - polygons in one feature class must be contained within polygons of another class	Ensure that hierarchical relationships are maintained (e.g., counties are completely covered by states)	Create a new polygon that fills the void

TABLE 6.3. Topology rules between feature types in a Geodatabase.

Feature(s) types	Rule	Example uses	Possible fixes
Polygon - line	**Boundary must be covered by** - boundaries of polygons must be covered by lines from another feature class	Ensure that area feature boundaries are marked by linear features (e.g., parcel boundaries are formed by major roads)	Create a new polygon that fills the void
Polygon - polygon	**Area boundary must be covered by boundary of** - boundaries of polygon features must be covered by boundaries of polygon features from another feature class	Ensure that polygons share boundaries when features naturally nest (e.g., parcels within a subdivision)	Create a new polygon that fills the void
Polygon - point	**Contains point** - a polygon contains at least one point from another feature class. Points must be in the polygon interior, not on the boundary.	Ensure that each polygon has at least one point associated with it	Add additional points
Line - line	**Must not overlap** - lines must not overlap (share an edge segment) lines within the same feature class, though lines can cross or intersect	Ensure that line segments are not duplicated (planar enforcement, e.g.,)	Subtract one line from the other
Line - line	**Must not intersect** - line features from the same feature class must not cross or overlap, though lines can share endpoints	Ensure that lines do not self-cross (e.g., a contour line)	Subtract one line from another Split a line at intersection
Line - line	**Must not have dangles** - a line feature must touch lines from the same feature class at both end points, though cul-de-sac or dead end streets are common exceptions	Ensure that lines from closed loops (e.g., a linear representation of a lake)	Extend line to intersect other line Trim part of line Snap end point to line
Line - line	**Must not have pseudo-nodes** - a line must connect to at least two other lines at each end point	Ensure closed loops or when line features should connect to two other features (e.g., a hydrologic network)	Merge the two features that share the pseudo-node
Line	**Must not intersect or touch interior** - a line must only touch other lines of the same feature class at the end points	Ensure that lines only be connected at end points	Subtract features Split features at intersection

TABLE 6.3. Topology rules between feature types in a Geodatabase.

Feature(s) types	Rule	Example uses	Possible fixes
Line - line	**Must not overlap with** - a line from one feature class must not overlap with line features of another class	Ensure that linear features do not share the same space (e.g., a road and a river)	Subtract features Move features
Line - line	**Must be covered by feature class of** - lines must be covered by lines from another feature class	Ensure that lines are coincident (e.g., a bus route follows a street network)	
Line - polygon	**Must be covered by boundary of** - lines must be covered by the boundaries of polygons	Ensure that linear features are coincident with polygon features (e.g., a lot line with the edge of a lake)	Subtract features
Line - point	**Endpoint must be covered by** - endpoints of linear features must be covered by points from another feature class	Ensure that a point feature occurs at all line junctions (e.g., a water line junction)	Create feature Remove pseudo-node
Line	**Must not self overlap** - a line feature must not overlap itself, though they can cross or touch themselves	Ensure that linear features like bus routes do not duplicate a segment, but can cross	Simplify
Line	**Must not self intersect** - line features must not cross or overlap themselves	Ensure planar topology (e.g. contour lines cannot cross themselves)	Simplify
Line	**Must be single part** - line features must be composed of only a single part	This is useful to reduce linear features to their elemental aspects	Explode
Point - polygon	**Must be covered by boundary of** - points must fall on the boundary of polygon features, not the interiors	Ensure markers are placed on the boundary	
Point - polygon	**Must be properly inside polygons** -points must fall in polygon interiors, not outside or on the boundaries	Ensure points are within an areal feature (e.g., a well inside an aquifer)	Delete features

TABLE 6.3. Topology rules between feature types in a Geodatabase.

Feature(s) types	Rule	Example uses	Possible fixes
Point - line	**Must be covered by endpoint of** - points must be covered by the end points of linear features	Ensure that markers are located only at the end of a line feature	Delete Move feature
Point - line	**Must be covered by line** - points must be covered by lines from another feature class	Ensure that points are located on a line (e.g., road sign locations on a road)	

6.7.2 Cluster tolerance

The *cluster tolerance* specifies the maximum distance between vertices of features that will be considered coincident. That is, if the distance between vertices is less than the cluster tolerance, then the vertices will be snapped together. With v8.3, a second aspect of map topology is the definition of the cluster tolerance. Usually the cluster distance is set to be a small distance to minimize the movement of features. The default tolerance is calculated as the minimum possible cluster tolerance. Increasing the tolerance causes more vertices to snap together, though large distances can begin to collapse features.

6.7.3 Topological or shared editing

The *Topology toolbar* provides additional editing tools. These include shared editing using the *Topology Edit tool*, validating topology, and fixing topological errors. Note that the first step in using the Topology tools is to set up map topology using the Map Topology button ( ).

6.7.3.1 Editing shared geometry

With the Topology Edit tool ( ) you can edit edges and nodes that may be shared by more than one feature. When you move a vertex, a node, or an edge, all of the features that share the vertices that are edited are updated as well. The *Show Shared Features* tool

( ) is useful to display the features that were selected using the Topology Edit tool. If you want to remove a particular feature from participating in the shared edit, you can interactively remove the feature from the check list. For example, the node located at the intersection of three counties in Colorado could be selected, but Eagle County might be removed from participating in the shared edit (see right above). Note that at the ArcView level, a few additional tools are provided, but are not typically located on the Topology toolbar, including the *Explode tool* (✳) that converts multi-part features to single-part features. With an ArcInfo license, additional ways to edit and create topological features are provided, including splitting lines at their intersections (Planarize Lines), constructing new features from different geometry types (Construct Features), and generalizing features (Generalize).

Editing shared geometry

Selecting and moving a node

1. From the *Topology* toolbar, click the Topology Edit tool (▣).

2. Click on the node you want to select (holding the N key down helps).

3. The node should be symbolized by a thick point (purple by default).

4. Click and drag the node to a new location. You can also move the node a specified distance by right-clicking, selecting Move To, and entering the absolute X and Y coordinates.

Selecting and moving an edge

1. From the *Topology* toolbar, click the Topology Edit tool (▣).

2. Click on the edge you want to select (holding the E key down helps).

3. The edge should be symbolized by a thick line (purple by default).

4. Click and drag the edge to a new location.

Modifying an edge

1. From the *Topology* toolbar, click the Topology Edit tool (▣).

2. Click on the edge you want to select (holding the E key down helps).

3. The edge should be symbolized by a thick line (purple by default).

4. Select Modify Edge from the Task dropdown arrow on the Editor toolbar.

5. To insert a new vertex, right-click a segment of the edge and select Insert Vertex. To delete a vertex, right-click on a vertex and select Delete Vertex. To move a vertex, click on a vertex and drag it to a new location. To split an edge, ctrl-click at the location where you want to split (you should see a circle symbolizing the "anchor"), then right-click and select Split Edge at Anchor.

6. To finish the sketch, right-click anywhere in the map and select Finish Sketch.

6.8 Geocoding

Most geographic datasets have their geometry derived either from paper maps or from GPS locations. Although relatively uncommon in the natural resources fields but commonplace in business applications, tabular datasets often have quasi-spatial attributes but are not tied to specific geometrical features. The most obvious example of this type of dataset is a file with customer names, addresses, and telephone numbers, and so these datasets are commonly called *address tables*. Through a process known as *geocoding* (also called *address matching*), these address tables can be combined with reference geographic datasets that have comparable attributes such as street address, street, city, and state names, and zip code. By linking the tabular data to the reference dataset through a series of rules, the locations of the tabular features (i.e. house locations) in the address table can be estimated. Geocoding databases power the browser mapping technologies such as MapQuest, allowing driving directions to be computed on the fly.

Occasionally the records in the address table can be referenced only to either a point or areal geographic feature. For example, if the address table contained just place names such as the city, state, zip code, or telephone area code (or a combination of these), then they could be linked only to point locations such as a city's x,y location or to polygons that represent a zip code. However, because usually there is no way to refine the location within a polygon, all the features are typically located to the center of the polygon. So, the spatial accuracy of the estimated locations in this case depend on the resolution of the polygon (e.g., five digit zip code vs. nine digit zip code), and typically this varies widely across different parts of a map (e.g., zip codes tend to be smaller in urban than rural areas).

It is fairly common, though, for an address table to have street addresses. By combining these data with a geographic dataset such as detailed roads that are attributed with address ranges, more accurate locations can be interpolated. For example, if you are trying to geocode the location of "950 West Oak Street," you would first find in a street database the polylines with their attributes "West Oak Street," and the starting address of 900 and ending address of 1000. Simple linear interpolation would then result in a point located at the midpoint of the street line. The reference geographic datasets for streets are available from a number of commercial vendors, including ESRI.[14]

Sounds great, in theory, but in practice it is slightly messier than this. Much of the messiness is caused by inconsistencies and data entry errors (e.g., "Georgetown" vs. "Georgetowne" vs. "George town"; "Street" vs. "St." vs. "St"), though these are fairly easy problems to clean up. Sometimes addresses are not unique, so that an address such as "1000 North College" may be a correct address for two different parts of town. More problematic are addresses that do not change linearly along a street, and the actual location of a house that may be set back some distance (e.g, a 1/4 mile or more in rural areas) from the street. For these reasons and others, agencies that provide emergency

---

14. For example, ESRI's StreetMap.

services (e.g., fire, police department, etc.) often need to expend huge effort to create and maintain accurate, up-to-date spatial databases. To reduce some of these problems, rural street addresses often correspond with the mileage (times 1000) from the start of the county road (e.g., the driveway of 1234 West County Road 29 is 1.234 miles from the start of County Road 29). Although this gets one closer to the house, this simply specifies the location of an intersection along a major road, and often houses are actually located some distance away along a complex network of private driveways.

6.8.1 Geocoding services

In ArcGIS, geocoding is provided through a series of *geocoding services*. A geocoding service defines the reference dataset(s) that has spatial features, rules for standardizing the descriptions of features in the address table, and rules for how they are matched to the reference data and how the new features are created. To match an address, the geocoding service: standardizes the address, searches the reference data for candidates, scores the candidates, and matches the best candidate. Before you create a service, you will need to understand the structure of your address table, particularly what fields have addresses, street names, directions, etc. For example, sometimes an address table will only have an "address" field (e.g., 950) and a "street" field (e.g., West Oak Street), while others may have the street broken into "street direction" (e.g., West), "street name" (e.g., Oak), and "street type" (e.g., Street).

A geocoding service is created in Arc-Catalog by locating the Geocoding Services folder in the Catalog, and then clicking on the Create New Geocoding Service folder to bring up the Create New Geocoding Service dialog. There are a number of different *geocoding styles* available—essentially you need to match how the reference geographic dataset is attributed. After the geocoding service is created and your address table matched,[15] you will likely want to examine your results. You can review the match scores, tweak some of the match parameters, and re-match your address table.

---

15. For more information, see the ArcGIS Desktop Help, Geocoding addresses section.

6.9 Editing attribute data

There are a couple of basic ways that attribute data can be edited. Recall that attributes can be edited from a feature-centric perspective by changing values for a particular feature through the Attributes dialog. A second way is to open an attribute table and edit it directly. Like a spreadsheet, attribute data can be edited cell-by-cell by simply typing in a value -- but this is available only when a dataset is in edit mode. The header cell of editable fields is shown in white. Values can be copied and pasted from one field to another. Note that to put the original value back into a cell, press Escape.

A third way to edit a table is through the *Field Calculator* dialog, which calculates the value of a field for all selected records (or on all records if no records are selected). For example, you might need to set all records to a constant value, perhaps 0.0, or, the value of a new field might be the product of two existing fields. Typically, calculations are done when you are *not* in edit mode.

The expression used to define the calculation can be simple or complex. To open the Field Calculator, use a field's context menu (right-click and then select Calculate Values...). Note that calculator expressions can be copied and pasted, and also saved to an *.cal* file.

Field Calculator

Fields	Type	Functions
OTHER	⊙ Number	Abs ( )
OWNER_OCC	○ String	Atn ( )
POP1990	○ Date	Cos ( )
POP2000		Exp ( )
Pop90_2000		Fix ( )
POP90_SQMI		Int ( )
RENTER_OCC		Log ( )
SEPARATED		Sin ( )
Shape		Sqr ( )

Pop90_2000 =   ☐ Advanced

[POP2000] - [POP1990]

`*` `/` `&`

`+` `-` `=`

Save... Load...

OK

Cancel

Below are some examples of common calculation expressions:

"Douglas fir" ' set field [Vegetation] to "Douglas fir" -- strings in double quotes

1000.0 ' set field [Area] to 1000.0

[Area] * 0.000247 ' convert area in square meters to number of acres in each polygon

[Perimeter] / [Area] ' set field [Poly_shape] to the perimeter/area ratio

[First] & " " & [Last] '' concatenate fields that contain first & last name into a single field

[FID] '' returns the record number

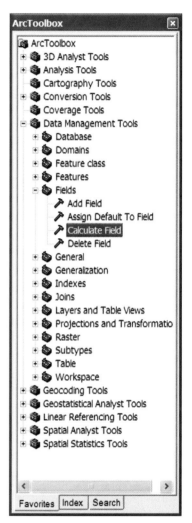

Saving a calculator expression

1. With the Field Calculator dialog open and the desired expression in the box, click on **Save**.

2. Navigate to the desired location and click **OK**.

Turn off annoying warning message

1. When using Field Calculator in regular (non-edit) mode, a warning dialog appears everytime you run a calculation (see below).

2. To turn it off, click Tools --> Options..., then click on the Tables tab.

3. In the middle of the dialog, there is a check-box option "Show warning when calculating field values out edit session" -- check this OFF, then click OK.

Field Calculator

You are about to do a calculate outside of an edit session. This method is faster than calculating in an edit session, but there is no way to undo your results once the calculation begins. Do you wish to continue?

Yes   No

6.9.1 Common problems with calculator expressions

Occasionally there can be problems with calculator expressions. If you get an error message, then try the following out:

1. Make sure strings are quoted.

2. Numbers cannot have commas, and a value less than 1 must be preceded with a zero (e.g., 0.124, not .124).

3. Dividing by 0 or doing a calculation on a value that is not a number will cause an error. One way to get around these problems is to first query the field to find the records that only contain non-zero values or strings that can be converted by using the query string "<field>.IsNumeric".

4. Make sure that the target field is specified as a data type that is large enough to handle the value — often you'll need a field of type Double rather than Short integer.

6.9.2 Advanced calculator expressions

A powerful feature of the Field Calculator is that, in addition to simple expression, virtually any VB Script function can be called within a more complicated expression. This provides access to a wide range of VB functions and ArcObjects, as well as basic programming statements (e.g., if then-else).[16] There is a range of functions to handle the various data types: date, numeric, text, and shape (Table 6.4), for example, to compute the area of a polygon (which is needed after you alter a feature through an operation such as clip or union, or

---

through interactive editing). To do this, right click on the target field and bring up the Field Calculator. Then, check the "Advanced" box and type the following into the pre-logic text box:

Dim dblX as double

Dim pArea as IArea

Set pArea = [shape]

dblX = pArea.area

The first and second lines set the dimension of a variable to store the area of a polygon (as a numerical value) and a variable to store the shape object (the polygon), respectively. The third line gets the polygon, and the fourth line requests the area of pArea (by the ".area" request), then assigns the area to the variable **dblX**. Finally, in the smaller text box below the field name, enter:

dblX

This last step tells ArcMap to put the value referenced by the variable **dblArea** back into the target field. Note that you cannot access other fields in this line. Also note that you can save and load these expressions, and you can comment your expressions (e.g., give them a name, describe the logic, etc.) using the single-quote comment character, where everything to the right is not evaluated. Building on this basic idea, you could request a number of properties about a shape object (by replacing the "dblArea = pArea.area" line), to include getting a polygon centroid, or X and Y location of a polygon's centroid.[17]

TABLE 6.4. Listing of VB functions that can be used in the Field Calculator for the date data type.

Function	Returns	Description
Date()	Date	Returns the current system date
DateAdd(<period>, <number>, <date>)	Date	Returns the result of adding or subtracting a given number of time periods ("yyyy"=year, "q"=quarter, "m" = month, "y" = day of year, "d"=day, "w"=weekday, "ww"=week, "h"=hour, "n"=minute, "s"=second. E.g., **DateAdd ("d", 2, Now)** adds two days onto the current day.
DateDiff(<period>, <date1>, <date2>)	Number	Returns the number of time periods between two dates. E.g., **DateDiff ("d", "11/5/2002", "12/31/2002")** adds two days onto the current day.

16. These functions are documented in the Visual Basic help, under: Visual Basic Language Reference -> Functions.

TABLE 6.4. Listing of VB functions that can be used in the Field Calculator for the date data type.

Function	Returns	Description
DatePart(<period>, <date>)	Number	Returns a component of the date or time (e.g., day, second, etc.). E.g., **DatePart ("m", "11/5/2002")** gets the month (11) as an integer two days onto the current day.
DateSerial(<year>,<month>,<day>)	Date	Returns a date specified by year, month, day. E.g., **DatePart (2002, 11, 5)** creates a date specifying the 5th of November 2002.
DateValue (<dat­eString>)	Date	Returns a date specified by string. E.g., **DateValue (2002, 11, 5)** creates a date specifying the 5th of November 2002.Note that a short cut is: "11/5/2002"
Now()	Date	Returns current date and time (to seconds). E.g., **Now()** returns current time. To get time precise to milliseconds, use Timer.
Timer()	Number (double)	Returns the current number of milliseconds since midnight. E.g., **Timer()**.

TABLE 6.5. Listing of VB functions that can be used in the Field Calculator for the number data type.

Function	Returns	Description
Abs(<number>)	Number	Returns the absolute value of a number. E.g., **Abs (-1)** equals 1; **Abs (1)** equals 1.
Atn(<radians>)	Number	Returns the arcTangent of a number in radians. To convert degrees to radians, multiply degrees by pi/180. To convert radians to degrees, multiply radians by 180/pi. E.g., **Atn(1 * (3.1415/180))** equals 0.017451 radians.
CDbl(<number>)	Number (double)	Returns the number as a type Double, which ranges from -1.79769313486232E308 to 1.79769313486232E308.
CInt(<number>)	Number (short)	Returns the number as an integer of type Short, which ranges from -32,768 to 32,767.
CLng(<number>)	Number (long)	Returns the number as an integer of type Long, which ranges from -2,147,483,648 to 2,147,483,647.
Cos(<radians>)	Number (double)	Returns the cosine of a number in radians, which ranges from -1 to 1.

17. For a helpful set of pre-specified calculator expressions, see Ianko Tchoukanski's EasyCalculate VBScripts, available on ESRI's ArcScripts page: http://arcscripts.esri.com/details.asp?dbid=12224.

TABLE 6.5. Listing of VB functions that can be used in the Field Calculator for the number data type.

Function	Returns	Description
CSng(\<number>)	Number (float)	Converts a value to a single or floating point type, which ranges from -3.402823E38 to 3.402823E38.
CStr(\<expression>)	Text	Returns a string representation of the expression. E.g., **CStr (10)** returns "10".
Exp(\<number>)	Number (double)	Returns the anti-logarithm of a number, to raise a number e (2.71282818). E.g., **Exp(2)** equals 7.389056..., or e^2.
Fix(\<number>)	Number (integer)	Returns an integer by removing the fractional part returning the next greater whole number. E.g., **Fix (-2.2)** equals -2.
Int(\<number>)	Number (integer)	Returns an integer by removing the fractional part returning the next greater whole number. E.g., **Int (-2.2)** equals -1.
IsNull(\<number>)	Number (boolean)	Returns a boolean flag if the number is Null.
IsNumeric(\<expression>)	Number (boolean)	Returns a boolean flag if the expression is numeric. E.g., **IsNumeric ("wow")** equals FALSE, **IsNumeric(10)** equals TRUE.
Log(\<number >)	Number (double)	Returns the natural logarithm of the number. E.g., **Log (0.4)** equals -0.916291...
RGB(\<red>, \<green>, \<blue>	Number (long)	Returns the RGB number for the specified component color values that range from 0 to 255, using the formula: RGB=red + (green * 256) + blue * 65536). E.g., **RGB(0, 255, 174)** returns 11468544.
Rnd ()	Number (double)	Returns a random number. To return a random integer in a range, use: **Int((high - low + 1) * Rnd() + low)**. Call Randomize(\<seed>) to reset the random number generator. Using Randomize() uses the system timer and creates a new series of random numbers each time.
Round(\<value>, \<places>)	Number	Returns a number rounded to the specified number of places. E.g., **Round (10.1234, 0)** returns 10, while **Round(10.1234, 2)** returns 10.12.
Sgn(\<number>)	Number	Returns the sign of a number: 1 if positive, 0 if 0, -1 if negative. E.g., **Sgn (-2345)** equals -1.
Sin(\<radians>)	Number (double)	Returns the sine of a number in radians.
Sqr()	Number (double)	Returns the square root of a number. E.g., **Sqr(2)** equals 1.1414...
Tan(\<radians>)	Number (double)	Returns the tangent of a number.

TABLE 6.5. Listing of VB functions that can be used in the Field Calculator for the number data type.

Function	Returns	Description
+	Number	Addition operator. E.g., **1 + 2** equals 3.
-	Number	Subtraction operator. E.g., **2 - 1** equals 1.
*	Number	Multiplication operator. E.g., **2 * 1** equals 2.
/	Number (floating)	Division operator. E.g., **1 / 2** equals 0.5.
\	Number (integer)	Integer division operator. E.g., **1 \ 2** equals 0.
mod	Number	Modulo operator, returns only the remainder. E.g., **1 mod 2** equals 1.
^	Number	Exponentiation operator, raises a number to the power of the exponent. E.g., **2 ^ 3** equals 8.

TABLE 6.6. Listing of ArcObject and Visual basic methods that can be used in the Field Calculator for the shape data type.

Function	Returns	Description
.Area	Number	Returns the area of a polygon shape in map units. The following lines must be in the pre-logic box: **Dim pArea as IArea** **Set pShape = [shape]** **dblX = pShape.area** In the expression box: **dblX**
.Centroid	Shape (point)	Returns the area-weighted centroid of a polygon (the centroid does not have to fall within the polygon). Replace dblX=pShape.Area (in .Area above) with: **dblX = pShape.Centroid**
.GeometryCount	Number	Returns the number of parts in a shape. **Dim pGeometryCollection As IGeometryCollection** **Dim lngX As Long** **Set pGeometryCollection = [Shape]** **lngX = pGeometryCollection.GeometryCount** In the expression box: **lngX**

TABLE 6.6. Listing of ArcObject and Visual basic methods that can be used in the Field Calculator for the shape data type.

Function	Returns	Description
.LabelPoint	Shape (point)	Returns the label point of a polygon (this is the same as the centroid if the centroid falls within the polygon, otherwise it is forced to fall in the polygon). Replace dblX=pShape.Area (in .Area above) with: **dblX = pShape.LabelPoint**
.PointCount	Number	Returns the number of vertices that comprise a shape. **Dim pPointCollection As IPointCollection** **Dim dblX As Double** **Set pPointCollection = [Shape]** **dblX = pPointCollection.PointCount** In the expression box: **dblX**
.Length	Number	Returns the perimeter of a polygon or length of a polyline. Use the following in the pre-logic box: **Dim pCurve As ICurve** **Dim dLength As Double** **Set pCurve = [Shape]** **dblX = pCurve.Length**
.X	Number (double)	Returns the X coordinate (in map units) of a point. E.g., replace dblX=pShape.area (in .Area above) with: **dblX = pShape.Centroid.X**
.Y	Number (double)	Returns the Y coordinate (in map units) of a point. E.g., replace dblX=pShape.area (in .Area above) with: **dblX = pShape.Centroid.Y**

TABLE 6.7. Listing of VB functions that can be used in the Field Calculator for the string data type.

Function	Returns	Description
&	Text	Concatenates two strings together. E.g., **"Yes"** & **"!"** equals "Yes!".
Asc(<string>)	Number	Returns the ANSI code of the first character in the string. E.g., **Asc ("a")** equals 97.
Chr(<number>)	Text	Returns the character for the given ASCII code . E.g., **Chr(97)** equals "a".

TABLE 6.7. Listing of VB functions that can be used in the Field Calculator for the string data type.

Function	Returns	Description
CStr(<expression>)	Text	Returns a string representation of the input expression. E.g., **CStr (1234)** equals "1234".
InStr(<searchString>, <findString>)	Number	Returns the starting position of the findString in search-String, or returns 0 if not found. E.g., **InStr("Colorado", "olo")** returns 2.
LCase(<String>)	Text	Returns the string in all lowercase. E.g., **LCase ("Colorado")** returns "colorado".
Left(<string>,<length>)	Text	Returns the left-most characters defined by length in the input string. E.g., **Left ("Colorado", 4)** returns "Colo".
Len(<string>)	Number	Returns the number of characters in a string. E.g., **Len("Colorado")** returns 8.
LTrim(<string>)	Text	Trims any leading spaces from input string. E.g., **LTrim (" Colorado")** would return "Colorado".
Mid(<string>, <start>, <length>)	Text	Returns the string that begins at start that is a length characters long from the input text. E.g., **Mid ("Colorado", 2, 4)** returns "olor".
Proper	Text	Actually, returning the "proper" form of a string (first character upper case, the rest lower case) can be created using a combination of functions. E.g., the string in the Text field is converted to "proper" form: **UCase (Left([text], 1)) & Right([text], Len([text]) - 1)**
Replace(<string>, <findString>, <replaceString>)	Text	Finds a string in a field and replaces it with a replacement string. E.g., **Replace([PlaceNames], "Sakagawea", "Sakakawea").**
Right(<string>, <length>)	Text	Returns the right-most characters defined by length in the input string. E.g., **Right ("Colorado", 4)** returns "rado".
RTrim(<string>)	Text	Trims any trailing spaces from input string. E.g., **LTrim ("Colorado ")** would return "Colorado".
Split(<expression>, <delimiter>)	Text	Parses a string into an array using a delimiter. To access the values in an array, simply indicate the position (starting at 0) in parentheses. The following returns "Jones". In the pre-logic expression: **Dim sArray** **sArray = Split("Mr. Jones", " ")** In the assignment expression: **sArray(1)**

TABLE 6.7. Listing of VB functions that can be used in the Field Calculator for the string data type.

Function	Returns	Description
StrComp(<string1>, <string2>)	Number	Determines whether string1 is equal to (0), greater than (1), or less than (-1) string2. E.g., **StrComp("Yes", "Yes)** returns 0, while **StrComp("Yes","Yes2")** returns -1.
String(<number>, <character>)	String	Returns a string with a single character repeated a specified number of times. E.g., **String(10, "x")** returns "xxxxxxxxxx".
Trim(<string>)	String	Trims any leading or trailing spaces from input string. E.g., **Trim (" Colorado ")** would return "Colorado".
UCase(<string>)	String	Returns the string in all upper case. E.g., **UCase ("Colorado")** returns "COLORADO".
Do...Loop		
Choose(<index>, <choice1>, <choice2>, <choiceN>...)		Use the index value to identify the choice to return. E.g., **Choice([Field], "red", "green", "blue")** returns "red" if the value in the field is 1, etc.
Constants		**vbTab** returns the tab character **vbCr** returns the carriage return character
Switch(<expression1>, <value1>, <expression2>, <value2>, ...)		For example, you can use this to reclassify values based on a series of ranges: Switch(([Id] >= 0 AND [Id] < 5),1 , ([Id] >=5 AND [Id] < 10), 2, ([Id] >10), 3)

TABLE 6.8. Listing of VB functions that can be used in the Field Calculator for miscellaneous functions.

Function	Returns	Description
Choose(<index>, <choice1>, <choice2>, <choiceN>...)		Use the index value to identify the choice to return. E.g., **Choice([Field], "red", "green", "blue")** returns "red" if the value in the field is 1, etc.
Constants		**vbTab** returns the tab character **vbCr** returns the carriage return character
Switch(<expression1>, <value1>, <expression2>, <value2>, ...)		For example, you can use this to reclassify values based on a series of ranges: Switch(([Id] >= 0 AND [Id] < 5),1 , ([Id] >=5 AND [Id] < 10), 2, ([Id] >10), 3)

Creating and editing feature data

Raster basics

7.1 Overview

In this chapter, the basics about raster datasets and setting up the analysis environment are provided. Next, the four fundamental classes of functions, local, focal, zonal, and global, are described. Basic functions that are provided through interfaces in Spatial Analyst are followed by a comprehensive listing of operations that can be used in the Raster Calculator. Advanced raster processing methods are described in the next chapter.

7.2 Raster representation

Geographic phenomena that varies continuously through space, such as elevation, are usually represented using the *field* data model and implemented using a raster data structure.[1] A raster contains a matrix or mesh of *cells* (or *pixels)* that contain a particular numeric value, such as a brightness value or a land cover type. A cell typically is square, and all cells

---

1. For a thorough introduction to raster data structures, see: Holroyd, F. and S.B.M. Bell. 1992. Raster GIS: Models of raster encoding. *Computers & Geosciences* 18(4): 419-426.

in a raster are the same size. There are three ways to store data at each cell. First, if the attribute of interest is either there or not there (present/absent), then this layer can be represented using a single layer of binary values. For example, the public/private land ownership pattern could be represented as private and not private by simply setting a binary flag for presence/absence. A second approach also represents just a single layer of interest but allows a number of values to occur at each cell. For example, land use categories could be represented with integer values (e.g., 1=grassland, 2=forest, 3=urban, etc.), or elevation could be represented with real values (e.g., Pikes Peak, Colorado is at 4301.2 meters). Finally, one could represent multiple themes at each cell, so cells could be stacked one upon another (like "crowning" in checkers). For example, a cell could have a 1 because it is private, and in the second level, 2 because it is forest. An advantage of the first (single-layer-binary-value) approach is that data can be stored in a very storage-efficient manner. However, it can become quite cumbersome when many layers are needed to represent seemingly related items (e.g., grassland/not grassland, forest/ not forest, urban/not urban, etc.). The second approach, called single-layer integer/ratio value, is commonly used in commercial systems because of its versatility and the direct association between a file and a layer. The third approach, the stacking-layer approach, is an efficient storage model but lacks versatility during analysis.

The file size for a raster dataset can be very large because it increases exponentially as the cell size decreases. Consequently, numerous ways have been developed to compress a file to reduce its size. One common method is called *run-length encoding*[2], which compresses data on a row-by-row basis, storing both the value and the number of times that a value occurs in successive columns (Figure 7.1). Adjacent pixels on a row that share the same value are represented as a pair of numbers. The more homogeneous (across columns) the data are, the better this compression scheme works. Note that run-length encoding works only on data represented as integer values, not real values.

There are numerous additional modifications to the standard raster data structure that attempt to address one or more limitations. For example, the *block code* data model is an extension of run-length encoding to two dimensions. Block codes store four numbers: the value, the origin x, the origin y, and the length of the square block. Essentially, space is partitioned into a set of space-filling, nested squares of varying sizes. This compression scheme works best for simple, homogenous shapes that result in large average-square size. Block codes are the basis for compression schemes commonly used by facsimile machines.[3] Another common raster data model is the *quad-tree*, which provides a compact representation of space by successively (recursively) dividing space into finer and finer hierarchical tiles.

---

2. Rutovitz, D. 1968. Data structures for operations on digital images. *Pictorial Pattern Recognition*, Cheng, G.C. et al. (eds). Thompson Book Co. p. 105-133.

3. Burrough, P.A. and R.A. McDonnell, 1998. *Principles of Geographical Informational Systems*. Oxford University Press. Page 54.

There are numerous data structures used to implement the raster data model; indeed, a number of books have been written on this topic.[4]

FIGURE 7.1. Raster data represented as a flat ASCII file (upper left), run-length encoded (upper-right), and graphic (lower). NoData values are value -9 (and shown in black).

Flat ASCII										Run-length													
-9	-9	1	1	0	1	0	1	-9	-9	2	-9	2	1	1	0	1	1	1	0	1	1	2	-9
-9	-9	1	1	2	2	2	1	1	-9	2	-9	2	1	3	2	2	1	1	-9				
-9	1	1	1	2	2	2	2	3	3	4	1	4	2	2	3								
1	1	1	1	2	2	2	2	3	3	4	1	4	2	2	3								
0	1	1	1	1	2	3	3	3	3	1	0	4	1	1	2	4	3						
0	0	0	1	1	1	1	1	1	1	3	0	7	1										
0	2	2	3	3	3	-9	4	4	4	1	0	2	2	3	3	1	-9	3	4				
0	2	2	3	3	3	3	4	4	4	1	0	2	2	4	3	3	4						
0	2	2	2	4	4	4	4	4	4	1	0	3	2	6	4								

□ 0
■ 1
□ 2
□ 3
■ 4

7.2.1 GRID

A GRID is an implementation of a raster data structure developed by ESRI. The *Spatial Analyst* extension is needed to conduct analyses on GRIDs, though GRIDs can be displayed and queried in ArcMap without Spatial Analyst. GRIDs are implementations of the single-layer, multiple value method. GRIDs have m columns and n rows of cells, and are ordered starting from the origin in the upper-left corner. There are two types of GRIDs: *integer GRIDs* and *real GRIDs*. Integer values are used to represent nominal, ordinal, and ratio data and cells that

---

4.   Samet, H. 1990. *The Design and Analysis of Spatial Data Structures.* Addison-Wesley, Reading, MA.

have the same integer values have the same attributes. Integer GRIDs can also be used to represent continuous phenomena.

Run-length encoding is used to compress GRIDs. For example, a GRID comprised of 1,000 columns and 1,000 rows containing all 1s requires about 30KB, but a checkerboard of alternating 0s and 1s (also 1000x1000) requires 358K, about 11 times as much disk space, because there is no row-wise correlation and therefore no compression! Floating-point values are used to represent truly continuous phenomena, but require much more disk space because they cannot be run-length encoded.[5]

One way to reduce the size of a GRID that represents continuous phenomena with floating-point values is to multiply values by an increment of 10 to convert the GRID to an integer GRID. For instance, you could represent the value 10.123 by multiplying the value by 1000, resulting in a GRID value of 10,123 (of course you'll need to remember to divide the value in subsequent analyses by 1,000). The maximum value an integer GRID can represent is 2,147,483,846 (a 4-byte, 32-bit integer), and the location of pixels and the extent of a GRID is stored using 8-byte floating point numbers (double precision). Previous to ArcGIS v9, the maximum size (m x n) of a GRID was limited by the maximum file size of 2.147 GB (a 32-bit system constraint), which limits an integer GRID to roughly 125,000 x 125,000 and a floating point GRID to roughly 23,000 x 23,000.[6] Raster datasets can be of unlimited size as of v9.

In an integer GRID, all cells that have the same value belong to the same *zone*. There is one attribute record per zone in the attribute table. A zone can be comprised of contiguous cells that have the same value, disjoint cells that are at some distance away, or both. For example, a number of disjoint patches of aspen would be represented by a single value (e.g., 1) for each cell that occurs within the patches. In contrast, when patches of aspen are represented as polygons (feature data model), the individual patches of aspen are each represented by a unique polygon (and therefore have a record in the polygon attribute table). In the GRID representation of the patches of aspen, all patches are represented by the same zone with a value of 1 (Figure 7.2).

---

5. In contrast to ArcView v3.x, attribute tables can be created for floating-point GRIDs in ArcGIS.
6. ESRI Online Technical Article #14575.

FIGURE 7.2. *Three patches of aspen embedded in sagebrush illustrate the difference between GRID and feature attribute tables, and zones and polygons.*

Type	Map	Attribute Table
Polygon		**ID Type** 1 Sage 2 Aspen 3 Aspen 4 Aspen
GRID (zone)		**Value Type** 1 Sage 2 Aspen
GRID (after region grouping)		**Value Type** 1 Sage 2 Aspen 3 Aspen 4 Aspen

In order to distinguish the unique patches of aspen in the GRID, contiguous *regions* of same-valued cells must be identified. That is, a cell is grouped with neighboring cells, using either the four adjacent (rook's or von Neumann's case) or eight adjacent and diagonal (queen's or Moore's case) cells that share the same value. The result of this region grouping process is a GRID that has zones with unique values. The use of the term *regions* in this context (for GRIDs) requires adjacency, while (unfortunately the same term is used) a region in a coverage (feature data structure) is able to store disjoint polygons as a single feature (remember the example of the seven islands of Hawaii).

The *spatial extent* of a GRID is defined by the number of columns (m) and rows (n) and the cell size or resolution, totaling C cells in the entire spatial extent (Figure 7.3). Note that the spatial extent of a GRID is always rectangular in shape. Within the spatial extent, the *NoData* value is used in a GRID to signify that the phenomenon of interest does not occur at that location, is outside the study boundary, or that data is missing at that location. Do not confuse NoData with the value 0.0, as 0.0 is valid in GRID. NoData values are ignored when computing statistics, and attribute data cannot be associated with them. You can control how different functions behave when they encounter NoData values so that NoData is returned, NoData is ignored and available values are used, or the value is estimated. Locations outside of the extent are considered to have NoData.

FIGURE 7.3. Analysis properties in Spatial Analyst. A GRID with 5 columns (m) and 5 rows (n), and total number of cells (C) equals $m \times n = C=25$. Note that there are 4 NoData (nd) values (lighter grey), and the valued cells (darker grey) constitute the analysis mask, which contains $C_{nd}=(m \times n)-nd$ cells.

7.2.1.1 GRID files

A GRID is actually a bunch of files grouped into two directories. The first directory is the *INFO* directory, which contains the attribute data. Note that the INFO file is shared by other GRIDs and coverages that are located at the same level in the directory structure. The second directory has the same name as the GRID name and contains a number of files with *.adf (arc data file) extensions. The files are as follows:

dblbnd.adf—This stores the rectangular boundary (the spatial extent) of the GRID.

hdr.adf—Stores the type of GRID (integer or floating point), as well as the cell resolution.

log—The log file, which stores the history of commands (in Map Algebra notation), including the date they were processed.

prj.adf—Stores the projection information (note this is a text file and can be opened in a word processor application).

sta.adf—Stores statistics about the GRID, such as minimum, maximum, mean, and standard deviation. There is a corresponding file in the INFO directory that points to the data stored here.

vat.adf—The value attribute table (for integer GRIDs only), which stores the unique cell values and count for each value. There is a corresponding file in the INFO directory that points to the data stored here.

w001001.adf—Stores the cell data.

w001001x.adf—Stores indexes to the values in w001001.adf.

7.2.1.2 *Pyramids*

The resolution of large GRIDs (i.e., larger than 1000 x 1000) typically exceeds the resolution of the display so that each pixel on the monitor has more than one GRID cell in it. As a result, the display of these GRIDs can be slow. *Pyramids* are lower resolution copies (at several levels of resolution) of the original GRID, such that the lower resolution copy displays more quickly. Pyramids are stored in a reduced resolution dataset file (*.rrd). However, sometimes GRIDs with pyramids do not display particularly well, especially when zoomed way out.

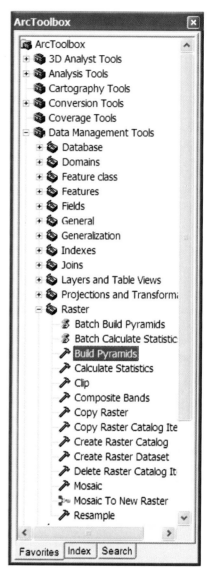

> ### *Creating pyramid files for a raster dataset*
>
> 1. Open ArcCatalog.
> 2. Navigate to locate the desired dataset.
> 3. Right-click on the dataset and select **Build pyramids**.

7.2.1.3 GRID properties

The Source tab on the Layer Properties dialog (shown at right) provides a number of characteristics about a GRID. The GRID type, directory location, name, status (permanent or temporary), and coordinate system are provided in the Data Source box. Note that the Data Source can be changed to another GRID (using the Set Data Source button). In the middle of the dialog are listings for

the number of rows and columns (10 each in the example), the number of bands (typically 1 for regular GRIDs, but remotely sensed images often have multiple bands), the *x* and *y* cell size (meaning the width and height in map units, not area!), the data type (integer or real), and whether pyramids have been created or not. At the bottom, a number of statistics are provided, including: minimum, maximum, mean, and standard deviation. Also note that the *sum* of all GRID values is displayed in the classification dialog (from the Symbology tab).

7.2.2 Images

Image data, which is also considered a raster dataset, includes remotely sensed satellite images and scanned aerial photographs. *Georeferenced images* have an associated header or world file that tells software where to place the image in space. For example, Digital Raster

---

Graphics (scanned, georeferenced images of topographic maps) are typically used as background maps, with spatial data drawn on top of them. Images do not contain attribute data about the features they show, so you cannot query them as you can GRID data. Most common image formats are supported in ArcGIS, such as TIFF, JPEG, and GIF. World files are recognized so that the images can be spatially georeferenced. See Table 7.1 for an overview of supported raster data formats.

FIGURE 7.4. A remotely-sensed image of the Picnic Rock fire west of Fort Collins, Colorado.

TABLE 7.1. Supported raster data formats.

Name	Description
Arc Digitized Raster Graphics (*.img, *.ovr, *.lgg-legend)	Geographically referenced arc-second raster map. Compressed (CADRG).
BMP (*.bmp)	Windows bitmap images: 1, 4, 8, or 24 bits per pixel. Compressed BMP files are not supported.
BIL, BIP, BSQ (*.bil, *.bip, *.bsq; *.hdr-header; *.clr-colormap; *.stx-statistics)	Single and multi-band images: band sequential (multi-band image), band interleaved by line, band interleaved by pixel. Header file describes layout of image data.
Compressed ARC Digitized Raster Graphics (CADRG)	CADRG Image.
DTED (Digital Terrain Elevation Data) (*.dt1, etc)	Created by NIMA (National Imagery and Mapping Agency).
ER Mapper (*.ers)	ER mapper format.
ERDAS (GIS file: *.gis; Imagine file: *.img; raw *.raw)	ERDAS Rev 7.3 and 7.4 *.lan and *.gis files.
GIF (*.gif)	ArcGIS can create GIF images — high quality, lossless compression.
GRID	ESRI format that supports 32-bit integer and 32-bit floating point raster grids. Without Spatial Analyst extension, a GRID is viewed as a single band image and looks for *.clr color map file.
Hierarchical Data Format (HDF)	National Center for Supercomputing Application's Hierarchical Data Format. There is no direct translator currently, but see: http://hdf.ncsa.uiuc.edu/.
IMPELL (*.rlc)	IMPELL Bitmap format which uses run-length compression for scanned monochrome images.
JPEG (*.jpg)	Standard compression technique for storing full color and gray scale images.
MrSid (*.sid)	A multi-resolution wavelet-based image format for high compression and fast access.
NITF	National Image Transfer Format.
Portable Network Graphics (*.png)	High-quality, lossless compression of graphics — a replacement for GIF. Supports 64-bit color, indexed-color images up to 256.
Sun (*.rs, *.ras, *.sun)	Sun rasterfiles for monochrome, grayscale, pseudocolor, and true color. Uses either 1, 8, 24, or 32 bits per pixel. These support a byte-level run-encoding scheme.
TIFF (*.tif, *.tff, *.tiff)	Tag Image File Forma— supports black and white (1 bit), grayscale (4, 8, 16, 24, or 32 bits), pseudocolor (4, 8, or 16), and true colors in compressed or uncompressed format. Multi-band images with 8 bits per band, unlimited number of bands. GeoTIFF 1.0 supported if the file is present. Also supports LZW compression.

7.3 Raster symbology

Rasters are displayed using symbology that is defined similarly to feature datasets. As with feature data, the symbology of choice depends on the data type that the raster represents. The *Unique Value* option is used for nominal data, to display land cover categories, for instance, while the *Classified* option is used for continuous data.

The *Stretched* option can also be used for continuous data. This option applies a contrast stretch to the values, which is designed to maximize the contrast based on different distributions. Stretch works by "mapping" the values found in the raster to the 0 to 255 found in the color maps. There are five types of stretches: none, custom, standard deviations (default), histogram equalize, and min-max. The None option will set the set the minimum value to the beginning of the color ramp and the maximum value to the end of the color ramp. To apply a *Custom* stretch, use the Histogram button and establish breakpoints by clicking in the graph. If raster statistics are not calculated, you will need to re-calculate them using the Calculate Statistics tool.

Some raster layers that are created using Spatial Analyst functions will create pre-defined color schemes. A good example of a pre-defined color scheme is for aspect GRIDs (see right).

Another interesting difference in raster symbology is the ability to display the *raster resolution*, which is the ratio of screen pixels to dataset pixels at the scale the raster is currently being displayed. A ratio of <1 means that each screen pixel is representing only a portion of the raster cell (zoomed in), while a ratio of >1 means that each screen pixel is showing only one of many raster values (zoomed out).

☐ ☑ Aspect of elevation
    <VALUE>
  ☐ Flat (-1)
  ■ North (0-22.5)
  ☐ Northeast (22.5-67.5)
  ☐ East (67.5-112.5)
  ☐ Southeast (112.5-157.5)
  ☐ South (157.5-202.5)
  ☐ Southwest (202.5-247.5)
  ■ West(247.5-292.5)
  ■ Northwest (292.5-337.5)
  ■ North (337.5-360)

7.4 Analysis environment

There are a number of analysis properties or options that can be controlled when conducting analysis on a raster dataset. The first of these specifies the directory where new GRIDs will be located. By default, the working directory is set to the system's temporary directory (usually c:\temp). Both temporary and permanent GRIDs will be saved there by default. Because analysis with GRIDs often requires a number of steps to get a final map, Spatial Analyst automatically creates *temporary* GRIDs by default. Temporary GRIDs can be made *permanent* in two ways. First, each desired GRID can be made permanent through its context menu (right click on a layer, then select Make Permanent). Second, all temporary GRIDs can be made permanent at once by saving the map document. Also, a permanent GRID will be created if a specific name (and path) of a GRID is provided when using a function. Note that GRID names cannot exceed 13 characters, and both the name and the directory path can contain only alphanumeric characters and the underscore ("_") character. Unpredictable errors can occur when a GRID has a hyphen ("-") and/or space in the name or path.

A second parameter in the Analysis Environment that can be set is the *analysis mask*. This parameter allows analysis to be performed only on certain cells within the analysis extent. The NoData cells in the *mask GRID* will carry through to any GRID created subsequently. Note that in addition to raster datasets, feature datasets can be used as the mask layer. If the coordinate system of a raster layer is different than the data frame coordinate system (in ArcMap), then the layer is on-the-fly projected using an approximation of the projection transformation. This transformation can introduce error. To ensure high-quality results, the raster layers should be projected into the same coordinate system as the data frame. Generally speaking, the errors introduced by the approximation are minimal for spatial extents smaller than a couple of degrees.

7.4.1 Analysis extent

The *analysis extent* determines the spatial extent or geographic coverage of a GRID. It is specified through the four *x,y* coordinates of a rectangle. By default, the analysis extent is set to be the *intersection of inputs*, which sets the extent of the output GRIDs to the extent made by the intersection of the input GRIDs. You also have the option of "snapping" the extent to that of an existing raster so that all subsequent layers will share the lower-left corner and cell size (recommended). The *snap extent to* option is especially useful when resampling layers.

The analysis extent can be set to the following:

> *Same as Display*—Sets the extent of output GRIDs to the current display extent. When working with really large data sets, numerous GRIDs, or complicated functions, you may want to set the extent to a small portion of the full extent so that processing is faster. First, zoom into a small portion of the overall extent, and then set the extent to *Same as Display*. Create your test GRIDs, and after you confirm

that the output GRID has worked as expected using the trial extent, reset the extent and rerun the analysis.

Union of Inputs – Sets the extent of output GRIDs to the union of all input layer extents.

Intersection of Inputs – Sets the extent of output GRIDs to the intersection of all input layer extents.

As Specified Below – Sets the extent by entering geographical coordinates for the top, bottom, left, and right of the extent.

Same As <layer> – Sets the extent to the extent of the selected layer. This is frequently used to create GRIDs that cover the same extent as some existing layer.

7.4.2 Cell size

The *cell size* or *resolution* of the output GRID can be specified using the cell size option. Cell size is the width (or height) of a cell – not the area – and is measured in map units specified by the coordinate system. The default cell size is set to the largest cell size of the inputs, the assumption reflecting that the output map is only as good as the coarsest resolution input GRID. There are, however, some instances where you might want to have the cell size smaller than the maximum, or specify your own size. However, realize that no new data is created, rather, cell values are interpolated. When converting a feature dataset to raster, the default cell size is calculated to get at least 250 columns and rows.

The following options allow you to specify how the cell size of output GRIDs will be set:

> *Minimum Of Inputs* – Sets the cell size to the size of the smallest found in the input GRID layers.
>
> *Maximum of Inputs* – The largest cell size of the input GRID layers.
>
> *As Specified Below* – The size you input. Note that the number of rows and columns is automatically updated when you type in the cell size. You can also enter either the number of rows or columns and the cell size is automatically calculated as well.

Same As <layer> — Sets the cell size to be the same as the selected layer.

Setting the analysis environment in Spatial Analyst

1. Add the Spatial Analyst extension by selecting **Tools -> Extensions...**, then checking the Spatial Analyst box.

2. Add the Spatial Analyst toolbar by selecting **View -> Toolbars -> Spatial Analyst**.

3. From the Spatial Analyst toolbar, select **Options.**

4. Select the desired tab: General, Extent, or Cell Size.

7.5 Raster-vector conversion

In the late 1970s and early 1980s, a hotly debated issue in the field of GIS was the particular advantages and disadvantages of one data model over another. One of the catchy (but misleading) adages that emerged from these debates was: "raster is faster, but vector is corrector."[7] But in actuality, *both* data models are useful for different purposes and so conversion routines between data models were developed. Spatial Analyst allows you to easily convert data between vector and raster data formats. However, conversion between formats can result in loss of information and can be problematic. Generally, using finer resolution produces better results, but the trade-off is that file sizes grow exponentially with increasing resolution. Also, beware that finer resolution can greatly overestimate linear and perimeter estimation of features.[8]

---

7. Chrisman, N. 1997. *Exploring Geographic Information Systems*. John Wiley & Sons. (page 117). Also see: Peuquet, D.J. 1984. A conceptual framework and comparison of spatial data models. *Cartographica* 21: 66-113.

8. Theobald, D.M. 2000. Correcting linear and perimeter measurement errors in raster-based data. *Cartography and Geographic Information Science* 27(2): 111-116.

7.5.1 *Vector to raster*

Any feature layer can be converted to a GRID. For point features, a cell is assigned the value of the point that is found within the cell. If two or more points intersect a single cell, the cell is assigned the value of the first point that is processed (in processing order[9]). For example, in the diagram to the right, the cell that has two points located within it (1 and 2) at the bottom is assigned a value of 1, but the cell on the right that has two points (also a 1 and

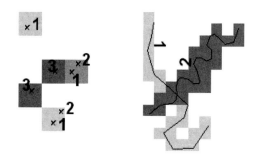

2) is assigned the value of 2. Increasing the raster resolution decreases the likelihood that a cell will share two or more points. After converting a feature to raster data, sum the count field to determine the number of cells, which should equal the number of points in the feature attribute table (if there are no multiple-point cells). Cells that do not have any points are assigned the NoData value.

For line features, cells are assigned values based on the line that intersects the cell (see above). This is similar to Bresenham's algorithm[10], where any cell that is intersected by the line is "turned on." Similar to points, if there are two or more lines that cross a cell, the cell value is assigned the value of the feature that is first encountered during processing.

There are three methods that are used to assign cell values for polygon features: centroid, dominant, and most important.[11] The *centroid method* assigns the value of the polygon found at the center of a grid cell. The *dominant method* assigns the value of the polygon that occupies the largest portion of a cell area. The *most important method* assigns the value of the polygon based on some specified ranking or weighting of polygon values. An advantage of using the centroid method is that small features (in relation to the cell size) are not systematically excluded, which happens with the dominate method. This is the method

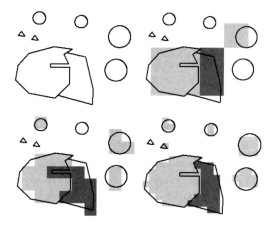

---

9. Features are processed in the same order as the feature ID value.
10. Foley, J.D. and A. van Dam. 1984. *Fundamentals of Interactive Computer Graphics.* Addison-Wesley.
11. Chou, Y.H. 1997. *Exploring Spatial Analysis in Geographic Information Systems.* Santa Fe, New Mexico: Onword Press.

that ArcGIS uses.[12] Notice in the graphic above that polygon features are *only* converted to GRID if the center of a cell falls within a polygon.

A number of factors should be considered when determining the appropriate cell size during vector to raster conversion. First, consider the minimum mapping unit (MMU) or smallest polygon size. Setting the cell size to one-half the width of the MMU may be reasonable *if* the source polygons are a regular, compact (circular or square) shape. But to resolve long, narrow features such as riparian zones along a river, the cell size should be one-half the width of the *narrowest* polygon. For all three feature types, cells that do not intersect a feature are assigned the NoData value.

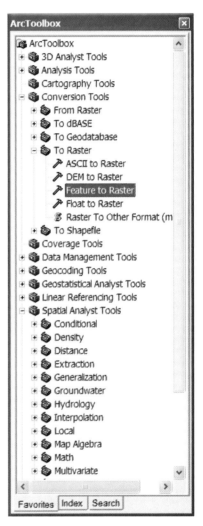

Converting features to raster[a]

1. From the Spatial Analyst toolbar, select **Convert -> Features to raster...**.

2. Select the feature layer to be converted (selected features are used).

3. Specify the output cell size.

4. Specify the output raster filename and location.

5. Click **OK**.

---

   a. This is the same functionality as Convert to GRID in ArcView v3.x.

---

12. ArcView v3.2 also uses the centroid method, while workstation ARC/INFO uses the dominant method by default.

7.5.2 *Raster to vector*

Raster can also be converted back to vector format, and Spatial Analyst allows you to select the resulting feature type.[13] When creating point features, a point will be created at the center of each cell for all non-NoData valued cells. For linear features, a polyline is created that links the center of all contiguous, same-valued cells. For polygon features, a polygon is built from regions of cells (same-valued, contiguous). For linear and polygon features, you have the option of using a generalization algorithm based on the Douglas-Peucker algorithm[14] to automatically smooth the "jagginess" of the resulting features. Note that only integer GRIDs can be converted

---

Converting raster to feature

1. From the Spatial Analyst toolbar, select **Convert -> Raster to features...**.

2. Select the raster layer to be converted (selected values are used). If a layer is not available in the list, make sure it is an integer GRID.

3. Specify whether generalization should be used or not.

4. Specify the output feature filename and location.

5. Click **OK**.

---

13. This is a welcome improvement over ArcView v3.x.

14. Douglas, D.H. and T.K. Peucker. 1973. Algorithms for the reduction of the number of points required to represent a digitized line or its caricature. *Canadian Cartographer* 10(2):110-122.

7.5.3 Image-GRID conversion

Although images and GRID data are both in raster format, the data values can be accessed only in a GRID. Occasionally you may want to convert a GRID to an image file so that it displays faster, is a smaller file size, or so that it can be used in another software program. GRIDs can be exported to images using the Export function. To convert an image to a GRID, the Image-to-GRID routine in ArcToolbox is used (requires ArcInfo license).

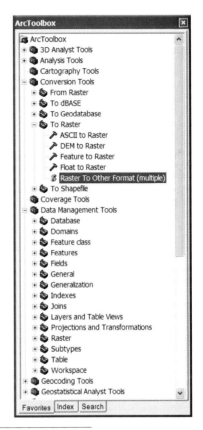

7.6 Local functions

There are four fundamental classes of functions that operate on raster data, grouped by the way they handle space: local, focal, zonal, and global.[15] Spatial Analyst provides direct interfaces to many of these functions through easy-to-use dialogs available from the Spatial Analyst toolbar. Many other functions are available through the Raster Calculator, which is discussed at length below.

---

15. Berry, J.K. 1987. Fundamental operations in computer-assisted map analysis. *International Journal of Geographical Information Systems* 1(2):119-136. Actually, the first paper that characterized cartographic modeling was: Tomlin, C.D. and J.K. Berry. 1979. A mathematical structure for cartographic modeling and analysis. *Proceedings of the 39th Symposium*, American Congress on Surveying and Mapping, Falls Church, Virginia, 269-283.

Local functions calculate output GRID values based on the values from a single or multiple GRIDs at the same location. That is, the output value for each cell is a function of the values of one or more input GRIDs *at that same location*. The values of neighboring cells do not have any influence on the output value. You can visualize local functions by thinking of a shish kabob: spear your stack of GRIDs with a skewer and then perform a function on the pierced cells (and repeat on all cells). A NoData value is returned in the output GRID for any cell that has a NoData value in any input GRID.

7.6.1 Cell Statistics

Often some statistic is needed that is calculated from a number of input GRIDs. For example, the 10-year average (mean) precipitation could be computed on a stack of GRIDs depicting precipitation from 1990 to 2000. A variety of *cell statistics* can be computed on two or more GRID layers.[16] The statistics available are: majority, maximum, mean, median, minimum, minority, range, standard deviation, sum, and variety (see Table 7.2).

Computing cell statistics

1. From the Spatial Analyst toolbar, select **Cell Statistics.**

2. Select the desired layers and add them to the Input Rasters list. Click on the Folder button to open a GRID that is not in the Layers list.

3. Select the type of statistic from the drop-down list.

4. Set the location of the output raster.

---

16. Up to 48 input GRIDs.

Local functions

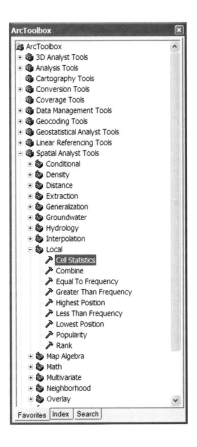

TABLE 7.2. Cell statistics available with examples of returned values for a stack of GRIDs with values: 3, 4, 2, 2, 3, 2, and 4.

Statistic	Returned value	Comments
Majority	2	Value that appears most often, tie results in NoData value
Maximum	4	Maximum value
Mean	2.857	Always returns a floating-point GRID
Median	3	
Minimum	2	
Minority	NoData	Value that occurs least often, tie results in NoData
Range	2	Maximum - minimum

TABLE 7.2. Cell statistics available with examples of returned values for a stack of GRIDs with values: 3, 4, 2, 2, 3, 2, and 4.

Statistic	Returned value	Comments
Standard deviation	0.899	Always returns a floating-point GRID
Sum	20	
Variety	3	

7.6.2 Reclassification

Although individual input values can be grouped so that they display with similar symbols, there is often the need to create new values to reflect new groupings. The *reclassification* function allows cell values from an input GRID to be replaced with new values. Often, reclassification is done to group a number of values into a few categories or classes (e.g., slopes that range from 0 - 5%=1, 5 - 10%=2, 10 - 20%=3, and 20 - 45%=4). Occasionally it is used to reassign classes on single values based on new information or a different set of assumptions (e.g., 1=2, 2=2, 3=3, 4=5) or to isolate the locations of a particular value (or range of values). Note that often reclassing data changes the data type. For example, reclassing slope values (ratio data) into categories (1 to 4) results in ordinal data. The input GRID to the reclass function can be both real and integer GRIDs, but it returns only an integer GRID. If the first GRID in the table of contents is a single-valued GRID, then a warning message may occur when bringing up the Reclassify dialog

GIS Concepts and ArcGIS Methods

To reclass a GRID, use the *Reclassify* interface.[17] A NoData value can be output by typing in "NoData" instead of a numerical value, or all input values that are not expressly listed in the dialog (the missing values) can be changed to NoData. Output classes can be specified by classifying the data (similar to classifying a legend) or by loading in a predefined reclass (a.k.a. *remap*) table that is stored as an INFO table. Note that because the option to change missing values to NoData is *not* saved in a reclass table, it is recommended to explicitly assign NoData values to the "missing values" rather than to rely on checking the NoData box.

Reclassifying a GRID

1. From the Spatial Analyst toolbar, select **Reclassify...**.

2. Specify the Input raster from the drop-down list.

3. Specify the reclass field from the second drop down list.

4. Set the desired "old values" through using the Unique button (if nominal data), through the Classify button (if quantitative data), or by clicking on the values and entering the desired values (must be in the form of "x - x", with a space, hyphen, space). Multiple entries can be selected (using shift-select) and deleted.

5. Save the remap table for documentation and later use.

6. Specify output GRID name and location.

7. Click **OK**.

---

17. This interface is essentially the same as ArcView v3.x. Unfortunately, ArcView v3.x reclass tables (*.avc) cannot be used in ArcGIS.

Although the same concept of reclassifying data applies to feature-based datasets, there is not a straightforward reclassification method for feature datasets. One way to reclassify feature attribute data is to use a combination of queries to get a desired selected set (e.g., all Lucodes value between 40 and 49) and then calculate the reclassed value in a new field (e.g., [Newlucode] = 4). Another method that works when reclassing nominal data is to create a summary table by summarizing on a field (e.g., [Lucode]). Then, add a reclass field onto the summary table and calculate the new values, then join the summary table back to the attribute table.

7.7 Focal functions

Focal functions create an output raster that is a function of the input value at a location *and* the values in the cells surrounding a location, specified by a *neighborhood*. Focal functions pass the same size and shaped neighborhood over the entire GRID. They are often used to smooth or filter a GRID by using the neighborhood values, or to compute the local variety of different land cover types, for instance. Note that the size of the neighborhood is typically defined to correspond to the functional aspect of interest. For instance, if a mammal has a one-hectare home range, then often habitat is averaged using a one-hectare neighborhood.

There are five *neighborhood* shapes available: rectangle, circle, annulus, wedge, and irregular (this last option is available only through the Raster Calculator).

Rectangle – The most common neighborhood shape is the rectangle (usually a square, e.g., 3x3). To simulate the four adjacent neighbors (rook's or von Neumann's case) use width and height values of 2. To get the eight adjacent and diagonal neighbors (queen's or Moore's case), use width and height values of 3. The *x,y* location of the processing cell – where the resultant value will be placed – is computed with respect to the upper-left corner of the neighborhood, by:

$$x = (w + 1)/2$$

$$y = (h + 1)/2$$

where w is the width and h is the height of the rectangle. If w or h is even, then the location is computed by truncation.

Circle – The size of the circle is specified by a radius value. Any cell whose center is within the radius value will be processed. (See Table 7.3 for a listing of the number of cells in the neighborhood of a given radius).

Annulus – You can specify a neighborhood such that cells immediately adjacent to the processing cell are not included, but cells slightly further away are included in the neighborhood. The inner radius specifies the area where cells will not be processed, while all cells that fall between the inner and outer radius will be processed. (This is also known as a "doughnut" neighborhood.)

Wedge – The wedge neighborhood allows you to specify a neighborhood that has a directional component. The start and end angle are specified in degrees (integer or floating point values) running from 0 to 360.

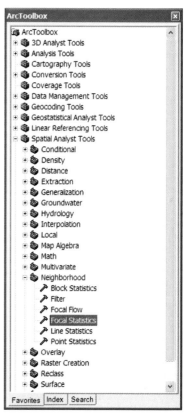

Computation time of focal operators typically increases rapidly (roughly exponentially) with the increasing size of the neighborhood. The length of processing time is dependent on the number of cells in the neighborhood, not the shape (or complexity) of the neighborhood.

TABLE 7.3. The number of cells in a circular neighborhood.

Radius (cells)	Area (# of cells)	Area (true circle)	Error
1	5	3.14	159.2%
2	13	12.5	103.5%
3	29	28.27	102.6%
4	49	50.26	97.5%
5	81	78.53	103.1%
6	113	113.09	99.9%
7	149	153.93	96.8%
8	197	201.05	98.0%
9	253	254.46	99.4%

TABLE 7.3. The number of cells in a circular neighborhood.

Radius (cells)	Area (# of cells)	Area (true circle)	Error
10	317	314.15	100.9%
15	709	706.83	100.3%
20	1257	1256.60	100.0%
30	2821	2827.35	99.8%
40	5025	5026.40	100.0%
50	7845	7853.75	99.9%

7.7.1 Neighborhood functions

As already discussed, *focal* functions move a neighborhood across an input GRID. There are two ways that these neighborhoods are moved or placed. Typically, focal operators place a *neighborhood* with respect to the *processing cell*, compute the new value and assign it to the output GRID at the location of the processing cell, then slide the neighborhood over one cell (and continue down to the next row). That is, the focal operation is computed for each and every cell in the input GRID. As the neighborhood or mask is moved across the GRID, the neighborhoods overlap. The number of neighborhoods N_f in a focal placement is:

$$N_f = C$$

where C is the number of cells in a GRID.

7.7.1.1 Block

In contrast to focal neighborhood movement, *block* functions move the neighborhood across in a non-overlapping fashion (though block operators are still considered to be focal operators). That is, block operators place a neighborhood with respect to the processing cell, compute the new value and assign it to *all* cells in the output GRID that fall underneath the neighborhood's minimum bounding rectangle, and then the neighborhood is lifted up and placed adjacent to the previous neighborhood (so the neighborhoods do not overlap). The resulting GRID typically has the same number of cells as the original. The difference between the focal and block placement methods is relatively small when the window or neighborhood is small (e.g., 3x3) but grows larger when bigger neighborhoods are used (e.g., >10x10).

The number of neighborhoods N_b in a block operation is:

$$N_b = C/B$$

where B is the number of cells in a block neighborhood.

7.7.2 Neighborhood statistics

Computing *neighborhood statistics* can be accomplished similar to Cell Statistics, through a dialog interface provided by Spatial Analyst. The following statistics can be computed for an annulus, circle, rectangular, or wedge neighborhood: majority, maximum, mean, median, minimum, minority, range, standard deviation, sum, and variety. This interface uses the focal (not block) method of moving the neighborhood across the input layer. Note that neighborhood statistics can be computed using a point layer as an input as well (only selected points are used). To compute density surfaces based on a specific number of points or for linear features, see the discussion on calculating density surfaces in the section on global functions.

Computing neighborhood statistics

1. From the Spatial Analyst toolbar, select **Neighborhood Statistics.**

2. Select the desired layer.

3. Select the field that contains the values.

4. Select the type of statistic from the statistics drop-down list.

5. Select the neighborhood type and settings.

6. Change the default output cell size, if desired.

7. Specify the location of the output raster.

7.8 Zonal functions

In the raster model, a *zone* represents a feature that is relatively homogenous, such as a vegetation patch or a political administrative unit like a state or district. A zone is composed of one or more cells that have the same (integer) value, and these cells are often contiguous but can also be disconnected or non-adjacent. A *region* is also composed of one or more cells that have the same value, but the cells must be contiguous. Thus, a zone can be composed of one or more regions. Zones represent areal features in a GRID. For example, the cells that represent each of the 50 United States would have a separate value, and the GRID attribute table would contain 50 records, one for each state.

A *zonal* function produces an output grid where the value of each cell depends on the value of the input GRID at that location and the association of that value with other cells of the same value across the input GRID. The number of zones equals the number of classes, not the number of regions. Even if more than one region has the same value, the number of zones remains equal to the number of unique values. Cells that are in the same zone often are adjacent to one another, but can be at any, often disjoint, location in the GRID. The layer that defines the zones is called the zone layer and can be either an integer GRID or a feature theme. Usually a zonal function will use the *zone* layer to specify the cells from the *value* layer to use when calculating a statistic.

7.8.1 Zonal statistics

One of the main uses of zonal functions is to compute a summary statistic for each zone in the *zone* layer using the cell values from the *value* layer. The output of this function is a table containing all of the summary statistics. For *value* GRIDs of integer type, you can compute the area, minimum, maximum, range, mean, standard deviation, sum, variety, majority, minority, and median value. For *value* GRIDs of floating-point type, you can compute area, minimum, maximum, range, mean, standard deviation, and sum.

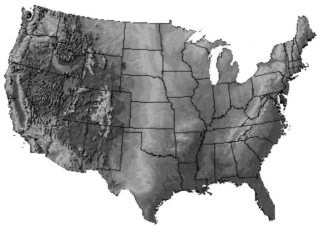

For example, zonal statistics can be used to determine which state is the "highest" in the US. This can be computed by using the *Zonal Statistics* interface provided by the Spatial Analyst. Note that the zone dataset can be either a feature or raster layer. Colorado turns out to be the highest (averages 2,094 m), Wyoming is the second highest (1,957 m), and Utah is third (1,843 m).

> ### *Computing zonal statistics*
>
> 1. From the Spatial Analyst toolbar, select **Zonal Statistics...**.
>
> 2. Set the Zone Dataset: to the layer that defines the zones to be summarized.
>
> 3. Select the zone field.
>
> 4. Set the Value raster: to be the GRID's values that will be summarized.
>
> 5. Check the options if you wish to ignore NoData, to join the summary output table to the Zone Dataset, or to create a chart.
>
> 6. Set the Output table name.
>
> 7. Click OK.

7.9 Global functions

Global functions manipulate values on an entire raster all at once. There is a wide variety of global functions, but the most commonly used ones are distance and density.

7.9.1 Distance

Distance is a fundamental factor in controlling the spatial relationships between different geographic features. Indeed, the *First Law of Geography* states that "Everything is related to everything else, but near things are more related than distant things."[18] Because of the importance of distance in GIS, there are a number of ways to calculate distance on raster data, and Spatial Analyst provides interfaces to four of the most common methods: straight line, allocation, cost weighted, and shortest path.

---

18. Tobler, W.R. 1970. A computer model of simulating urban growth in the Detroit region. *Economic Geography* 46: 234-240.

7.9.1.1 Straight line

Straight-line distance (a.k.a Euclidean or "as the crow flies") measures the distance from a location to the nearest feature of interest. Distance is measured from the center of each cell to the center of the nearest cell representing some feature of interest, and uses the Pythagorean theorem to compute the Euclidean distance. Distance from features is typically used when conducting a suitability analysis. For example, the distance from cities (yellow to red) could be used as an indicator of the relative *remoteness* in the western US. So, to "get away from it all," one might be inclined to find those red areas (see right) that are furthest away from cities (and so much of Nevada is fairly remote). Note that the output raster is a surface of real-valued distance values.

Related to straight-line distance is the notion of the Euclidean *direction* GRID, which provides the compass direction pointing back to the nearest feature of interest. This directional information might be useful when one wants to return from the isolated areas. Also note that in addition to finding the distance from features of interest, the particular feature that is closest can be identified for each location in a cell, which is known as *allocation*. This function is often used to locate the "service area" of a store, for example. The tesselations created by allocation zones can also be converted into polygons that are called *proximity regions*, area of influence polygons, or *Thiessen* or *Voronoi* polygons (Figure 7.5). These allocation polygons have been used in a wide variety of applications, from determining mathematical surfaces to interpolating precipitation averages.[19] Spatial Analyst provides interfaces to compute distance, direction, and allocation GRIDs.

---

19. Thiessen, A.H. 1911. Precipitation averages for large areas. *Monthly Weather Review* 39: 1082-1084.

FIGURE 7.5. The author succumbing to a Thiessen polygon in Death Valley, California (note old ArcINFO t-shirt!).

Calculating straight-line distance

1. From the Spatial Analyst toolbar, select **Distance -> Straight line...**.

2. Select the layer to compute the distance from. This is typically a point or line feature layer (selected features are used). If you input a raster layer, distance is computed from *all* valued (but not NoData) cells.

3. Input a maximum distance (if desired) in map units. Cells beyond this distance will be given the NoData value.

4. Set the output cell size.

5. Check the Create direction and/or Create allocation options if you wish.

6. Specify the Output raster name.

7. Click **OK**.

Note: a common reason for the "Error in opening or reading VAT" is that the input layer (e.g., representing point or linear features) is not in the same projection as the data frame's coordinate system — try re-projecting the feature layer to the same coordinate system.

Calculating allocation zones

1. From the Spatial Analyst toolbar, select **Distance -> Allocation...**.

2. Select the layer to compute the allocation zones around (selected features are used).

3. Set the output cell size.

5. Specify the Output raster name.

6. Click **OK**.

7.9.1.2 Cost weighted

A second approach to computing distance is to recognize that there may be geographic conditions that affect how far a particular location is from another, from a functional perspective. Restating the First Law of Geography slightly: some equidistant things are closer than others. That is, it is likely that some equidistant locations may take longer to get to than others. This is often the case when one thinks about how "far" away a location is in terms of the time it takes to get there rather than straight-line distance. Returning to the *remoteness* example, some remote locations in wilderness areas take much longer to access, and remoteness changes dramatically by the mode of travel (e.g., driving or walking). For example, the speed with which one can hike depends largely on the steepness of a road or trail. One estimation of the relationship between a hiker's velocity in km/hr (V) and slope in degrees (S) is:

$$V = 6e^{-3.5 \times abs(\tan(S/57.29578) + 0.05)}$$

so that on flat terrain a typical hiker averages 5.04 km/hr.[20] So, how can we reflect these geographic conditions when computing distance?

Cost weighted distance incorporates such factors that influence movement across a surface. Cost weighted distance computes distance in terms of cost units and accumulates these units at locations away from features of interest. For example, because mountainous areas are more difficult to access, our measure of remoteness should reflect this and hence some of the interior ranges of the west have a higher level of remoteness. To compute cost weighted distance, two input GRIDs are needed: the *source* GRID that defines the features of interest (all non-NoData values); and the *cost* GRID that contains the cost (or impedance) to travel across a location, for all cells. In the hiker example, the source GRID would mark the trailhead location, while the cost GRID would specify the cost based on some function (like the one above) of slope.

The cost weighted distance algorithm utilizes graph theory and represents a raster by assuming there is a node at the center of each cell connected by a link to each of the eight

---

20. From Tobler, W. 1993. *Three presentations on geographical analysis and modeling*. Technical report 93-1, National Center for Geographic Information and Analysis, University of California, Santa Barbara; based on empirical values estimated by Imhof, E. 1950. *Gelaende und Karte*, Rentsch, Zurich.

neighboring cells. The accumulative cost of a link (a) is computed by averaging the costs of two adjacent cells (c_1 and c_2):

$$a = (c_1 + c_2)/2 \text{ (for orthogonal links) and } a = (\sqrt{2(c_1 + c_2)})/2 \text{ (for diagonal links).}$$

Using an iterative process, the averaged cost is accumulated in steps away from the source cells (see Figure 7.6). Note that cost weighted distance is equivalent to straight-line distance if all cells in the cost GRID equal 1. Also, allocation and direction GRIDs can be created that reflect the cost weighted surface.

FIGURE 7.6. An example of using cost-weighted methods to compute the time to travel from trailheads in eastern Yosemite Valley to all locations within Yosemite National Park, California. Accessibility computed here reflects trail slope[21] and is weighted by off-trail slopes.

Calculating cost weighted distance

1. From the Spatial Analyst toolbar, select **Distance -> Cost weighted...**.

2. Select the layer to compute the distance from. This is typically a point or line feature layer (selected features are used). If you input a raster layer, distance is computed from *all* valued (non-NoData) cells.

3. Select the cost GRID.

4. Input a maximum distance (if desired) in map units. Cells beyond this distance will be given the NoData value.

5. Set the output cell size.

5. Check the Create direction and/or Create allocation options if you wish.

6. Specify the Output raster name.

7. Click **OK**.

Computing shortest paths

1. From the Spatial Analyst toolbar, select **Distance -> Shortest path...**.

2. Set the Path to: layer that specifies the source location(s).

3. Select Cost distance raster: to the desired cost-weight GRID.

4. Select the Cost direction raster.

5. Select the path type.

6. Specify the Output raster name.

7. Click **OK**.

---

21. Computed using data from van Wagtendonk, J. W., and J. M. Benedict. 1980. Travel time variation on backcountry trails. *Journal of Leisure Research* 12(2): 99-109

The *shortest path function* is used to find the least-cost path or route that is guaranteed to be the cheapest cost to travel between two locations. The shortest path is often used to help plan new construction, to identify where to locate a new road or trail, for example.[22] To compute the shortest path in Spatial Analyst, first cost-distance and cost-direction GRIDs (using the cost weighted distance method) must be created. The *destination layer* then specifies a source, or set of sources, that the path will be found to a destination. There are three possible *path types* to control the number of paths created. *For Each Cell* finds a path to each cell in each zone defined in the destination layer. *For Each Zone* finds the one least-cost path from the destination to each zone. *Best Single* finds the shortest or least-cost path for all zones. The output for the shortest path function is a feature dataset (line type).

---

22. A good example of using cost weighted methods to locate a new road can be found in the ArcGIS Desktop Help, search on "Finding the least-cost route for a road."

7.9.2 Density

Typically, continuous *density surfaces* are created to "smooth" or spread out counts located at points so that concentrations or "hot spots" can be more readily identified. An underlying assumption is that the process or geographic phenomena being mapped is continuous in nature. For example, a density surface representing population is often used to visualize where urban concentrations are located. Density surfaces can be created from both point and line layers. Essentially, density for each GRID cell is computed by determining the features (e.g., cities) within a given neighborhood (typically defined by a circle), summing the value of interest (e.g., population in 2000) for those features, and then computing the average number of occurrences per square unit area (e.g., square miles).

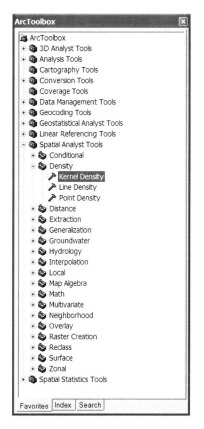

There are two density methods: simple and kernel. The *simple density* method calculates density by summing the values of a *population field* for all features found within the search radius or neighborhood, and then dividing by the neighborhood area. The density values can be expressed in a variety of units (roughly from largest to smallest): mi^2, km^2, acres, hectares, yds^2, ft^2, in^2, m^2, cm^2, and mm^2. Note that using larger areal units will result in smaller density values, and that because the values are specific to the areal units used, it is best to include the units in the GRID name to explicitly record the units of the GRID values.[23] The *kernel density* method calculates density similarly to the *simple* method, but a smoothly curved surface (based on a quadratic kernel function) is fit through each sample point, resulting in a smoother output.[24] The value is weighted highest at the center and diminishes with increasing distance from the center. The search radius (in map distance units) determines the distance to search for points from each cell in the output GRID layer. The default radius equals 1/30 of either the width or height of the extent, whichever is smaller. However, it is best to provide a

---

23. Unfortunately there is no way to record the units that the GRID value represents. However, units could be stored in the GRID's meta-data in the *entity attribute* section.
24. The kernel function is described in: Silverman, B.W. 1986. *Density Estimation for Statistics and Data Analysis.* New York: Chapman and Hall. (p. 76, equation 4.5).

radius that corresponds to the spatial scale of the process or phenomenon under study. Larger radii smooth or average the values, while smaller radii result in "peakier" surfaces.

> ### *Calculating a density surface*
>
> 1. From the Spatial Analyst toolbar, select **Density...**.
>
> 2. Select the input layer (typically a point feature, but it can also be a line feature type).
>
> 3. Select the "population" field (should represent counts).
>
> 4. Select the density type, either Simple or Kernel.
>
> 5. Specify the search radius (in map units).
>
> 6. Set the area units of the output GRID.
>
> 7. Specify the cell size.
>
> 8. Specify the output raster filename and location.
>
> 9. Click **OK**.

Often a map showing the density of linear features, such as *road density* or *stream density*, is needed. For example, a number of studies have found that in the Great Lakes region of the US (Wisconsin and Minnesota), wolves (*Canis lupus*) do not persist in areas with road densities greater than about 0.5 km/km^2. Some of these studies, however, have computed road density by summing the total length of roads in each county, then dividing by the area of each county.[25] If the distribution of roads is heterogeneous within a county (e.g., many roads near a city, few in the countryside), then the average road density in a county may be misleading. Ideally, road density is computed using a focal operator because the analytical unit (the area that is used to compute the denominator of the density) can be controlled by specifying the neighborhood size so that it is meaningful to the

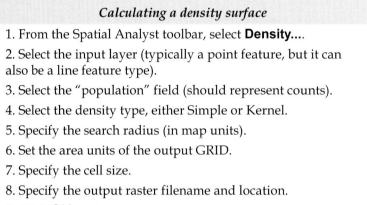

25. Mech, L.D. 1989. Wolf population survival in an area of high road density. *American Midland Naturalist* 121:387-389. Thiel, R.P. 1985. Relationship between road densities and wolf habitat suitability in Wisconsin. *American Midland Naturalist* 113:404-407.

process or organism under study. This type of computation can be accomplished using the *Density* interface in Spatial Analyst (the *linestats* function can also be used in Map Algebra).

Computing road density

1. From the Spatial Analyst toolbar, select **Density...**.
2. Set the Input Data: to the line layer with roads.
3. Leave the population field as <none>.
4. Set the Density type: to be Simple.
5. Set the search radius (the circle radius).
6. Set the Output cell size.
7. Set the name of the output GRID.
8. Click **OK**.

7.9.3 Surface analysis

We have long examined the intricacies of the earth's surface to understand topographic relief and variation and how these influence other geographic phenomena. Powerful GIS methods have been developed to manipulate and analyze elevation data that represent surfaces through digital terrain models (DTMs) or digital elevation models (DEMs).

DEMs represent surfaces by "posting" an elevation at equal-spaced locations, usually at the center of every GRID cell. A wide variety of data sources for DEMs are available. For instance, the US National Imagery and Mapping Agency developed the Digital Terrain Elevation Data (DTED), a 30 arc-second resolution (Level 0).[26] GTOPO30 provides global coverage at 30 arc second (roughly 1 km) resolution and is composed of a variety of different sources, including DTED and US Geological Survey (USGS) DEMs. If the source of the 1 km data was finer resolution (e.g., 90 m), then instead of using the average or the center cell, the average of the dominant geomorphic feature (ridge or valley) was used.[27] In the United States, the USGS provides DEMs at varying scales: 7.5' (~10 m and ~30 m) and 1° (3 arc-second: ~90 m).[28] At the fine resolution, a number of methods have been used to create DEMs from aerial photographs, including an automated photogrammetric system known as the Gestalt Photo Mapper II that estimated elevations in "patches," manual profiling using photogrammetric stereomodels that recorded postings along successive east-to-west and west-to-east terrain profiles, and interpolation of digital line graph (DLG) hypsographic (i.e. contour lines) and hydrographic

---

26. DTED is available from: http://www.fas.org/irp/program/core/dted.htm.
27. US Geological Survey, 1996. GTOPO30 documentation. http://edcdaac.usgs.gov/gtopo30/README.html.
28. USGS DEMs: http://edc.usgs.gov/glis/hyper/guide/usgs_dem.

lines. The USGS found the last method produces the most accurate DEMs and is their preferred method for production. More recently the USGS has embarked on the National Elevation Dataset (NED), which is a seamless, edge-matched dataset that provides standardized and pre-processed DEMs for large expanses (i.e. broader than a single quadsheet).[29] Most recently, a joint effort between the National Imagery and Mapping Agency and the National Aeronautics and Space Administration is producing the Shuttle Radar Topography Mission (SRTM), whose goal is to map 80% of the world at 1 arc-second (~30 m) resolution using radar interferometry.[30] Also, surfaces are commonly represented using Triangular Irregular Networks as well.[31]

There are two types of errors found in DEMS: systematic and random. Systematic errors are relatively common in the "older" DEMs. These are usually visible as "seams," such as abrupt changes or *slivers* of missing data at map sheet boundaries (e.g., at the border of two quad sheets,) or *stripes* introduced by the method used to produce the DEM. Random errors are very difficult to spot visually in a DEM, but they rear their ugly heads when using DEM's particular surface analyses, such as watershed basin delineation. The most common types of random errors are artificial pits and peaks.[32] *Pits* are cells that are surrounded by higher elevation values, though some of these may be natural (e.g., in a karst landscape). Artificial pits cause breaks in hydrologic drainage. *Peaks* are cells that are surrounded by cells of lower value.

The Spatial Analyst extension provides interfaces to six of the most common surface analysis methods: contours, slope, aspect, hillshade, viewshed, and cut/fill (see Figure 7.7 for examples of these at different resolutions). Also, note that *any* raster data with ratio values can be analyzed using these methods, so that surfaces representing phenomena other than elevation can be analyzed.

29. Gesch, D., M. Oimoen, S. Greenlee, C. Nelson, M. Steuck, and D. Tyler. 2002. The National Elevation Dataset. Photogrammetric Engineering & Remote Sensing 68(1), available online at: www.asprs.org/asprs/publications/pe&rs/2002journal/january/january_frame.html

30. http://srtm.usgs.gov/.

31. Kumler, M.P. 1994. An intensive comparison of triangulated irregular networks (TINs) and Digital Elevation Models (DEMs). *Cartographica* 31(2):1-99.

32. Mark, D.M. 1988. Network models in Geomorphology. In: Modeling in Geomorphologic Systems. John Wiley. Also see Mark, D.M. 1983. Automated detection of drainage networks from digital elevation models. *Proceedings of the Sixth International Symposium on Automated Cartography* 2: 288-295.

FIGURE 7.7. Examples of surface functions at different resolutions (top to bottom: 90 m, 30 m, and 10 m) for Redstone Canyon, west of Fort Collins, CO, USA. Left to right, the images show elevation (white higher), hillshade, slope (red steeper, green flatter), and aspect (north red, east yellow, south turquoise, west blue, and flat in gray).

7.9.3.1 Contours

Contours represent points of equal elevation (technically, contours are for above sea level elevations, while bathymetric contours or *isobaths* are used for below-sea level). Often the term contour is used synonymously with the more general *isoline*, which connects points of equal value. Isolines not only show elevation, but they are also used to display numerous other types of data, such as isobars (pressure) and isohyets (precipitation). Spatial Analyst interpolates from a smooth surface, it does not merely connect lines to the center of cells with the same value.

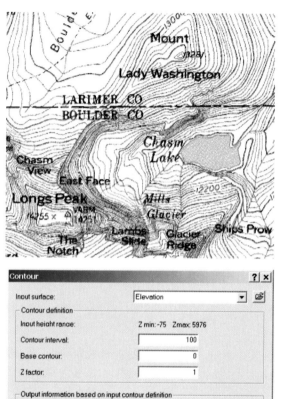

Contours have long been used to visualize topographic relief: steep hillsides are shown in contours with little space between them, while flat areas have widely spaced contours. The *base contour* establishes the lowest contour and all contours build from it. The *contour interval* defines the vertical distance between contours—the smaller the interval, the more detailed the portrayal of topography. However, if the interval is too small, then the resulting map is too messy and will be difficult to read. It might be helpful to make use of ArcMap's ability to display layers at different scales so that as one zooms in, the contour layer with smaller intervals is shown.

Contour lines can also be created interactively by using the *contour tool* ( ) on the Spatial Analyst toolbar. ArcGIS finds the contour for the value at that location for the top-most visible GRID.

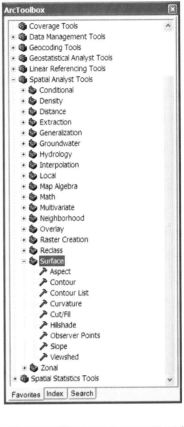

Creating a contour layer

1. From the Spatial Analyst toolbar, select **Surface analysis -> Contour....**

2. Select the input GRID that contains the elevation values.

3. Specify the contour interval.

4. Specify the base contour elevation.

5. Set the Z factor to convert vertical units (e.g., m to ft).

6. Enter the name of the output polyline shapefile.

7. Click **OK**.

7.9.3.2 Hillshade

Although contour maps remain very useful, a newer method that is used frequently to help readers visualize surfaces is the *hillshade* map. Hillshade maps represent data from an *orthographic* perspective. The *azimuth* is the angle of the light source (e.g., the sun) using 0° and 360° as north, increasing clockwise. The default value is 315° (northeast). Hillshade maps are customarily created using an azimuth that is in the north (between 0° to 90° and 270° to 360°). Because we generally read maps with north at the top and because light comes from above, we perceive ridge and canyon features correctly. If the light source was from the south (or we flipped the hillshade map 180°), we would perceive ridges to be canyons and vice versa. The altitude or *zenith* defines how high the sun is in the sky; the higher the value, the flatter the hillshade looks, and only areas with steep relief will cast shadows. In contrast, low altitude values will accentuate relief. A zenith of 45° is commonly used. Typically, hillshades are displayed using a dark to light gray color ramp so that high values have lighter colors (this is the reverse of most other graduated color legends).[33] Hillshade maps are often used as the base, with another layer draped on top and the *transparency* set so the topographic relief can be seen.Because both the direction of the sun (azimuth) and its height in the sky (zenith) need to be defined, many different hillshade GRIDs can be created for the same surface, each highlighting different aspects of the terrain. It is also useful for analysis, for example, to determine the number of hours of direct sunlight for a particular location. There are also techniques to do simultaneous hillshading.

Two types of blemishes are common in hillshade maps. The first is a fine-scale horizontal striping caused by an defect in the process used to create many DEMs — typically by semi-automatic profiling of stereo-pairs of aerial photographs. The elevation values are recorded consecutively in an east-west direction, and, as a result, the elevation values in different E-W rows were recorded from the opposite direction. That is, the systematic sampling results in stronger autocorrelation within, as compared to between, rows. A second blemish occurs at quadsheet boundaries, where an abrupt discontinuity in elevation is noticeable. Both of these types of blemishes can be reduced by using advanced filtering methods.[34]

Creating a hillshade GRID

1. From the Spatial Analyst toolbar, select **Surface analysis -> Hillshade....**

2. Select the input GRID that contains the elevation values.

3. Specify the azimuth (in degrees, north is 0, clockwise).

4. Specify the altitude (in degrees, 90 is straight overhead).

5. Check the model shadows box if make shadow cells = 0.

6. Set the Z factor to convert vertical units (e.g., m to ft).

7. Enter the output cell size.

8. Enter the name of the output GRID.

9. Click **OK**.

---

33. Schruben, P. 1999. *Color shaded relief map of the coterminous United States*. USGS Open-file Report 99-11. http:// pubs.usgs.gov/openfile/of99-011/index.html

GIS Concepts and ArcGIS Methods

In addition to using contours or hillshades to visualize topographic features, three-dimensional modeling can provide oblique perspectives using the *3D Analyst* extension (Figure 7.8).

FIGURE 7.8. Redstone Canyon, Colorado viewed from the southeast (looking northwest).

---

34. For details on removing striping from DEMs, see: Russell, E. and H. Ochis. 1996. *Mitigation methods for systematic errors in USGS DEMs*. www.ctmap.com/gis_journal/filtering_wp.pdf.

7.9.3.3 Slope

Slope can be derived directly from an elevation GRID. Slope is the maximum rate of change at all locations on a GRID or TIN layer. Slope is calculated by fitting a plane at a location using a 3x3 window to average the maximum slope. Therefore, slope is resolution dependent.[35] If the value of one of the 3x3 cell is NoData, the center cell's elevation value is substituted in the missing cell when calculating slope. Although any GRID layer can be input, calculation of slope assumes a continuous phenomenon (ratio data).

Slope is found using the *rise* (horizontal distance) over *run* (vertical distance), and is expressed in degrees ($S°$), where:

$$S° = \tan\theta = \frac{rise}{run}$$

or in percent (S'), where:

$$S' = \frac{rise}{run} \times 100 \quad .$$

When the *z* (elevation) units of a GRID are not the same as the coordinate system (x,y) units, a *z-factor* must be used to account for the unit change. For example, if a GRID is in UTM meters but elevation values are in feet, then use a z-factor of 0.3048. Note that slope (the maximum rate of change at a location) cannot be used directly for the slope of linear features, such as streams, roads, or trails, because the direction of the linear feature does not have to coincide

---

35. Burrough, P.A. and R.A. McDonnell, 1998. *Principles of Geographical Informational Systems*. Oxford University Press.

with the direction of the steepest slope (i.e. the "fall line"). Rather, only those cells that fall on the linear feature can be used when calculating slope.

Creating a slope GRID

1. From the Spatial Analyst toolbar, select **Surface analysis -> Slope...**.

2. Select the input GRID that contains the elevation values.

3. Specify the whether you want the output in degrees or percent.

4. Set the Z factor to convert vertical units (e.g., m to ft).

5. Enter the output cell size.

6. Enter the name of the output GRID.

7. Click **OK**.

7.9.3.4 Aspect

Related to slope is *aspect*, which is the direction of maximum slope. Output values are expressed in degrees, with 0° and 360° at north, increasing clockwise. Cells that are flat are assigned a value of -1. If the input surface is a GRID, then aspect is calculated using a 3x3 window. If the input surface is a TIN, then cells are assigned the aspect of the triangle its center

falls in. The default legend for an aspect GRID is optimized to show the 360° nature of aspect. Also note that aspect is a *cyclical* data type. Often the average aspect is needed, and one way to get around the cyclical data is to convert it to N-S values and not differentiate E-W directions. That is, if an aspect is greater than 180°, then the normalized aspect equals the aspect - 180°.

Creating an aspect GRID

1. From the Spatial Analyst toolbar, select **Surface analysis -> Aspect...**.

2. Select the input GRID that contains the elevation values.

3. Enter the output cell size.

4. Enter the name of the output GRID.

5. Click **OK**.

7.9.3.5 *Viewshed*

A *viewshed* is composed of the places that are viewable from a given location (Figure 7.9). Viewsheds are important when siting features such as cell towers or buildings, or for understanding amenity (view) values. A viewshed can be calculated from either a single position or a number of positions, defined by an *observation* theme with either point or line features. That is, from an observation point, you can identify the locations that are visible.

A number of options can be specified for each of the observation points. These settings must be defined in the *observation* layer's (observer points) attribute table, not interactively through a series of dialogs. The value in the *spot field* in the attribute table of the observation table is used for the elevation value. The elevation value is interpolated (bilinear) from the input GRID if the field is not in the table. An observation point is excluded from the analysis if the value of the nearest cell is NoData.

The value in the *Offseta field* specifies a vertical distance (in surface units) to be added to the elevation value of the observation point. This value is added to either the *Spot* or interpolated elevation value (it must be positive). By default, a value of 1 is added if the *Offseta* field does not exist. The value in the *Offsetb* field specifies a vertical distance to be added to the elevation values to each cell in the input GRID. By default, a value of 0 is added if the *Offsetb* field does not exist.

The values in the *Azimuth1* and *Azimuth2* fields specify the beginning and ending horizontal angles of the scan. The scan proceeds in a clockwise direction from angle 1 to angle 2. If these fields do not exist, a full 360° scan is implemented. The values in the *Vert1* and *Vert2* fields define the upper and lower limit of the scan, respectively. Default values are 90° and -90°.

FIGURE 7.9. Areas on the northern Colorado Front Range where Longs Peak (lower left cross) can be seen are shown in green.

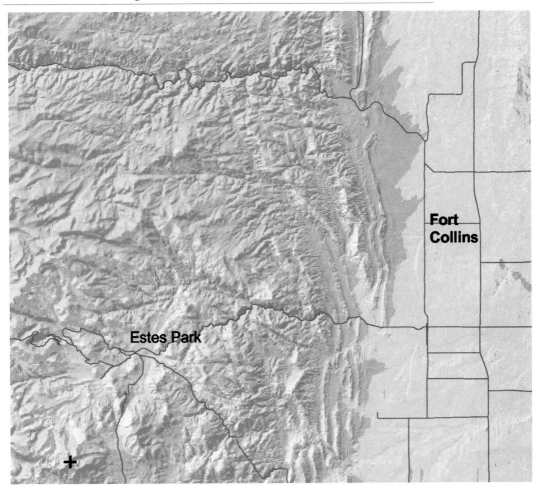

You can also limit the search distance from each point by specifying a short and far search radius in the *Radius1* and *Radius2* fields. Locations closer than the short radius will not be visible in the output GRID but can block the visibility beyond that location. Locations beyond the far radius are excluded from the analysis. The default values are 0 and infinity, respectively. By default, the distances are three-dimensional line-of-sight distances. You can use planimetric distances by inserting a negative sign in front of the distance values.

Creating a viewshed GRID

1. From the Spatial Analyst toolbar, select **Surface analysis -> Viewshed...**.

2. Select the input GRID that contains the elevation values.

3. Select the layer (point or line) that contains the observations.

4. Check the box if you wish to account for Earth's curvature.

5. Enter the Z factor (to convert units).

6. Enter the output cell size.

7. Enter the name of the output GRID.

8. Click **OK**.

7.9.3.6 Cut and fill

The differences between two surfaces, in terms of area and volume, can be computed by cut and fill analysis. Most often this operation is used for planning construction projects, but it is useful in other applications as well, such as examining population growth patterns, changes in river geomorphology, or lake sedimentation.[36]

Cut and fill analysis

1. From the Spatial Analyst toolbar, select **Surface analysis -> Cut/fill...**.

2. Select the input GRID that contains the "before" surface.

3. Select the input GRID that contains the "after" surface.

4. Enter the Z factor (to convert units).

5. Enter the output cell size.

6. Enter the name of the output GRID.

7. Click **OK**.

---

36. For a detailed description of cut and fill operations, see: Price, M. 2002. Deriving volumes with ArcGIS Spatial Analyst. ArcUser (October-December):52-55. www.esri.com/news/arcuser/1002/files/volumes.pdf

7.9.4 Surface generation (interpolation)

Often geographic data are sampled at various locations, rather than a complete census, because of time or money constraints. To create a surface from sampled data, that is to estimate the values at all non-sampled locations, one needs to *interpolate*. There is a variety of interpolation methods, but all make use of the First Law of Geography, that things closer together tend to be more similar than those farther away. Spatial Analyst provides ready-access to three methods: inverse distance weighted (IDW), spline, and kriging. Which method should you use? It depends, mostly on the assumptions that you can make with a given dataset. It is best to assess the accuracy of the model chosen, either through cross-validation[37] or through tests against a set of "test points." To illustrate the differences between these methods and the results they provide, we'll use an example dataset of 509 elevation test points, randomly selected from a 30 m DEM (Figure 7.9). Because we know the "truth" for the rest of the elevations, we can assess the accuracy of the interpolation methods. Although any point layer with integer or real values can be input, interpolation assumes that the geographic phenomena represented by the surface values is *continuous*.

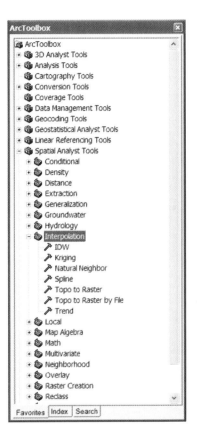

---

37. Note that the Geostatistical Analyst extension provides a flexible interface to explore the accuracy of different models.

FIGURE 7.10. Elevation with Xs showing the 509 sampled locations.

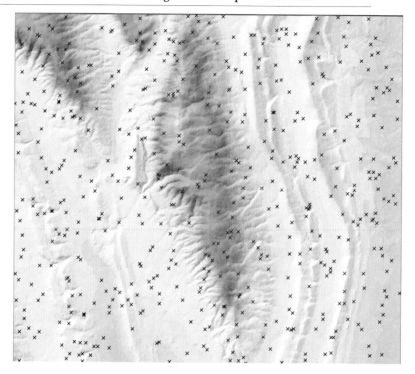

7.9.4.1 Inverse distance weighted

The inverse distance weighted (IDW) method assumes a distance decay function using a linearly weighted set of sample points, so that the influence of a point declines with increasing distance from that point. Therefore, points closer to the processing cell have greater weight than those farther away. The interpolation algorithm uses either a specified number of nearest points or all points within a given radius. The power parameter affects the rate of decline in influence with distance. As the power parameter value approaches 0 (but is not less than), the influence of distant points increases. As the value increases, the influence of distant points decreases. Reasonable results can be obtained using values from 0.5 to 3. The default value is 2. A *barrier* layer (of line feature type) can be specified to break the limit of search for sample points using linear features.[38] The nearest neighbor method is typically used when the phenomenon exhibits the behavior that more distant locations have less influence. Neighbors can be specified by using either a fixed or variable search radius. Fixed neighborhoods use all points that are found within a given radius (though a minimum number of points can be required as well). Variable search neighbors use the nearest n neighbors, where n is specified (and a maximum distance can be defined as well). The *barrier* theme is useful when there are geographic features, such as ridges, cliffs, rivers, highways, or some feature that interrupts the continuous distribution of the phenomenon of interest.

The *root mean square error* (RMSE) is typically used to compute error in surfaces (Figure 7.11). RMSE is the square root of the average squared difference between the estimated value (x) and the "true" value (x_0):

$$RMSE = \sqrt{\left(\sum (x - x_0)^2\right)/n}$$

where n is the number of points (also usually randomly selected).

FIGURE 7.11. IDW-interpolated surface (left), with error surface (right—darker blues show overestimation, light cyan and yellow show little error, while darker reds show underestimation). The RMSE was 21.5 m.

38. Phillip, G.M. and D.F. Watson. 1982. A precise method for determining contoured surfaces. *Australian Petroleum Explanation Association Journal* 22: 205-212; Watson, D.F. and G.M. Phillip. 1985. A refinement of Inverse Distance Weighted interpolation. *Geo-Processing* 2:315-327.

Interpolating using IDW

1. From the Spatial Analyst toolbar, select **Interpolate to raster -> Inverse distance weighted...**.

2. Select the input layer that contains the points.

3. Select the field that contains the "elevation" values.

4. Set the Power factor (typically 0.5 to 3).

5. Specify the search radius type as Variable or Fixed.

6. If Variable, then specify the number of points in a neighborhood and the maximum distance. If fixed, then enter the search radius (in map units) and the minimum number of points needed.

7. Check the box to use barrier polylines, and specify the polyline shapefile.

8. Enter the output cell size.

9. Enter the name of the output GRID.

10. Click **OK**.

7.9.4.2 *Spline*

The *spline* interpolation algorithm fits a two-dimensional, minimum-curvature surface through the sample points using a mathematical function (Figure 7.12). The resulting surface passes exactly through the input points. This method is best for surfaces that exhibit smooth, gentle variations, such as water table heights or precipitation. It is not appropriate for surfaces that have abrupt changes (use the IDW with a barrier theme). You have the option of using a *regularized* method, which produces a smooth surface by using the specified weight parameter to define the weight of the third derivative in the curvature minimization equation. Higher values produce a smoother surface, and typically range from 0.0 to 0.5. The *tension* method produces a "stiffer" surface and uses the specified weight parameter for the tension weight and the specified number of points to establish the number of points required during local approximation. The greater the weight, the coarser the surface, and typical values range

---

from 1 to 10. The greater the number of sample points required, the smoother the resulting surface.

FIGURE 7.12. Spline-interpolated surface (left), with error surface (right — darker blues show overestimation, light cyan and yellow show little error, while darker reds show underestimation). The RMSE for the spline surface is 21.2 m.

Interpolating using spline

1. From the Spatial Analyst toolbar, select **Interpolate to raster -> Spline...**.

2. Select the input layer that contains the points.

3. Select the field that contains the "elevation" values.

4. Specify the spline type: Regularized or Tension.

6. Specify the weight and number of points in a neighborhood.

7. Enter the output cell size.

8. Enter the name of the output GRID.

9. Click **OK**.

7.9.4.3 Kriging

Kriging is an interpolation method that includes the autocorrelation of the values of the input points (Figure 7.13). It is similar to IDW in that the surrounding measures are weighted, but kriging also utilizes the spatial arrangement of the weights. The interface allows ordinary and universal kriging and a number of common semivariogram models: spherical, circular, exponential, Gaussian, and linear. Importantly, kriging allows the creation of a surface of predicted variance. There are number of books that discuss kriging methods in detail.[39]

Kriging	? x
Input points:	elevation_points
Z value field:	GRID_CODE
Kriging method:	● Ordinary ○ Universal
Semivariogram model:	Spherical
	Advanced Parameters...
Search radius type:	Variable
Search Radius Settings	
Number of points:	12
Maximum distance:	
Output cell size:	31.92496901
☐ Create variance of prediction:	<Temporary>
Output raster:	<Temporary>
	OK Cancel

FIGURE 7.13. Kriging-interpolated surface (left), with error surface (right—darker blues show overestimation, light cyan and yellow show little error, while darker reds show underestimation). For this model, the RMSE was 33.1 m.

---

39. See: Bailey, T.C. and A.C. Gatrell. 1995. *Interactive spatial data analysis*. Prentice Hall; Isaaks, E.H. and R.M. Srivaastava. 1989. *Applied geostatistics*. Oxford University Press; O'Sullivan, D. and D.J. Unwin. 2002. *Geographic Information Analysis*. John Wiley and Sons.

Global functions

Raster basics

Advanced raster analysis

8.1 Overview

Although Spatial Analyst provides a number of interfaces to access commonly used functions, there is a wide variety of additional functions "under the hood." These functions are accessible through the *Raster Calculator*, which is a dialog where expressions containing functions and operations can be typed and run. The format and rules of these functions are based on *map algebra*, which treats entire maps as variables and operations on maps are analogous to traditional mathematical operations.[1] The Raster Calculator not only provides access to additional functions, it also allows more complex expressions to be built. Moreover, lists of map algebra "models" can be saved to word processing files to document your work and provide models for others to use.

---

1. Berry, J.K. 1987. Fundamental operations in computer-assisted map analysis. *International Journal of Geographical Information Systems* 1(2):119-136

8.2 Advanced raster analysis

8.2.1 Map algebra

Map algebra statements contain functions and operators. Functions (e.g., **sin(<inGrid>)**) require an input(s) to be specified and their parameters separated by commas. Parameters can be additional datasets, keywords, or numbers. Operators (e.g., +, /, etc.) are generally placed between raster datasets, and spaces between the operand and datasets are mandatory. In general, functions are processed in left-to-right order. However, many functions have a *precedence order* that modifies this left-to-right processing. The best way to ensure that Spatial Analyst processes the statement according to your desires (and understanding) is to explicitly set precedence using parentheses.

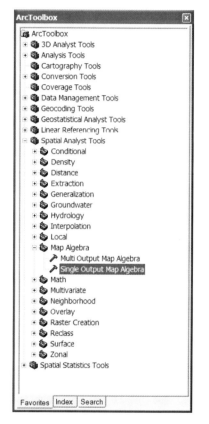

8.2.2 *Raster Calculator*

The *Raster Calculator* provides an interface in which map algebra expressions can be entered. The dialog provides a list of the raster layers currently included in ArcMap (upper left), a number of buttons for often-used operations (upper right), and an *expression text box* where map algebra expressions or statements are formed (lower). The output GRID created after an expression is evaluated is automatically added to ArcMap after processing. Raster datasets can be accessed from the raster calculator a number of ways. If the raster data set is listed as a layer, then the layer name must be enclosed by brackets ([ ]).[2] For example:

[Calculation] * 1

Other datasets (permanent rasters, feature datasets, tables) that have not been added to ArcMap can be accessed by specifying the entire path and filename:

c:\temp\roads * 2

By default, the resulting output GRID is created as a temporary GRID in the working directory. Permanent GRIDs can be created directly by explicitly assigning an output GRID name:

c:\temp\roads2 = c:\temp\roads * 1

By default, the values in the *Value* field in the GRID's attribute table are used in the calculations. However, other fields in the attribute table (e.g., Count) can be accessed using what is known as "<grid>.<item>" notation[3] (no spaces before or after the period):

[Calculation].count * 1

c:\temp\roads.count * 1

---

2. Note that when layers are created by the raster calculator, their name has an extra trailing space, which needs to be included for the layer to be properly recognized—so [Calculation] is correct, while [Calculation] is not.

3. In ArcView v3.x, this functionality is provided by the .Lookup request.

If your expression grows very long, or if you would like to break it into multiple parts on different lines to make it more readable, use the *line continuation* character ("~"):

con ([Calculation] > 4, ~

    [Calculation2], ~

    [Calculation3])

Multiple lines of map algebra expressions can be processed as well, enabling you to build complex models.[4] Output GRID names must be enclosed by brackets so that they can be accessed later in the statement. However, do not confuse the temporary output GRIDs created (on the left of the equal sign) with layers in ArcMap. Each line in a multi-line expression must be separated by a carriage return. Also, the dialog box can be dragged downward to enlarge the expression text box, and the font of the expression text box can also be changed for easier reading.[5]

[R1] = rand()

[b_w] = con ([R1] > 0.5, 1, 0)

If you are unclear what parameters are used for a given function, the *usage* of a function can be obtained quickly by typing in the function name (e.g., REGIONGROUP), highlighting it, then right-clicking and selecting **Usage**. Usage describes a function's inputs, e.g., focalsum(). Options that are enclosed with "<>" are required, those enclosed with "{}" are optional. There are many types of options: conditions, expressions, values, keywords, input GRIDs, and output GRIDs. For example, the simple usage for focalsum() is:

FocalSum(<grid>, {DATA | NODATA})

where <grid> is a required input GRID and the DATA or NODATA parameter is optional (e.g., FocalSum([G1]) is valid). Note that default values are used if they are not explicitly specified. Because there are a variety of neighborhoods that can be specified for focal functions, there are some additional ways to use FocalSum:

FocalSum(<grid>, <RECTANGLE>, <width>, <height>, {DATA | NODATA})

FocalSum(<grid>, <CIRCLE>, <radius>, {DATA | NODATA})

FocalSum(<grid>, <ANNULUS>, <inner_radius>, <outer_radius>, {DATA | NODATA})

FocalSum(<grid>, <WEDGE>, <radius>, <start_angle>, <end_angle>, {DATA | NO-DATA})

FocalSum(<grid>, <IRREGULAR>, <kernel_file>, {DATA | NODATA})

---

4. Starting at ArcGIS v8.2.
5. This is also a nice feature, as brackets and parentheses were remarkably difficult to distinguish in the Map Calculator dialog in ArcView v3.x. Try: Courier, 10 pt., regular, which seems to work well.

FocalSum(<grid>, <WEIGHT>, <kernel_file>, {DATA | NODATA})

Parameters like <RECTANGLE> distinguish the neighborhood type, while <width> is a required number value (e.g., FocalSum ([G1], RECTANGLE, 3, 3)).

Sometimes the usage defines a <condition> or <expression>. For example, the usage for con() is: con(<condition>, <trueExpression>, <FalseExpression>). A condition must equal true or false, while full expressions can be simple or complicated:

con ([G1] > 0, 1, 0)

con ([G1] > 0, sin([G1]), log([G1]))

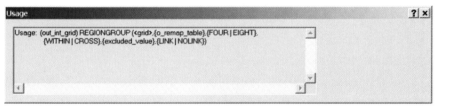

Recent map algebra expressions can be accessed as well by right-clicking in the text box, then selecting *recent expressions*. Copy the expression(s) that you are interested in, then paste it into the text box. It is good practice, however, to paste the expressions that you ultimately used into a word processor document to save for later use, because these expressions are not saved with the map document file.

8.2.3 Integer and floating-point math

When you are calculating values using integer GRIDs, you need to be careful about your assumptions of how Spatial Analyst handles decimal places. First of all, Spatial Analyst *truncates* decimal points, rather than rounding. For example, if you calculate the following (in Map Calculator):

(2 / 3)

the resulting integer GRID would have a value of 0, not 1. Furthermore, the decimal places cannot be accessed by multiplying a GRID by a factor of 10, as in the following:

((10 / 3) * 1000)

This results in a GRID with a value of 3000, not 3333. The consequence of this is that your everyday mathematical equation, such as: $y=(4/3)*3$, is not calculated the way we might expect. For instance, y should equal 4, but:

((4 / 3) * 3)

equals 3! In other words, the values are not simply truncated at the end of the calculation, but throughout the equation! To force Spatial Analyst to utilize the decimal places, you will need to call *Float()* for every part of an equation that uses integer GRIDs, but should use real-value computation. For example:

((float(4) / 3) * 3)

will result in a value of 4, but the following will result in a value of 3:

((4 / 3) * float (3))

8.2.4 Advanced map algebra expressions

As discussed above, Spatial Analyst provides access to a number of commonly used functions through dialog interfaces. These dialogs gather the input parameters from the user, and then process the request. The exact same requests could be accomplished directly through the Raster Calculator. Returning to the focal averaging example, finding the mean habitat value within a 1000 m radius could be found with:

Focalmean ([Habitat], CIRCLE, 1000)

As was asserted earlier, there are numerous additional functions that may be useful—now that we know about map algebra and the Raster Calculator, we can explore these functions in detail.

8.2.4.1 Local

In addition to statistical operators, there are a wide variety of additional local operators, including mathematical and logical operators (arithmetic, bitwise, boolean, combinatorial, logical, and relational), conditional, and reclassify. A couple of the more commonly used local functions are described in detail below. The most powerful and most commonly used conditional function is *Con*. Con essentially allows "if-then" logic and has three components: **Con(<condition>, <true>, <false>)**. For example, imagine you wanted to create a map to locate areas that are not so steep (>15) they preclude development. Two categories are needed: OK to develop (1), and too steep to develop (0). Con could be used to do this:
con([slope] > 15, 1, 0)

Note that NoData values could be used in place of the 0s if you do not specify the <false> parameter:

con([slope] > 15, 1)

Con statements can also be imbedded to incorporate more complex logic, for example, to add the constraint that development must be 100 m or further away from water:

con([slope] > 15, ~

    con([d2water] > 100,~

        1,~

        0), ~

    0)

When using the reclassify function through the Raster Calculator, text-based remap tables can be used in addition to INFO remap tables. For example, the remap table (slope1.txt) for the slope example above would look like:

      0 5 : 1
      5 10 : 2
      10 20 : 3
      20 45 : 4

and would be called in the Raster Calculator using:

Reclass ([slope], slope1.txt)

There are a few *built-in variables* that can be accessed in the Raster Calculator that are quite useful: **\$\$COLMAP** (column number), **\$\$ROWMAP** (row number), **\$\$NCOLS** (number of columns), **\$\$NROWS** (number of rows), **\$\$CELLSIZE** (cell size in map units), **\$\$XMAP** (x coordinate), **\$\$YMAP** (y coordinate), **\$\$WX0** (minimum x value), **\$\$WX1** (maximum x value), **\$\$WY0** (minimum y value), and **\$\$WY1** (maximum y value).

These variables can be used in expressions to create a wide variety of GRIDs. For example, to identify column and row locations, beginning with 0,0 in the top-left corner, use:

[column] = \$\$colmap

[row] = \$\$rowmap

To compute a GRID where the value of the cell is the x and y locations, use:

[x] = \$\$xmap

[y] = \$\$ymap

Another use of these variables is to create a GRID where every cell has a unique integer value (here shown by unique colors at right), in row-major (moving from left to right: 0, 1, 2, 3, 4; continuing at the next row: 5, 6, 7, 8, 9; etc.) (see Figure 8.1):

$$COLMAP + ($$ROWMAP * $$NCOLS)

To create a GRID with unique values in row-prime, or *boustrophedon*[6], ordering (left to right: 0, 1, 2, 3, 4; continuing at the next row right to left: 9, 8, 7, 6, 5; etc.), use:

$$COLMAP + ($$ROWMAP * $$NCOLS) + ~

(($$ROWMAP MOD 2) * (($$NCOLS - 1) - ($$COLMAP * 2)))

Note that sections in the US Public Land Survey System follow a row-prime order.

An interesting hierarchical raster ordering scheme is attributed to Guy Morton's work at IBM in the 1960s, known as the Morton or "N" (or "Z") order (note that the Morton ordering in Figure 8.1 is a "backwards N" order).[7] To create a GRID with Morton order values (1 to 4) at a given level of resolution, use:

(($$COLMAP mod 2) * 2) + ($$ROWMAP mod 2) + 1

Also note that by converting these unique-valued GRIDs into polygons (without generalization), a *fishnet* or mesh of squares (as polygons) can be created.

To compute a *checkerboard* pattern of alternative values, use:

($$colmap + $$rowmap) mod 2

---

6. Boustrophedon is derived from a Greek adverb that means "like an ox turning" or "as a field is plowed"—*The Concise Oxford Dictionary of Linguistics*. 1997. Oxford University Press.

7. A comparison of these ordering schemes is provided in: Goodchild, M.F. and A.W. Grandfield. 1983. Optimizing raster storage: an examination of four alternatives. In *Proceedings of AutoCarto 6*, Ottawa, Canada. Pgs. 400-407.

FIGURE 8.1. A comparison of raster ordering methods: row-major (top left), row-prime (top right), Morton or "N" ordering (bottom left), and Morton hierarchical addressing (bottom right).

0	1	2	3	4	5	6	7
8	9	10	11	12	13	14	15
16	17	18	19	20	21	22	23
24	25	26	27	28	29	30	31
32	33	34	35	36	37	38	39
40	41	42	43	44	45	46	47
48	49	50	51	52	53	54	55
56	57	58	59	60	61	62	63

0	1	2	3	4	5	6	7
15	14	13	12	11	10	9	8
16	17	18	19	20	21	22	23
31	30	29	28	27	26	25	24
32	33	34	35	36	37	38	39
47	46	45	44	43	42	41	40
48	49	50	51	52	53	54	55
63	62	61	60	59	58	57	56

0	2	8	10	32	34	40	42
1	3	9	11	33	35	41	43
4	6	12	14	36	38	44	46
5	7	13	15	37	39	45	47
16	18	24	26	48	50	56	58
17	19	25	27	49	51	57	59
20	22	28	30	52	54	60	62
21	23	29	31	53	55	61	63

111	113	131	133	311	313	331	333
112	114	132	134	312	314	332	334
121	123	141	143	321	323	341	343
122	124	142	144	322	324	342	344
211	213	231	233	411	413	431	433
212	214	232	234	412	414	432	434
221	223	241	243	421	423	441	443
222	224	242	244	422	424	442	444

A comprehensive list of local operators and functions is provided in Table 8.1.[8]

TABLE 8.1. Local operators and functions available through the Raster Calculator.

Group	Usage	Example	Comments

TABLE 8.1. Local operators and functions available through the Raster Calculator.

Arithmetic	+ (addition)	G1 + G2	If G1 = 2 and G2 = 3, then G3 = 5
	- (subtraction)	G1 - G2	If G1 = 2 and G2 = 3, then G3 = -1
	* (multiplication)	G1 * G2	If G1 = 2 and G2 = 3, then G3 = 6
	/ (division)	G1 / G2	If G1 = 2 and G2 = 3, then G3 = 0.666. DIV and "/" are equivalent.
	MOD (Modulo)	G1 MOD G2	Returns the integer remainder. If G1 = 7 and G2 = 2, then G3 = 1. Use FMOD to calculate the remainder between two floating point GRIDs.
Bitwise	!! (exclusive OR)	G3 = G1 !! G2	If G1 = 5 and G2 = 3 (Bitwise G1 = 000000101 and G2 = 00000011), then G3 = 6 (00000110).
	&& (AND)	G3 = G1 && G2	If G1 = 5 and G2 = 3 (Bitwise G1 = 000000101 and G2 = 00000011), then G3 = 1 (00000001).
	<< (left shift)	G1 << G2	If G1 = 1 (0001) and G2 = 2, then it results in a value of 4 (0100). G2 specifies the number of places to shift.
	>> (right shift)	G1 >> G2	If G1 = 7 (0111) and G2 = 1, then it results in a value of 3 (0011). G2 specifies the number of places to shift.
	^^ (complement)	G2 = ^^G1	If G1 = 5 (00000101) then G2 = -6 (11111010) .
	| | (OR)	G3 = G1 | | G2	If G1 = 5 and G2 = 3 (Bitwise G1 = 000000101 and G2 = 00000011), then G3 = 7 (00000111).
Boolean	! (Exclusive OR)	G1 ! G2	Any value other than 0 is TRUE, 0 is FALSE.
	& (AND)	G1 & G2	If the values of both G1 and G2 not 0, then G3 = 1, otherwise 0. The values of floating-point GRIDs are truncated to integer before operation is performed.
	^ (complement)	G2 = ^G1	If G1 is TRUE, then G2 = FALSE, and vice versa.
Combina-torial	CAnd	G3 = G1 CAnd G2	G3 is a unique value for each unique combination where G1 and G2 are non-zero (TRUE) values.
	Combine(<GRID, ..., GRID>)	G3 = combine (G1, G2)	Combine creates a new unique number for each unique combination of input GRIDs, and the value of each cell is listed in the output GRID's attribute table.
	COr	G3 = G1 COr G2	G3 is a unique value for each unique combination where G1 or G2 are non-zero (TRUE) values.
	CXor	G3 = G1 CXor G2	G3 is a unique value for each unique combination where G1 xor G2 are non-zero (TRUE) values.

8. To access further details, see: ArcGIS Help --> Spatial Analyst --> Spatial Analyst Functional Reference --> Operators.

TABLE 8.1. Local operators and functions available through the Raster Calculator.

Condi-tional	Con(<condition>, <TrueExpression>, <FalseExpression>)	G3 = con(G2 > G1, 1, 0)	Implements if-then-else logic, so that if the value of G2 > G1, then output value equals 1, otherwise 0.
	Pick(<IndexGRID>, <GRID, ..., GRID>)	G5 = Pick(G1, G2, G3, G4)	Uses the value of an input GRID as an index to select which GRID's values will be output. I.e., if G1 = 1, then G1 values will be output, etc.
	SetNull(<condi-tion>, { GRID | number })	G3= Setnull(G1 > 2, G2)	If G1 > 2, then G3 = NoData, otherwise G3 = G2.
	Test(<GRID>, <logi-calExpression>)	G3 = test(G1, "value > 2")	Tests or "thresholds" a single GRID based on a conditional statement, so that if the value of G1 > 2 then the output value equals 1, otherwise 0.
Logical	Diff	G3 = G1 DIFF G2	If G1 is different than G2, then G3 = G1, else G3 = 0.
	<GRID	number> In {<list>}	G3 = G1 IN {<list>}	If value in G1 is in a list of values, then G3 = value. E.g., G3 = G1 IN { 0, 1, 2}.
	Over	G3 = G1 OVER G2	If G1 is non-zero, then G3 = G1, else G3 = G2.
Mathe-matical	Abs (<GRID | num-ber>)	G3 = Abs(G1)	If G1 = -1, then G3 = 1; if G1 = 1, then G3 = 1.
	Ceil (<GRID | num-ber>)	G3 = Ceil(G1)	Returns the next highest integer value. If G1 = 1, then G3 = 1; if G1 = 1.1, then G3 = 2.
	Exp (<GRID | num-ber>)	G3 = Exp(G1)	Calculates the base e (natural) exponent. If G1 = 0.1, then G3 = 1.1.
	Exp10 (<GRID | number>)	G3 = Exp10(G1)	Calculates the base 10 exponent. If G1 = 1, then G3 = 10.
	Exp2 (<GRID | number>)	G3 = Exp2(G1)	Calculates the base 2 exponent. If G1 = 1, then G3 = 2.
	Float(<GRID | num-ber>)	G3 = Float (G1)	Converts values to floating-point values.
	Floor(<GRID | num-ber>)	G3 = Floor (G1)	Returns the next lowest integer value. If G1 = 1, then G3 = 1, if G1= 1.1, then G3 = 1.
	Int (<GRID | num-ber>)	G3 = Int(G1)	Truncates floating-point to integer. If G1 = 1.1, then G3 = 1; if G1 = 1.7, then G3 = 1. To round the number, then use: Int(G1+0.5)
	IsNull(<GRID>)	G3 = IsNull(G1)	Returns 1 if the value in G1 is NODATA. This is often used with Con, e.g., G3=con(IsNull(G1), 99, G1) replaces NODATA cells with 99.
	Ln (<GRID | num-ber>)	G3 = Ln(G1)	Calculates the natural log. If G1 = 2, then G3 = 0.7.
	Log10 (<GRID | number>)	G3 = Log10(G1)	Calculates the base 10 log. If G1 = 2, then G3 = 0.3

TABLE 8.1. Local operators and functions available through the Raster Calculator.

Mathe-matical	Log2 (<GRID | number>)	G3 = Log2(G1)	Calculates the base 2 log. If G1 = 2, then G3 = 1.0
	LPos(<GRID, ..., GRID>)	G4 = LPos (G1,G2,G3)	Finds position of GRID in list with lowest value. E.g., G4=2 if G1=3, G2=2, G3=4.
	Majority(<GRID, ..., GRID>)	G4=Major-ity(G1,G2,G3)	Returns the majority value in list of GRIDs.
	Max(<GRID, ..., GRID>)	G4=Max(G1,G2,G3)	Returns largest value in list of GRIDS
	Mean(<GRID, ..., GRID>)	G4=Mean(G1,G2,G3)	Returns mean value in list of GRIDs.
	Med(<GRID, ..., GRID>)	G4=Med(G1,G2,G3)	Returns median value in list of GRIDs.
	Min(<GRID, ..., GRID>)	G4=Min(G1,G2,G3)	Returns smallest value in list of GRIDs.
	Minority(<GRID, ..., GRID>)	G4=Minor-ity(G1,G2,G3)	Returns most infrequent value in list of GRIDs.
	Pow	G3=Pow(G1,G2)	Raises value in G1 to the power of value in G2.
	Range(<GRID, ..., GRID>)	G4=Range(G1,G2,G3)	Returns the range (max - min) value in list of GRIDs.
	Rank(<GRID, ..., GRID>)	G4=Rank(2,G1,G2,G3)	Returns the value at a given rank ordering. If G1=2, G2=5, and G3=1, then G4=2.
	SetNull(<condi-tion>, <GRID | number>)	G3=Set-Null(G1,G2)	If G1 is TRUE, then G3=NO DATA, else G3=G2.
	Sqr(<GRID | num-ber>)	G2= Sqr(G1)	Squares a GRID (raises the values to the 2nd power).
	Sqrt(<GRID | num-ber>)	G2= Sqrt(G1)	Computes the square root of the values in G1.
	Std(<GRID, ..., GRID>)	G4=Std(2,G1,G2,G3)	Returns the standard deviation of the values in list of GRIDs.
	Sum(<GRID, ..., GRID>)	G4=Range(G1,G2,G3)	Returns sum of values in list of GRIDs
	UPos(<GRID, ..., GRID>)	G4 = UPos (G1,G2,G3)	Finds position of GRID in list with highest value. E.g., G4=2 if G1=3, G2=2, G3=4.
	Variety(<GRID, ..., GRID>)	G4=Range(G1,G2,G3)	Returns variety (the number of different values) in a list of GRIDs.

TABLE 8.1. Local operators and functions available through the Raster Calculator.

Reclassify	Reclass(<GRID>,<re mapTable>, {DATA | NODATA}, {InField}, {OutField})	G2 = Reclass (G1, remap1.txt)	Reclassifies G1 based on classes specified in a remap table (e.g., remap1.txt).
	Slice(<GRID>, TABLE, <remapT-able>, {InField}, {OutField}, {InMin}) Slice(<GRID>, EQAREA, <NZones>, {Base-Zone#}, {InMin}, {InMax}) Slice(<GRID>, EQINTERVAL, <NZones>, {Base-Zone#}, {InMin}, {InMax})	G2 = Slice (G1, table, slice.txt)	Changes ranges of values.
Relational	<> (not equal to)	G2 = G1 <> <num>	If G1 does not equal <num>, G2 = 1, else G2 = 0. E.g., G2 = G1 ^= . Same as "^=" or "NE".
	== (equal to)	G2 = G1 == <num>	If G1 equals <num>, then G2 = 1, else 0. This is used to differentiate "=" which is the assignment operator.
	<= (less than or equal to)	G3 = G1 <= G2	If G1 <= G2, then G3 = 1, else G3 = 0.
	<> (not equal to)	G3 = G1 <> G2	If G1 <> G2, then G3 = 1, else G3 = 0.
	> (greater than)	G3 = G1 > G2	If G1 > G2, then G3 = 1, else G3 = 0.
	>= (greater than or equal to)	G3 = G1 >= G2	If G1 >= G2, then G3 = 1, else G3 = 0.
	< (less than)	G1 < G2	If G1 < G2, then G3 = 1, else G3 = 0. Note: For all conditional operators, the resulting GRID will always have values of 0, 1, or NODATA. If any of the input GRIDs has a value of NODATA, the output will equal NODATA.

8.2.4.2 Focal functions

There are a few additional focal functions that are not available directly through the neighborhood statistics dialog, including block functions (see Table 8.2). Also, in addition to annulus, circular, rectangular, and wedge neighborhoods, *irregular* neighborhoods can be used in Map Algebra expressions. Irregularly shaped neighborhoods are created by directly specifying the cells in a neighborhood that will be processed through a *kernel* file. Typically, the kernel file is used simply as a mask to include or exclude particular neighboring cells. For example, the following kernel file (i.e. irr4x4.txt) specifies a 4x4 neighborhood.

```
4 4
0 1 1 1
1 1 1 0
1 1 1 0
0 1 1 0
```

An example expression that would use an irregular neighborhood is:

Focalmean ([Habitat], IRREGULAR, irr4x4.txt)

This neighborhood is used only as a mask, however. Using an additional keyword WEIGHT, the neighborhood values will be multiplied times the cell values, which is similar to *spatial convolution filtering*.[9] This is useful for spatial filtering and image processing. For example, a high-pass filter (e.g., high.txt) that enhances edges looks like:

```
3 3
-0.7 -1.0 -0.7
--1.0 6.8 -1.0
-0.7 -1.0 -0.7
```

and would be called using:

Focalmean ([Habitat], WEIGHT, high.txt)

Another interesting use of focal functions is to implement *cellular automata* (CA) models. A CA model is typically computed using a 2-D array of regular cells where the state of a cell at time t is defined by a set of transition rules that govern local behavior of each cell using the cell's neighboring values. One of the most popular CAs is John Conway's *Game of Life*.[10] This modeling approach is a natural for GRID processing with focal functions[11], and a number of GIS implementations of Life have been developed using map algebra expressions.[12] On the next page is an elegant, single-line expression, that, when used iteratively, implements the rules, assuming an initial GRID *G0*:[13]

[G1] = abs(focalsum([G0]) * 2 - [G0] - 6) <= 1

9. Jensen, J.R. 1996. *Introductory digital image processing: A remote sensing perspective*. Prentice-Hall.
10. Gardner, M. 1972. The fantastic combinations of John Conway's new solitaire game "Life."*Scientific American* 233(4):120-123.
11. Theobald, D.M. and M. Gross. 1994. EML: A modeling environment for exploring landscape dynamics. *Computers, Environmental, and Urban Systems* 18(3): 193-204.
12. For example: Wagner, D.F. 1997. Cellular automata and geographic information systems. *Environment and Planning B* 24:219-234.
13. This was created by Bill Huber, 2000. For more information, go to the ESRI ArcScripts web site and search for "Life": http://arcscripts.esri.com/details.asp?dbid=D2AE23B0-71D5-11D4-943200508B0CB419

TABLE 8.2. Focal functions available through the Raster Calculator.

Usage	Description
BlockMajority() BlockMax() BlockMean() BlockMedian() BlockMin() BlockMinority() BlockRange() BlockStd() BlockVariety()	Computes the statistic in the function name, using the cells defined in the *block* neighborhood. The options below apply to each function, except the WEIGHT option, which does not apply to majority, max, min, minority, and variety. BlockMean(<GRID>, <RECTANGLE>, <width>, <height>, {DATA | NODATA}) BlockMean(<GRID>, <CIRCLE>, <radius>, {DATA | NODATA}) BlockMean(<GRID>, <ANNULUS>, <inner_radius>, <outer_radius>, {DATA | NODATA}) BlockMean(<GRID>, <WEDGE>, <radius>, <start_angle>, <end_angle>, {DATA | NODATA}) BlockMean(<GRID>, <IRREGULAR>, <kernel_file>, {DATA | NODATA}) BlockMean(<GRID>, <WEIGHT>, <kernel_file>, {DATA | NODATA})
FocalMajority() FocalMax() FocalMean() FocalMedian() FocalMin() FocalMinority() FocalRange() FocalStd() FocalSum() FocalVariety()	Computes the statistic in the function name, using the cells defined in the *focal* neighborhood. The options below apply to each function, except the WEIGHT option, which does not apply to majority, max, min, minority, and variety. FocalMean(<GRID>, <RECTANGLE>, <width>, <height>, {DATA | NODATA}) FocalMean(<GRID>, <CIRCLE>, <radius>, {DATA | NODATA}) FocalMean(<GRID>, <ANNULUS>, <inner_radius>, <outer_radius>, {DATA | NODATA}) FocalMean(<GRID>, <WEDGE>, <radius>, <start_angle>, <end_angle>, {DATA | NODATA}) FocalMean(<GRID>, <IRREGULAR>, <kernel_file>, {DATA | NODATA}) FocalMean(<GRID>, <WEIGHT>, <kernel_file>, {DATA | NODATA})
LineStats(<LINES>, {item}, {CellSize}, {Statistic}, {Radius})	Computes a statistic using linear features as input. The item name options are: RAND_INT, RAND_FLOAT, or NONE. The statistic options are: MIN, MAX, MEAN, RANGE, MIDRANGE, MEDIAN, MAJORITY, MINORITY, VARIETY, or LENGTH.
PointStats(<POINTS>, {item}, {cellsize}, {statistic}, {neighborhood})	Computes a statistic using point features as input. The item name options are: RAND_INT, RAND_FLOAT, or NONE. The statistic options are: MIN, MAX, MEAN, RANGE, MIDRANGE, MEDIAN, MAJORITY, MINORITY, VARIETY, or NPOINTS. The neighborhood options are: {CIRCLE, {radius} | RECTANGLE, {width}, {height}, {angle} | ELLIPSE, {axis1}, {axis2}, {axis1_angle} | RINGS, {radius1}, {radius2}, ... | WEDGES, {radius1}, <from_angle1>, <to_angle1>, {radius2}, {from_angle2}, {to_angle2}, ... | POLYGON, <vertex_file>}

8.2.4.3 Zonal

There are a number of other zonal functions that can be used to analyze the shape of zones in a GRID (Table 8.3). Some of these measure the shape of a zone through area, perimeter, thickness, and orientation measures.

The *regiongroup* function assigns a unique value to a group of contiguous cells that have the same value. Recall that a region differs from a zone in that a *region* is a group of contiguous cells, while a *zone* can be composed of disconnected cells. For example, to find the regions (patches) of a classified vegetation image, the *regiongroup* function would be used in the Raster Calculator:

RegionGroup ([vegetation])

However, there are a couple of different ways to define contiguity with neighboring cells. A common method is to use only the four orthogonal neighbors (a.k.a. rook's or Von Neumann's case), use:

RegionGroup ([vegetation], #, FOUR)

Another method is to use both the four orthogonal and four diagonal neighbors (a.k.a. queen's or king's or Moore's case) are considered. The *excludedValue* specifies the value to be used that breaks connectivity in a region. Use:

RegionGroup ([vegetation], #, EIGHT)

TABLE 8.3. Zonal functions available through the Raster Calculator.

Usage	Description
ZonalArea(<GRID>)	Calculates the area of each zone of the input GRID, and outputs a GRID with the corresponding zone area in each cell.
ZonalCentroid(<GRID>)	Creates an output GRID with the centroid cell for each zone (all other cells are NoData).
ZonalGeometry (<GRID>, {Geometry-Type}, {MaxThickness})	Calculates an aspect of the geometry of zones, based on the GeometryType keyword: AREA, PERIMETER, THICKNESS, ELLIPSE, and ALL.
ZonalFill(<ZoneGRID>, <WeightGRID>)	Creates an output GRID with values filled in using minimum value.
ZonalMajority(<Zone-GRID>, <ValueGRID>)	Outputs a GRID whose cell values contain the majority value found in a given zone.
ZonalMax(<Zone-GRID>, <ValueGRID>, {DATA | NODATA})	Outputs a GRID whose cell values contain the maximum value found in a given zone.
ZonalMean(<Zone-GRID>, <ValueGRID>, {DATA | NODATA})	Outputs a GRID whose cell values contain the mean value found in a given zone.

TABLE 8.3. Zonal functions available through the Raster Calculator.

ZonalMedian(<Zone-GRID>, <ValueGRID>, {DATA | NODATA})	Outputs a GRID whose cell values contain the median value found in a given zone.
ZonalMin(<Zone-GRID>, <ValueGRID>, {DATA | NODATA})	Outputs a GRID whose values contain the mean of the <ValueGRID> for the zones defined in <ZoneGRID>.
ZonalMinority(<Zone-GRID>, <ValueGRID>, {DATA | NODATA})	Outputs a GRID whose cell values contain the minority value found in a given zone.
ZonalPerimeter (<GRID>)	Outputs a GRID whose cell values contain the perimeter of a given zone.
ZonalRange(<Zone-GRID>, <ValueGRID>, {DATA | NODATA})	Outputs a GRID whose cell values contain the range value found in a given zone.
ZonalStats(<Zone-GRID>, <ValueGRID>, {StatisticName}, {DATA | NODATA})	Computes the statistic using values from <ValueGRID> for the zones defined in <ZoneGRID>. Valid statistic names are: MAJORITY, MEAN, MIN, MAX, RANGE, SUM, STD, VARIETY, MINORITY, MEDIAN, ALL, EXTREME (returns Min and Max), MOMENT (returns Mean and Std). If no statistic name, then returns MEAN, MIN, and MAX.
ZonalStd(<ZoneGRID>, <ValueGRID>, {DATA | NODATA})	Outputs a GRID whose cell values contain the standard deviation found in a given zone.
ZonalSum(<Zone-GRID>, <ValueGRID>, {DATA | NODATA})	Outputs a GRID whose cell values contain the sum of values found in a given zone.
ZonalThick-ness(<GRID>, {MaxThickness})	Outputs a GRID whose cell values contain the thickness value found in a given zone.
ZonalVariety(<Zone-GRID>, <ValueGRID>, {DATA | NODATA})	Outputs a GRID whose cell values contain the number of different values found in a given zone.

8.2.4.4 Global and application functions

There are a number of advanced global and application-specific functions, and below a few of the more commonly used functions are described (see Table 8.4 for a complete listing of global functions).

Earlier, *cost-weighted distance* was used to compute a *remoteness* surface for the western US. A significant refinement to the previous method used to compute remoteness is to recognize that we travel in different modes: via planes, trains, and automobiles, as well as by boats, buses, and bicycles, and on horseback, and on foot as well. Ideally then, a distance surface might reflect these different modes of travel, at least the most likely modes. Building on the earlier example of remoteness, let's use the average speed of car travel along different road types, for example: 70 mph on Interstates, 55 mph on highways, and 40 mph on secondary roads; and the average speed of walking given different slopes: 4 mph on flat ground, 3 mph on 1-3°, 2 mph on 3-5°, 1 on >5°. Because we want to express cost in terms of the time it takes to move across a single cell, we'll convert these values to km per hour (corresponding to 1 km cells). Finally, we'll use the inverse (number of hours it takes to cross one cell). The result is a map of remoteness, expressed in hours to access a location from a city, that formalizes our assumption that places closer to large cities are less remote (Figure 8.2).

Computing travel time from cities via car and feet

1. Reclass road type to number of hours it takes to drive across one cell (ROADS).

2. Reclass the slope to the number of hours it takes to walk across 1 cell (Reclass of Slope of Elevation).

3. Compute the cost weight GRID:

con (isnull ([ROADS]), 1.0 / [Reclass of Slope of Elevation], 1.0 / [ROADS])

4. Run the cost weighted distance routine, calculating distance from Cities, using the cost weight GRID just created.

FIGURE 8.2. Remoteness in the western US (1 km resolution). Isolated areas (dark green) are further from cities (crosses), defined in terms of travel time via automobile along major roads (interstates shown in black) and then by walking from roads.

A common need is to clean up a raster to remove specks or "salt and pepper," which are small (often just a single cell) regions (Figure 8.3). Typically these specks are regarded as noise and are removed by a focal filter. For example, fine-grained (30 m resolution) land cover maps (e.g., USGS National Land Cover Dataset[14]) created from remotely sensed images often have specks in them, yet to make a more generalized map of land cover, we may want to remove them. Because these are nominal values (land cover classes), they can be removed using a specialized filter, *MajorityFilter*:

MajorityFilter ([nlcd], EIGHT, MAJORITY)

This filter replaces the center cell with the majority value of the eight surrounding cells (note that four orthogonal cells could be used as well). To require that the majority be at least half of the neighboring cells, use:

MajorityFilter ([nlcd], EIGHT, HALF)

If there is not a clear majority (i.e. a tie), or if the majority does not meet the half constraint, then a NoData is assigned to the center cell. Typically these NoData values are simply replaced with the original values:

[G2] = MajorityFilter ([nlcd], EIGHT, HALF)

Con(IsNull ([G2]), [nlcd], [G2])

One difference between MajorityFilter and FocalMajority is that MajorityFilter does not use the center cell:

FocalMajority ([nlcd])

If you know that certain locations or cell values are incorrect, then use the Nibble command, which replaces those identified locations (those in the "mask" input with NoData) with the value of the nearest neighbor (Euclidean distance):

[mask] = setnull([nlcd] == 23, [nlcd])

Nibble ([nlcd], [mask])

---

14. http://landcover.usgs.gov/natllandcover.html

FIGURE 8.3. Example of generalizing a land cover map (upper left) using MajorityFilter with EIGHT neighbors (upper right), FocalMajority using 3x3 neighbors (lower left), and Nibble to replace yellow linear feature (lower right).

Often raster datasets are used as covariates in a statistical model, and so a common task is to obtain the raster values' particular locations. Raster values (e.g., [G1], [G2], [G3], etc.) can be sampled at particular locations using a point (e.g., points.shp) or raster layer:

c:\temp\samplesG123 = Sample (c:\temp\points.shp, [G1], [G2], [G3])

The output textfile (space delimited) provides a listing of the point number, x,y location, and GRID values.

Typically, random location points are created with feature-based techniques (i.e. identify random x and y, test to see if it is within a study boundary, then create the random point). However, random points can also be created in continuous space using raster functions, and there are three notable advantages.[15] First, and probably least important, it may be time-consuming to create random points that fall within the study area for study areas that are not rectangular or have *exclusion zones* (e.g., lakes for vegetation survey or private land that cannot be sampled). Second, it is straightforward to constrain random locations so that clumping of random points is precluded. That is, simple random sampling is often criticized for creating sample points that can be overly clustered or clumped. Third, continuous surfaces allow an easy means to specify *inclusion rates* for different zones so that sampling intensity varies across the study area according to some stratification or desire to sample some areas more or less intensely.

Let's begin with a *simple random sampling* (SRS) design. The first step is to determine the cell resolution, which should be consistent with the spatial precision that is important for a particular process. It also determines in an indirect way the minimum distance between two random points. If the cell size is too large, then using the center of the randomly selected cells may create a systematic bias. If the cell size is too small, then two points may be too close to one another and would be overly clustered (not well balanced). Second, create a GRID that reflects the study area, where all locations within the study are 1 and locations outside (including exclusion zones within the spatial extent) are NoData. The analysis mask is set to the study area GRID. Note that the total number of cells in the study area (at a given resolution) is listed in the count field in the attribute table of the study GRID. Third, compute a threshold value (t):

$$t = s / C$$

---

15. See Bill Huber's ArcView v3.2 *Sample* extension: www.quantdec.com/sample/index.htm.

where s is the number of desired random points and C is the number of cells in the study area. Fourth, find the cell values of a random GRID with values ranging from 0.0 to 1.0 (uniformly distributed) that are less than the threshold t. The resulting GRID contains the sample locations, which can then be converted to a point feature dataset. For example, if we wanted 100 random points from a 100 x 100 GRID, then $t = 100/10000=0.01$:

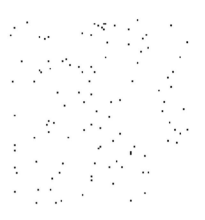

```
[r] = rand()
```

```
con ( [r] < ( 0.01 ), 1)
```

We can also incorporate the number of desired sample locations (i.e. 100) and the number of cells in the study area directly as:

```
[study] = 1
```

```
[study_sum] = zonalsum ( [study], [study] )
```

```
con ( [r] < ( 100.0 / [study_sum] ), 1)
```

Note that the number of sample cells needs to be entered as a floating-point value.

These 100 points could also be stratified, for example, so that 10 quadrats (from a 10x10 GRID) are first selected, and then 10 points within each selected quadrat are found. In this case, first change the cell size so that there are 10 x 10 columns and rows, then create a new study GRID ([studyq]) and random GRID ([rq]) using the coarser cell size. Then, select the quadrats:

```
[studyq] = 1
```

```
[study_sumq] = zonalsum([studyq], [studyq] )
```

```
[qpts] = con ( [rq] < ( 10.0 / [study_sumq] ), 1)
```

Now, reset the analysis environment so that the cell size is back to 100x100. Next, substitute the quadrat points GRID in place of the study area GRID, and recall that we want 100 points total:

```
[studyqpts] = 1
```

[study_sumq] = zonalsum ([studyqpts], [studyqpts])

[rpts] = con ([rq2] < (100.0 / [study_sumq]), 1)

One of the difficulties with this method, you may have noticed from the graphic on the previous page, is that although it is likely that the desired number of points will be created using this methodology, the exact number is not guaranteed since we are drawing from a distribution of numbers. A straightforward way to address this limitation is to tweak the threshold value slightly to get the exact number of points for that given distribution of random points.

Now, imagine the situation where there are three different zones that require different numbers of samples, perhaps reflecting different geology or land cover types, where the number of points desired for zone 1 = 10, zone 2 = 70, and zone 3 = 20. First, the number of points would need to be converted to a GRID; we'll call it: [ZonePts]. Also noticed that there is a "hole" in the middle — this is our exclusion zone where no random points can be located. Following our logic above (creating a study mask GRID of 1), use:

[study_sum] = zonalsum([zonePts], [study1])

con ([r] < ([zonePts] / [study_sum]), 1)

TABLE 8.4. A comprehensive listing of global functions available through the Raster Calculator.

Group	Usage	Comments
Distance	CostAllocation(<Source-GRID>, <CostGRID>, {OutAccumCostGRID}, {OutBacklinkGRID}, {MaxDistance}, {ValueGRID})	For each cell, the value of the output GRID is the allocation zone from the sources using <SourceGrid> across a weighted surface using <CostGrid>.
	CostBackLink(<SourceGRID>, <CostGRID>, {OutAccumCost-GRID}, {OutBacklinkGRID}, {MaxDistance}, {ValueGRID})	Finds the neighbor on the least-cost path from a cell to a set of course cells.
	CostDistance(<SourceGRID>, <CostGRID>, {OutAccumCost-GRID}, {OutBacklinkGRID}, {MaxDistance}, {ValueGRID})	Computes the cost weighted distance from each source cell specified in <SourceGRID>, reflecting the impedance values of <CostGRID>.
	CostPath(<FromCellGRID>, <AccumCostGRID>, <Back-linkGRID>, {BYCELL | BYZONE | BYLAYER})	Creates a GRID with the least-cost paths from <FromCellGRID> to closest source defined in <AccumCostGRID>.
	Corridor(<AccumGRID1>, <AccumGRID2>)	For each cell, it sums the accumulative cost GRIDs.
	EucAllocation(<SourceGRID>, { OutDistanceGRID}, {OutDirectionGRID}, {MaxDistance}, {ValueGRID})	Computes the zone of the closest (straight-line) source cell.
	EucDirection(<SourceGRID>, { OutDistanceGRID}, {OutDirectionGRID}, {MaxDistance}, {ValueGRID})	Computes the direction of each cell from the closest source cell.
	EucDistance(<SourceGRID>, { OutDistanceGRID}, {OutDirectionGRID}, {MaxDistance}, {ValueGRID})	Computes the distance of each cell from the closest source cell.
	PathDistance(<SourceGRID>, {CostGRID}, {SurfaceGRID}, {HorizFactorGRID}, {HorizFactorParm}, {VertFactorGRID}, {VertFactorParm}, {OutBacklinkGRID}, {OutAllocateGRID}, {MaxDistance}, {ValueGRID})	Computes the least-cost distance from a source cell.

TABLE 8.4. A comprehensive listing of global functions available through the Raster Calculator.

Generalize	Aggregate (G1, <CellFactor>, <Statistic>, { EXPAND | TRUNCATE }, {DATA | NODATA})	Resamples a GRID to coarser resolution using sum (default), minimum, maximum, mean, or median value of input cells covered by the square spatial extent of the output cell, defined by the *cell factor*. The cell size of the new grid equals the original cell size times <cellFactor>. The extent of the new grid is smaller if TRUNCATE (if the number of rows or columns is not divisible by <cellFactor>). If DATA, then any of the input values are NODATA, then the output grid's values are NODATA. The following <statistic> types are valid: MAX, MEAN, MEDIAN, MIN, SUM. This request should only be used on continuous (ratio) data (use resample for nominal data).
	BoundaryClean(<GRID>, {NOSORT | DESCEND | ASCEND |}, { TWOWAY | ONEWAY })	Cleans the boundary between zones by expanding and shrinking the boundary. Priority is set by: NOSORT (no sorting by size, but zones with larger values have higher priority); DESCEND (descending order by size); or ASCEND (ascending order by size). The cleaning process is done only once if ONEWAY, otherwise it is done twice, with the second pass reversing the priority. Can only be done on integer grids.
	Expand (<GRID>, <NCells>, LIST, <ValueList>)	Expands zones in <GRID> listed in <ValueList> by <NCells>.
	MajorityFilter(<GRID>, {FOUR | EIGHT}, {MAJORITY | HALF})	Filters values in <GRID> using a majority statistic. This is similar to FocalMajority, but you can require that at least half the cells are the same value with HALF.
	Nibble (<GRID>, <MaskGRID>, {ALL | DATAONLY})	Replaces the cells of <GRID> if the cells in <MaskGRID> are NoData, and the replacement values are the nearest neighbors. If DATAONLY, then only neighbors with non-NoData values are used.
	Shrink(<GRID>, <NCells>, LIST, <ValueList>)	Shrinks zones of <GRID> defined in the <ValueList> by <NCells>. <GRID> must be integer.
	Thin(<GRID>, {POSITIVE | DATA}, {NOFILTER | FILTER}, {ROUND | SHARP}, {thickness})	Thins linear features in <GRID>. All non NoData values are thinned. Boundaries are smoothed if FILTER; right-angled corners are preserved if SHARP. Thickness defines the maximum thickness of linear features in map units.

TABLE 8.4. A comprehensive listing of global functions available through the Raster Calculator.

Geometric transformation	Flip(<GRID>)	Flips<GRID> in the Y direction (top to bottom).
	Merge(<GRID>, ..., <GRID>)	Merges <GRID>s. When the cells overlap, the priority is determined by their order.
	Mirror(<GRID>)	Flips<GRID> in the X direction (Left to right).
	Mosaic(<GRID>,..., <GRID>)	Mosaics <GRID>s, but overlapping cells are averaged to create a smooth transition. Do not use this on GRIDs with nominal values.
	Resample (<GRID>, {CellSize}, {NEAREST | BILINEAR | CUBIC | SEARCH })	Creates a new GRID with the specified resolution <CellSize> using nearest neighbor (for nominal data), bilinear interpolation, cubic convolution, or SEARCH (extended nearest neighbor).
	Rotate(<GRID>, <Angle>, {NEAREST | BILINEAR | CUBIC })	Rotates <GRID> clockwise about the lower-left corner by <Angle> in degrees, using nearest neighbor, bilinear interpolation, or cubic convolution.
	Shift(<GRID>, <XMin>, <YMin>, {CellSize})	Creates new GRID that is shifted by x,y (in map units) with cells that are <CellSize>.
	Warp(<GRID>, <LinkFeature | LinkFile>, {Order}, {NEAREST | BILINEAR | CUBIC }, {FORWARD | BACKWARD}, {OutCellSize})	Transforms all cells according to a polynomial transformation, achieving the best overall fit within the points specified in <Link...>.
Groundwater	DarcyFlow(<HeadElevGRID>, <PorosityGRID>, <ThicknessGRID>, <TransmissivityGRID>, {OutDirectionGRID, OutMagnitudeGRID})	Computes groundwater volume balance using Darcy's Law.
	ParticleTrack(<FlowDirGRID>, <FlowMagGRID>, <x,y>, {StepLength}, {Time}, {OutTrackCoverage})	Computes the path of a particle through a velocity field
	PorousPuff(<TrackFile>, <PorosityGRID>, <ThicknessGRID>, <Mass>, {time}, {longDispersivity}, {DispersRatio}, {RetardFactor}, {DecayCoeff})	Calculates distribution of mass per volume of a solute.
Hydrologic	Basin (<DirectionGRID>)	Delineates all drainage basins with spatial extent using <DirectionGRID>.
	FlowAccumulation(<DirectionGRID>, { WeightGRID })	Accumulates the number of cells above a cell that would flow into or contribute runoff into it. <DirectionGRID> has flow direction values, <WeightGRID> assigns weight to each cell.

TABLE 8.4. A comprehensive listing of global functions available through the Raster Calculator.

Hydro-logic	FlowDirection(<GRID>, {ODropGRID}, {NORMAL | FORCE})	Calculates the flow direction in <>. If ODropGRID is specified, then an optional GRID that shows the ratio of the maximum change in elevation is output. All cells on the edge of the surface will flow away if FORCE.
	FlowLength(<DirectionGRID, {WeightGRID}, {DOWN-STREAM | UPSTREAM})	Calculates the accumulated flow length to each cell. The impedence to move through a cell is specified by WeightGRID. Length is calculated from the top of the drainage down to the cell if DOWNSTREAM.
	FocalFlow(<GRID>, {Thresh-Value})	Determines which of the eight neighboring cells flow into the center cell. The ThreshValue is added to the center cell's value. Because there is a possibility that all neighboring cells are greater, the value is encoded in a binary scheme, where, starting to the right of center and working clockwise, are the values 1, 2, 4, 8, 16, 32, 64, and 128.
	Sink(<DirectionGRID>)	Computes the pits or sinks in <DirectionGRID>. Usually Sink is used to pre process data to remove (usually) spurious pit artifacts in the data.
	SnapPour(<GRID | Point>, <AccumGRID>, {SnapDistance})	Snaps pour points to highest flow accumulation.
	StreamLink(<NetGRID>, <DirectionGRID>)	This is used to identify stream sections, and assigns a unique value for each section of raster linear network.
	StreamOrder(<NetGRID>, <DirectionGRID>, { STRAHLER | SHREVE })	Assigns a stream order to stream segments of <GRID>, using Shreve ordering (adds segments downslope, so that when two segments intersect, their magnitudes are added) or Strahler (stream order increases downstream only when streams of the same order intersect).
	StreamShape(<NetGRID>, <DirectionGRID>, {NOWEED | WEED})	Converts a GRID representing a stream network to a polyline shapefile. This uses <DirectionGRID> to aid in vectorizing cells. If WEED, then generalization using Douglas-Peucker algorithm is used.
	Watershed(<DirectionGRID, <SourceGRID>)	Creates a GRID that represents watersheds or basins using <DirectionGRID>, from all non-NoData values in <Source-GRID>.
Surface	Aspect (<GRID>)	Computes the direction of maximum change in surface <GRID>, in degrees (0 North, increasing clockwise).
	Contour(<GRID>, <INTER-VAL>, <InterVal>, { base })	Creates isolines for the input< GRID>, starting at base, and incrementing every <InterVal>. This returns a polyline shapefile.
	Curvature(<GRID>, {Out-ProfCurve}, {OutPlanCurve}, {OutSlope}, {OutAspect})	Computes the 2nd derivative of a surface <GRID> by fitting a 4th order polynomial through each cell. Convex upward are positive values, convex are negative.
	CutFill	Not implemented at v8.2.

GIS Concepts and ArcGIS Methods

TABLE 8.4. A comprehensive listing of global functions available through the Raster Calculator.

Surface	Hillshade(<GRID>, {Azimuth}, {Altitude}, {ALL | SHADE | SHADOW }, {ZFactor})	Computes illumination of surface <GRID>, with source at <Azimuth>, and zenith or Altitude. ALL considers both local illumination angles and shadows; SHADE does not consider shadows; SHADOW finds only shadows and returns 0s (shadow), 1 (not shadow).
	Slope (<GRID>, {DEGREE | PERCENTRISE}) Slope (<GRID>, {ZFactor}, {DEGREE | PERCENTRISE})	Computes slope of <GRID> using ZFactor of 1.0 and returns values in DEGREES or PERCENTRISE.
	Visibility (<GRID>, <Feature>, {POINT | LINE}, {FREQUENCY | OBSERVERS})	Computes the visibility on a surface <GRID> from source location <Feature>. FREQUENCY records the number of times a cell can be seen from input points (<17). OBSERVERS records whether the observation point can be seen from that cell.

8.3 Importing raster data

Just as with feature data, ArcGIS recognizes a variety of raster spatial data formats that can be brought directly into ArcMap or ArcCatalog, but some raster formats need to be imported into ArcGIS. Again, an ArcINFO license is required to import most formats using ArcToolbox tools. A complete list of supported raster formats is provided in Table 8.5.

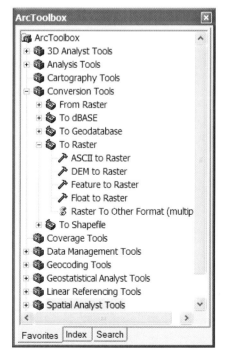

TABLE 8.5. Raster data formats that can be imported into ArcGIS (with ArcINFO license).

Name	Description
ADRG	US National Image and Mapping Agency's Arc Digitized Raster Graphics (ADRG).
ASCII	An ASCII file in a space-delimited text file in the format below, where NCOLS = number of columns, NROWS = number of rows, XLLCENTER | XLLCORNER = either the x coordinate for the center or lower left corner of the lower left most cell in the grid, YLLCENTER | YLLCORNER = either the x coordinate for the center or lower left corner of the lower left most cell in the grid; CELLSIZE = length of a cell's edge; NODATA_VALUE = the value representing unknown values, which is optional and defaults to -9999 if not specified. <NCOLS xxx> <NROWS xxx> <XLLCENTER xxx | XLLCORNER xxx> <YLLCENTER xxx | YLLCORNER xxx> <CELLSIZE xxx> {NODATA_VALUE xxx} ROW 1 ROW 2 ROW n
DEM	US Geological Survey's Digital Elevation Model (*.dem) files. See: http://gisdata.usgs.net/NED/default.asp.
DTED	US National Image and Mapping Agency's Digital Terrain Elevation Data (DTED) file.
E00	ESRI's ArcINFO export interchange file (*.e00). Available in ArcToolbox.
Floating point	An IEEE floating-point format, 32-bit signed file of binary floating point values.
STDS	US Geological Survey's Spatial Transfer Data Standard (STDS).

Single-layer analysis

9.1 Overview

In this chapter, basic analytical techniques are described that operate on a single map of either feature or raster type. Most often, simple summary statistics are computed for feature attributes. But various aspects of features themselves are computed as well, such as area, length, and shape, and the relationship between features, such as average distance between features. Proximity analysis buffers features to examine how relationships change with distance. Finally, features are occasionally transformed from one type to another to facilitate spatial analysis.

9.2 Summarizing attributes

A basic way to analyze data is to compile statistics for selected features of a map. This allows you to answer questions such as: How many total acres do the Great Lakes occupy? How many miles of interstate highway are there in the western US? How many people are there along the forest fringe in the western US?

9.2.1 Basic statistics

Probably the most common way to analyze geographic features is to compute basic statistics. For example, how many people are there in United States in 2000? What is the average population by county? Many statistics can be computed for the attributes of selected features in a layer, but typically the following are used: count, minimum, maximum, sum, mean, and standard deviation. For example, the arithmetic mean value ($\bar{X}$) is computed by:

$$\bar{X} = \sum_{i=1}^{n} x_i / n$$

where x represents the attribute of interest and n is the number of data points (features or records).

There are three ways to compute statistics in ArcGIS. First, in ArcMap, the *Selection Statistics* dialog can be opened without first specifying the layer or attribute field. This dialog allows differences between layers to be easily compared by selecting layers from the drop-down list. Note that only layers that have some selected features are available through the dialog,[1] and that statistics can be performed only on numerical fields that are listed in the field drop-down list. For example, the average population by US county in 2000 equals 87,631. The Selection Statistics dialog is not modal, so you can change the feature selection (either through the Select by Attributes dialog or interactively on the map) and the statistics will be dynamically updated. The second method, also in ArcMap, is to compute statistics directly on a field from a particular attribute table. Unfortunately, the text

1. If none of the layers have selected features, then the menu is greyed out. Note that this is inconsistent with the rest of the Arc-Map interface that assumes that no features being selected is the same as if all features are selected.

in the dialog box cannot be copied (and then pasted into another application). Statistics can also be computed from the attribute table when opened through ArcCatalog.

Calculating statistics for layers using Selection Statistics

1. In ArcMap, select Selection-->Statistics.

2. Select the layer to compute the statistics on.

3. Select the field from the selected layer to compute statistics on.

4. Close the dialog when finished.

Calculating statistics for tables using Statistics

1. In ArcMap, open the attribute table that contains the field to be analyzed by right-clicking on the desired layer and selecting Open Attribute Table.

2. Right-click on the field that contains the values to analyze and select Statistics....

3. The results of the various statistics of the selected records are listed in the lower-left box.

4. Close the dialog when finished.

9.2.1.1 Weighted statistics

When using count values (e.g., population) collected in analytical units that vary broadly in size, it may be more appropriate to weight the values by the area or length of the collection unit. The *weighted mean* ($\bar{X}$) is computed by:

$$\bar{X} = \frac{\displaystyle\sum_{i=1}^{n} w_i x_i}{\displaystyle\sum_{i=1}^{n} w_i}$$

where w is the weight. For example, the area-weighted mean population in 2000 by county is 106,561.9. This makes more sense for computing area for counties, particularly because the

---

minimum and maximum county area is nearly five orders of magnitude different! Other statistics (such as standard deviation) can be computed in a similar fashion.

Calculating area-weighted mean

1. In ArcMap, open the attribute table.

2. Add a field called Weighted of type Double.

3. Calculate the Weighted field to equal the attribute of interest times the [Area] field, e.g.: [Area] * [Pop2000].

4. Compute the sum of the Weighted field and write it down.

5. Compute the sum of the field that was used to weight, e.g.,: [Area], and write it down.

6. Divide the sum of the Weighted field by the sum of the area field.

9.2.2 Summarize

Another common way to analyze data is to summarize attribute data based on unique occurrences of a value within a field containing any type of data (i.e. qualitative as well as quantitative). When you summarize an attribute table, ArcMap creates a new table that counts the occurrences of each value of a field from the selected set of records. Each record in the new table contains at least two fields: the first lists the unique values found in the selected field and the second lists the number of records that have this value. These tables can be related, though the relationship may be one-to-one or many-to-one.

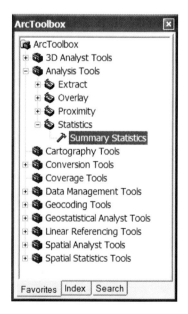

Also, additional numerical fields can be selected to summarize using a statistical method, including: minimum, maximum, mean, standard deviation, sum, and variance. A typical use of this function is to identify all unique values that occur in a field that contains nominal or class data. For example, if you wanted to find the number of land cover polygons and the total area of the polygons by land cover type, you would summarize on the "type" field by making it active (e.g., Lucode). Then, you can add a statistic by selecting on the "area" field, selecting the "Sum" statistic and adding it to the table. Note that the field you are summarizing on (the active field) is not available for other statistics.

Summarizing data is a convenient way to filter or preprocess data to discover possible data entry or logical errors in a dataset before you invest a lot of time creating maps and computing statistics. For example, summarizing a field that represents nominal values is a quick way to determine all classes represented in an attribute table, and often data entry errors can be discovered. A summary table can also be created from an attribute table, then joined back to the attribute table to calculate various proportions, differences from average values, etc. For example, if you want to calculate the proportion of the total class area occupied by each polygon, you would first create the summary table, then relate the tables based on the class code field ("Lucode"). Then, add another field in which to calculate the proportion (e.g., [Area] / [Total area in Class]). Note that in order to combine adjacent features (dissolving the shared boundaries), you need to use the Dissolve tool.

9.3 Measurement

Many ways have been developed to measure different aspects about geographic features that are represented on a map. Below are some of the more commonly used methods.

9.3.1 Number

A basic way to measure a map is to simply count the number of features. This can be obtained easily using either the *statistics* or *summarize* tools. Note that the number of selected features in a layer is displayed in the status bar (lower-left) of ArcMap, and in the lower-left hand portion of an attribute table.

9.3.2 Area

Before the age of electronic mapping, there were two basic methods to measure *area* from a map. The first was to estimate the area by placing a sheet of plastic containing a grid of dots on top of a map and counting the number of dots found in a polygon of interest.[2] A second method was to trace the boundary of a polygon using a mechanical device called a *planimeter*. These methods were tedious, time consuming, and error prone.[3] In fact, the Canadian Land Inventory (what is recognized as the first GIS) was justified by a cost-benefit analysis that showed that it was more cost effective to compute the area of a land resource unit electronically, even with 1965 computer technology![4]

The standard method to compute area in GIS is based on finding triangles or trapezoids using the vertices of a polygon. For example, to compute the area of a simple polygon (assuming a plane), sum the product of the vertex vectors.[5] An alternative method is to sum trapezia formed by every segment of a polygon and the baseline through the origin.[6] The following is used to compute the area (A) using triangles, and assumes that the polygon vertices (x,y) are in clockwise order:

$$A = -\frac{1}{2}\sum_{i=1}^{n-1}(x_i y_{i+1} - y_i x_{i+1})$$

Within ArcMap, feature area can be calculated using a short equation in the Field Calculator (see Chapter 6). For raster data, the area of a zone in a GRID (A_z) can be computed by:

$$A_z = c \times r^2$$

where c is the number of cells in the count field and r is the cell resolution (width of a cell). The area units are the same as the coordinate system units (a.k.a. map units). It is wise to set the field name to specify the units (e.g., "hectares" rather than "area").

9.3.3 Length

A central characteristic of a linear feature is its *length* (and perimeter for areal features). Length is computed by summing the length of each straight-line segment calculated using the

2. Wood, W.F. 1954. The dot planimeter: a new way to measure area. *Professional Geographer* 6:12-14.
3. For example, see: Frolov, Y.S. and D.H. Maling. 1969. The accuracy of area measurement by point counting techniques. *Cartographic Journal* 6:21-35.
4. Longley, P.A., M.F. Goodchild, D.J. Maguire, and D.W. Rhind. 2002. *Geographic Information Systems and Science*. Wiley & Sons.
5. Worboys, M.F. 1995. *GIS: A Computing Perspective*. Taylor & Francis. Page 214.
6. Jones, C.B. 1997. *Geographical Information Systems and Computer Cartography*. Longman. Page 65.

Pythagorean theorem. Because line segments are not always able to capture the small turns and wiggles of real-world linear features (e.g., a road or trail), map-based measurement of length underestimates "true" length slightly. Typically, the finer the scale of the map, the less underestimation is involved. In addition, length is typically thought of in two-dimensional space, where the third dimension, topographic variation, is ignored.

Estimation of length or perimeter using raster datasets is subject to artifacts that can cause severe underestimation and overestimation. If a very coarse resolution GRID is used to represent a sinuous linear feature (e.g., a winding road up a hillside), then the length can be significantly underestimated. On the other hand, orientation artifacts can cause significant problems, so that a linear feature aligned at 45° to the GRID can overestimate length by up to 41%.[7]

9.3.4 Shape

Shape is often measured for areal features to distinguish those features that are long and skinny from those with a compact or round shape.

9.3.4.1 Compactness index

Although the perimeter (P) to area (A) ratio can be used, it is more common and useful to measure shape by comparing a polygon to a normal form, usually a circle (but occasionally a square, especially for raster data). The equation to compute the compactness index (S_c) for a circle is:[8]

$$S_c = \frac{P}{2\sqrt{\pi A}}$$

---

7. Theobald, D.M. 2000. Correcting linear and perimeter measurement errors in raster-based data. *Cartography and Geographic Information Science* 27(2): 111-116.
8. Patton, D.R. 1975. A diversity index for quantifying habitat 'edge'. *Wildlife Society Bulletin* 3:171-173.

Values of S_c range from 1 (compact) to greater than 1 (less compact, more distended).

Computing compactness (relative to a circle)

1. In ArcMap, open Field Calculator dialog.
2. Check Advanced box and in the pre-logic box enter:

Dim dblArea as Double
Dim dblLength as Double
Dim dblC as Double
Dim pArea as IArea
Dim pCurve As ICurve
Set pArea = [shape]
dblArea = pArea.area
Set pCurve = [Shape]
dblPerimeter = pCurve.Length
dblC = dblPerimeter / (3.544908 * sqr (dblArea))

3. In the field expression box, enter:

dblC

4. Click OK.

9.3.4.2 Zonal geometry

For raster-based features, basic aspects about the shape of zones can be obtained through the Zonal functions. In addition to area and perimeter, the *ZonalGeometry* function computes thickness and a number of parameters based on fitting an ellipse to each zone. *Thickness* is the radius (in cells) of the largest circle that can be fit wholly within a zone. The *major* and *minor* axes of the best-approximating ellipse are dimensioned so that the ellipse area equals the zone area, and the *orientation* specifies the angle between the axes. The ellipse is placed at the *x,y* centroid.

9.3.4.3 Sinuosity

Although less common, the sinuosity (S_s) of a linear feature (a.k.a. "wiggliness") represented as a polyline is measured as the ratio of the straight-line distance from the start to the end of a line (L_e), divided by the full (meandering) length of a line (L_f):

$$S_s = \frac{L_e}{L_f}$$

Values of S_s run from 0 (very sinuous) to 1 (straight).

Computing sinuosity
1. In ArcMap, open Field Calculator dialog.
2. Check Advanced box and in the pre-logic box enter:
Dim dblLe as Double
Dim dblLf as Double
Dim dblS as Double
Dim pCurve As Icurve
Dim pFPoint As IPoint
Dim pTPoint As IPoint
Set pCurve = [Shape]
Set pFPoint = pCurve.FromPoint
Set pTPoint = pCurve.ToPoint
dblLe = Sqr((pFPoint.x - pTPoint.x) ^ 2 + (pFPoint.Y - pTPoint.Y) ^ 2)
dblLf = pCurve.Length
dblS = dblLe/dblLf
3. In the field expression box, enter:
dblS
4. Click **OK**.

9.3.5 Fragmentation

A wide variety of fragmentation indices have been developed, including simple metrics such as the number of patches (though this is really only meaningful if the patches are defined functionally). More useful measures have been developed, particularly in the landscape ecology field, that evaluate fragmentation based on the *landscape composition* or *landscape structure* (a.k.a. *configuration*) of patches. A number of stand alone and hybrid GIS programs have been developed to compute these indices as well. For example, the classic *FRAGSTATS* program provides description of a variety of landscape metrics.[9] However, a number of basic metrics can be easily computed in GIS.

---

9. McGarigal, K., and B. J. Marks. 1995. *FRAGSTATS: spatial pattern analysis program for quantifying landscape structure.* USDA For. Serv. Gen. Tech. Rep. PNW-351. Available at: http://www.umass.edu/landeco/research/fragstats/fragstats.html

FIGURE 9.1. Clear-cut patterns in national forests generated some of the early concern over landscape fragmentation, for example adjacent to Yellowstone National Park, USA.

NATIONAL FOREST | YELLOWSTONE NATIONAL PARK

CLOUDS

FOREST CLEARCUTS BETWEEN 1972 & 1986

CLEARCUTS BETWEEN 1986 & 1992

9.3.5.1 Fragmentation index

Fragmentation (*p*) of a map can be calculated as the ratio of the number of contiguous map regions (*m*), or the number of polygons that would result after classifying and dissolving the boundaries between same-valued neighboring polygons, to the number of original polygons (*n*):[10]

$$p = \frac{m - 1}{n - 1} .$$

This *fragmentation index* ranges from 1, complete fragmentation (where *m=n*), to 0, completely connected (where *m=0*). For raster data, *m* equals the number of regions (the number of records in the attribute table after using *RegionGroup* function), while *n* equals the number of cells in the GRID.[11] As an example, consider the land cover pattern shown in Figure 9.2. Site A has a *p* of 0.059 = (473-1)/(7979-1), while Site B has a *p* of 0.009 =(74-1)/(7979-1) and indeed, Site B looks more connected than Site A. Note that this requires that some classification and dissolving occurs. Otherwise, *m* and *n* are the same with a polygon dataset.

FIGURE 9.2. Sites A (left) and B (right) showing land cover patterns. Coniferous forest is shown in green.

10. Chou, Y.H. 1997. *Exploring spatial analysis in GIS*. Onword Press. Note that this was originally proposed by Monmonier, M.S. 1974. Measures of pattern complexity for choroplethic maps. *The American Cartographer* 1(2): 159-169.
11. This does not necessarily equal the number of rows times columns, but can be found by summing the Count field.

9.3.5.2 Relative size of the largest patch

Another measure of fragmentation is the *relative size of the largest patch metric* (RS_i).[12] RS_i is the ratio of the area of the largest patch (a_i) to the area of all the patches of the same class as the largest patch (A_i):[13]

$$RS_i = \frac{a_i}{p_i \times A_i}$$

The area of a_i can be found by using the Statistics tool on the area (feature based) or count field (GRID based). RS_i for a connected landscape approaches a value of 1.0, while fragmented landscape approach 0.0. For the example landscapes, the RS_i for Site A = 0.705 = (4368/6192) and for Site B = 0.999 = (7589/7594).

9.3.5.3 GISFrag

The GISFrag metric computes fragmentation by computing the average distance from the nearest patch and accounts for the configuration of patches.[14] This metric assumes a binary landscape (e.g., habitat/non-habitat), and is computed by finding the straight-line distance away from patches. Smaller values (>0) indicate less fragmented landscapes and larger values indicate higher levels of fragmentation. GISFrag is simply the mean distance value (including the 0s in the cells that represent the patches), and is calculated in the Raster Calculator using:

[GISFrag] = EucDistance(con([study] == 42, 1))

where 42 is the value representing habitat. Assessing the fragmentation of the coniferous vegetation on the study sites, GISFrag for Site A = 8.74 and for Site B = 1.33, indicating that Site A is more fragmented than Site B.

9.3.5.4 Landscape signature

Both the shape and configuration of patches in a landscape can be examined by measuring how the proportion of a landscape that is occupied by patches changes when patches are enlarged (buffering out) and shrunk (buffering in) across a range of scales. This can be computed by calculating both the straight-line distance away from and into the patches (Figure 9.3). These areas are then normalized to the total study area and expressed as a cumulative distribution function.[15] Notice that the proportion of "habitat" is found at the

---

12. Turner, M.G., R.H. Gardner, and R.V. O'Neill. 2001. *Landscape Ecology in Theory and Practice*. Springer.
13. For a polygon feature type, select the features of the appropriate class, then sum the areas. For a raster representation, this can be found from the zonal attribute table in the count field.
14. Ripple, W.J., G.A. Bradshaw, and T.A. Spies. 1991. Measuring forest landscape patterns in the Cascade Range of Oregon, USA. *Biological Conservation* 57: 73-88.
15. It is probably easiest to do this in a spreadsheet like Microsoft Excel.

---

intersection with 0 (~85%). The shape of the curve with positive values indicates the configuration of the patches, while negative values indicate the number, shape, and size of the patches. Note that this method can also incorporate cost weighted distances and continuous valued (0.0 to 1.0) data as well.

FIGURE 9.3. Landscape signature for Site A using coniferous forest as patch. The top graph shows the cumulative distribution function of the proportion of study area. The bottom map shows within-patch areas in green, outside patches in blue. Deeper color indicates further in or out from the edge of patches.

The landscape signature GRID can be computed using the following, where [patch] contains 0s and 1s:

[g1] = int(EucDistance ([patch] == 1, 1)) * 1)

[g2] = int(EucDistance (con([patch] == 0, 1)) * -1)

[patch_sig] = [g1] + [g2]

9.3.6 Distance

There are a number of different methods for computing distances between zero-dimensional objects (points), and a couple of these are discussed below. However, some assumptions need to be made when calculating distances between line or polygon features. Often the centroids of linear and areal features are used when calculating distances, but distances can also be computed from the nearest part of a feature or the average distance from all parts of a feature. When creating distance surfaces from linear and polygon features, the closest edge-to-edge distance (not centroid to centroid) is computed. The differences between the centroid and other measurement methods is more important as the ratio of the length or area of a feature to the distance between features increases. For example, if the distance between polygons is an order of magnitude or more than the thickness of a polygon, then approximating the polygon with the centroid will cause minimal bias.

9.3.6.1 Spherical

Calculating distance using geographic coordinates requires using spherical geometry, and the formula to calculate *spherical distance* (D_s) uses the Law of Cosines:

$$D_s = R \cos \angle 1 [\sin \phi_1 \sin \phi_2 + \cos \phi_1 \cos \phi_2 \cos(\lambda_1 \angle \lambda_2)]$$

where R is radius of a spheroid (typically 6,370,997 m is used), ϕ (phi) is latitude, λ (lambda) is longitude. It is not recommended to use this formula to calculate distances shorter than about 2 km, however, because it is pushing the lower limit of precision that a computer computes inverse cosine values. Also, at higher latitudes (toward the poles), the length of a degree of longitude decreases. At the equator, one degree of longitude is 111.321 km, at 60° latitude it decreases to 55.802 km, and at the poles it is 0.0 km. Because distance (and area) changes with latitude, it is recommended to compute area using projected (not geographical) coordinates.

9.3.6.2 Euclidean

The most common way to calculate the *Euclidean* or straight-line distance (D_E) between two points (x_1,y_1 and x_2,y_2) uses the Pythagorean theorem:

$$D_E = \sqrt{(x_2 \angle x_1)^2 + (y_2 \angle y_1)^2}.$$

To interactively measure the distance between two features (or locations) on a map, use the *Measure Distance* tool (⊞). To measure the distance between a given feature and another feature in the same layer, unfortunately, is not easy to do using the standard interface of ArcGIS (with ArcView license) without a custom program. A straightforward way of computing the distances from a single feature to all other features in a layer is to create a distance surface with just the feature of interest, and then to "overlay" the other features on the distance surface. Note that the precision of the distance values is controlled by the cell size of the raster. Also, the *direction* from a feature to all other features could be computed in this fashion by using the option to create the direction GRID when creating the distance surface. However, the *Point Distance tool* in the Proximity group of tools in ArcToolbox (requires ArcInfo license) will compute the nearest feature for coverage datasets.

Distance from a feature to all other features in a layer

1. Select the feature of interest from a layer.

2. Create a distance surface from the feature of interest by selecting, from the Spatial Analyst toolbar, Distance -> Straight Line.

3. Clear the selected feature of interest.

4. Select Zonal Statistics from the Spatial Analyst toolbar.

5. Set the original layer as the Zone dataset (and choose an appropriate field).

6. Set the distance surface GRID just created as the Value raster.

7. Set the chart statistic to Mean.

8. Specify the output table and click OK.

9. Join the resulting table back to the original layer's attribute table using the Zone Field.

9.3.6.3 Constrained distance

The Manhattan metric distance[16] between two points x_1,y_1 and x_2,y_2 on a plane assumes that movement is constrained to allow only orthogonal movement (e.g., the road network, assuming it is oriented with the coordinate system). It is computed using:

$$D_M = |x_2 - x_1| + |y_2 - y_1|$$

---

16. So called because of driving on orthogonal streets.

9.3.6.4 Weighted distance

In addition to Euclidean and constrained distances, recall from Chapter 7 that another approach to computing distance is to recognize that there may be geographic conditions that affect how far a particular location is from another, from a functional perspective. *Cost-weighted distance* incorporates such factors that influence movement across a surface. Cost-weighted distance computes distance in terms of cost units and accumulates these units at locations away from features of interest.

9.3.7 Pattern

Geographic features can be characterized by their pattern or degree of dispersion: *regular, random,* and *clustered* patterns. There are numerous statistics and metrics that quantify the spatial pattern or arrangement of features. However, many of these require specialized

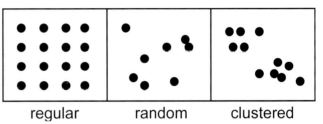

regular   random   clustered

programs to run, though increasingly these are built as user-defined extensions to ArcGIS software.[17] Rather than providing a comprehensive review, below I describe some of the more common statistics that are useful and relatively straightforward to implement in the standard ArcGIS interface.

---

17. Lee, J. and D.W.S. Wong. 2001. *Statistical Analysis with ArcView GIS.* John Wiley & Sons. 192 pgs. (Information is online at: http://www.wiley.com/products/subject/geography/gis/lee/). Note: this is for ArcView v3.X.

9.3.7.1 Mean center

The most common way to quantify a feature theme is to simply count the number of features. But themes with the same number of features can differ substantially in their spatial pattern. Another common way to differentiate patterns is to quantify the mean geographic center of x,y points:

$$\bar{x} = \frac{\sum\limits_{i=1}^{n} w_i x_i}{\sum\limits_{i=1}^{n} w_i} \;,\; \bar{y} = \frac{\sum\limits_{i=1}^{n} w_i y_i}{\sum\limits_{i=1}^{n} w_i} \;.$$

For example, the US Census Bureau has tracked the center of population since 1790 (Figure 9.4).

FIGURE 9.4. The western march of the US population center from 1790 to 1990.[18]

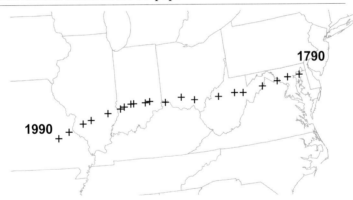

---

18. Data from US Census Bureau: http://www.census.gov/population/censusdata/popctr.pdf

9.3.7.2 Nearest neighbor

The *nearest neighbor* index (*N*) measures the degree of spatial dispersion of features based on the minimum distance between individual (point and line) features. A scattered distribution has a greater average distance, while a clustered distribution has a smaller average distance. This index is computed by averaging all the distances from a point to its nearest neighbor:[19]

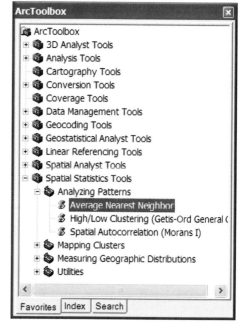

$$N = \left(\sum_{i=1}^{n} d_i \right) / n$$

where d_i is the distance from location i to its nearest neighbor. This can be computed using a custom VBA program.[20]

9.3.7.3 Quadrat analysis

Quadrat analysis is a common technique that can be used to detect non-randomness in spatial distributions. This technique requires that *quadrats*, usually squares, are superimposed over the points of interest. Then, the number of points that fall within each quadrat are counted. Finally, the observed number of points per quadrat (i.e. the average number of points per quadrat) are compared with the number of points that would be expected if the points were randomly distributed (the variance).[21] To create a listing of the quadrat classes and their frequency, convert the point feature dataset to a GRID. However, because only one feature per cell is recognized when using simple feature-to-raster conversion, you will need to use a function that counts the number of points in a cell. The Neighborhood Statistic dialog can be parameterized to use a single-cell neighborhood to

19. Chou, Y.H. 1997. *Exploring Spatial Analysis in Geographic Information Systems.* Sante Fe: New Mexico: Onword Press.
20. For example, M. Sawada's Nearest Neighbor Analysis: http://arcscripts.esri.com/details.asp?dbid=12227
21. Muehrcke, P.C. and J.O. Muehrcke, 1992. *Maps Use: Reading, analysis, and interpretation.* Madison, Wisconsin: JP Publications.

count the number of features. The attribute table of the resulting GRID lists the frequency of class counts (note that there is no 0 class).

Creating count frequency table

1. Create a field (e.g., COUNT) in the feature attribute table with the value of 1. (use LongInt type).

2. Select **Neighborhood Statistics...** from the from the Spatial Analyst toolbar.

3. Set the input data layer to be the point layer of interest.

4. Set the field input to be the newly created Count field.

5. Set the statistic type to be **Sum**.

6. Set the Neighborhood type to **Rectangle**.

7. Set both the height and width to 1 (to count just the features within a single cell).

8. Set the output cell size and raster name.

9. Click **OK**.

One difficulty with this method is that the results are especially dependent on the quadrat size – different quadrats will produce different results. One suggestion for the optimal quadrat size[22] sets the cell size (width) (r) to:

$$r = \sqrt{A/n}$$

where A is the study area and n is the number of points in the study area. However, because the results are dependent on the cell size, it would be useful to examine how the results change with a range of cell sizes, and in this way the *scale* of the process represented by the point distribution could be examined.

---

22. Greig-Smith, P. 1952. The use of random and contiguous quadrats in the study of the structure of plant communities. *Annals of Botany* 16: 312.

9.3.7.4 Autocorrelation

Recall that the First Law of Geography states that near things are more related than distant things.[23] To test this law and make use of this information, a number of methods have been developed to directly measure *autocorrelation*, including joint counts, Moran's *I* and Geary's *c*. These techniques are mostly implemented in the *Geostatistical Analyst* extension,[24] but a number of advanced tools have been developed in the Spatial Statistics toolbox as well.

9.4 Proximity analysis

There are numerous situations that require knowing the distances between features. This "distance from" notion is entrenched in laws and prescribed in regulations, for example, all neighbors within 1000 feet of a proposed zoning change must be notified, and a drug-free zone is typically established around schools. Buffering is the basis for *proximity analysis* and creates a buffer feature that is a polygon feature type. Although most often you will want to create a new layer that represents buffered features, particularly if the layer will be used in an overlay operation (e.g., clip or union) with another layer. But if the buffer layer will simply be used to select features from another layer, recall from Chapter 5 that a *buffered selection* can be done using the *Select by location* interface.

23. Tobler, W. 1970. A computer movie simulating urban growth in the Detroit region. *Economic Geography* 46(2):234-240.
24. See: Johnston, K., J. M. ver Hoef, K. Krivoruchko, and N. Lucas. 2001. *Using ArcGIS Geostatistical Analyst*. ESRI Press.

9.4.1 Buffering

Point, line, and polygon features can all be *buffered* by expanding outward in all directions a defined distance from a feature. Typically buffer analysis uses a single, equidistant zone around a feature. Multiple zones can also be created to examine how the results of an analysis might change with a range of distances. The buffer distance might also vary with an attribute of the feature. So, for example, points that represent warehouses might be buffered further than points representing houses. Or, the buffer distance could vary with direction (e.g., in response to differences in wind strength at the edge of a forest) or with the characteristics of a polygon's edge (e.g., exposure is greater at a grassland-forest edge compared to a shrubland-forest edge).

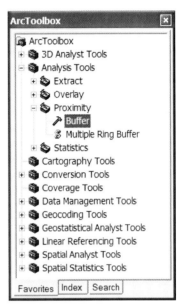

The *Buffer tool* can be used to create buffers around the selected features of a feature layer . First, you'll need to select the layer of interest and choose whether to use all the features or just the selected ones. Note that the number of selected and total features is displayed in the dialog.

There are three ways buffer distances can be defined. *At a specified distance* allows you to set a distance that is applied to all selected features in the layer. This is the default. *At a distance from an attribute field* allows you to set the buffer distances based on the value in the field you specify. This allows you, for example, to change the buffer distance based on some feature attribute. *As multiple rings* allows you to create multiple rings at a defined, uniform increment. Notice that at the bottom of the dialog the distance units can be changed.

Specify a number of characteristics about the output from the buffering operation. You can choose to dissolve barriers between buffers (or not). Dissolving barriers removes the polygon boundaries if two polygons overlap. This enforces buffer polygons to be embedded in a two-dimensional plane. Not dissolving barriers allows the buffer polygons that overlap to remain intact. If the features to be buffered are polygons, then you have the choice of buffering them so that the resulting buffer polygon is both inside and outside, outside only, inside only, or outside only with the core included (see Figure 9.4). Note that a fifth option shrinks a polygon boundary, and is accomplished by entering a *negative buffer* value (e.g., using -200 in the *at a specified distance* option) using the *outside only with the core included* option. Lastly, specify how the buffers are to be saved. The default is to create them in a new layer. They can also be saved as graphics in the data frame or added to an existing editable layer.[25]

Although buffers are typically created on feature datasets, the concept also applies (and in some ways is easier to implement) to raster datasets. That is, buffers can be created using distance surfaces by specifying a maximum distance when calculating the Straight Line distance, or in the Raster Calculator using:

EucDistance ([lakes], #, #, 400)

Multi-rings of equal distances can also be created easily by dividing (using modulo division) a distance surface by the interval distance (e.g., 200 m):

[DS] = int (EucDistance([lakes]))

con([DS] == 0, 0, (int([DS] / 200) * 200))

---

25. Kudos to ESRI for implementing several improvements over the ArcView v3.2 Buffer Wizard, especially breaking dissolved polygons into single-part polygons, as well as setting the defaults to create a new layer and tracking (some of) the parameters used from the last time it was used.

FIGURE 9.5. Different buffer types that can be created using the Buffer tool on a polygon feature (top left): inside and outside (top center); only outside (top right); only inside (bottom left); outside and include inside (bottom center); and outside and include inside with a negative value (bottom right). The resulting buffer polygon is shown in grey and the original polygon is a black ring.

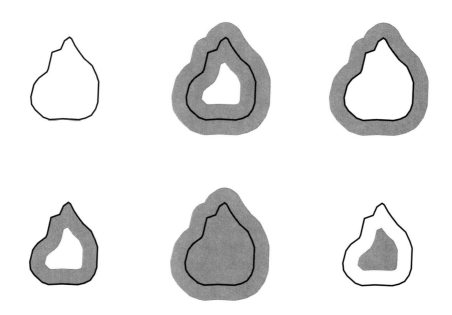

9.4.2 *Variable buffers*

Although frequently buffer zones are specified using a straight-line distance (e.g., 300-foot buffer zone), the concept of a *variable buffer* whose width changes in response to geographic variation is very attractive.[26] For example, riparian zones are often modeled in GIS by simply buffering stream lines a certain distance (perhaps using different distances for each stream order), and this is a useful — but a first — approximation. In reality, the width of both the stream and flood channel typically changes in response to bedrock geology and the dynamics of stream flow. As a result, it would be useful to represent buffers that vary in response to these changing channel characteristics. Recall the recent discussion about creating buffers using distance surfaces? A natural extension of this approach is to create variable buffers using weighted surfaces. That is, rather than assuming straight-line distance away from stream lines,

26. This is also called effective distance. See: Berry, J.1993. *Beyond mapping: Concepts, algorithms, and issues in GIS*. Wiley & Sons.

GIS Concepts and ArcGIS Methods

a cost-weighted surface that represents the valley geomorphology could be used, based on the slope of the adjacent valley walls. Riparian zones are more likely to be found in areas that gently grade away from the stream channel as opposed to narrowly incised valleys (Figure 9.5).

FIGURE 9.6. Variable-buffer fit around a stream created using cost-weighted distance (shown in teal). Fixed-width buffer is shown in red for comparison.

Creating a variable buffer

1. Create a cost-weighted distance surface based on the continuously varying factor that influences the buffer width (e.g., slope classes).

2. Select **Distance -> Cost weighted...** from the from the Spatial Analyst toolbar.

3. Set the cost raster to be the cost weighted distance surface (e.g., slope classes).

4. Set the maximum distance to be the buffer width.

5. Specify the output raster name.

6. Click **OK**.

9.4.3 Neighborhoods

Neighborhood analysis finds features that are adjacent to one another (usually polygon features). You will need to identify features that are adjacent to a particular feature. Finding the directly adjacent neighbors is typically accomplished on polygon features (but is not limited to polygons) such as counties. It can be easily accomplished using a "what is adjacent?" query (see Chapter 5). This analysis can be extended to find second- and third-order (and so on) neighbors by using the selected neighborhood features as the selected set. Another type of neighborhood analysis identifies nearby features that are within some defined distance. For instance, a typical planning application is to identify potentially affected neighbors who are within 500 feet of a home whose owner is proposing a zoning change. A third type of neighborhood analysis identifies features that are adjacent but that have particular attributes. For example, it might be important to identify patches of coniferous forest that are adjacent to urban areas because fire protection efforts might need to be focused there in the event of a forest fire. In this case, you will need to select the urban patches that are adjacent to coniferous forest patches from a map of land cover types. Finally, *zones of influence* neighborhoods could also be created, as we did in Chapter 7 (called proximity zones or Thiessen polygons). These proximal neighborhoods can be created using the Allocation interface in Spatial Analyst, through the *Create Thiessen Polygons tool* in the Proximity group in ArcToolbox (requires ArcInfo license), or through a custom program.[27]

9.5 Transformations

There are many GIS operations that transform a feature of a particular type to another type: from and to point, line, polygon, and raster (see Table 9.1). This contrasts with a *projection*, which changes the coordinates of the vertices used to represent features, but the features themselves remain represented by the same feature type. Because many of these *transformations* are not typical tasks, only the relatively common ones are covered below. Also, many of these transformations are not easy to accomplish in standard ArcGIS, although a

---

27. For example, see the "Create Thiessen Polygons 3.0" Extension written by Tim Lomas (2002) at: http://arcscripts.esri.com/details.asp?dbid=11958. For an in-depth discussion of algorithms used to compute Thiessen polygons and Voronoi diagrams (page 157), see O'Rourke, J. 1998. *Computational geometry in C.* Cambridge University Press.

number of user-created extensions and programs are available to do them. (Note that conversion to raster data is also considered a transformation, but is handled in Chapter 7.)

TABLE 9.1. Common transformations.[a]

From Type	To Point	To Line	To Polygon	Raster
Point	Interpolation Merge Sample	Interpolation	Buffer Convex hull Interpolation Thiessen polygon	Conversion
Line	Nodes Vertices	Generalize	Buffer	Conversion
Polygon	Centroid Label center Vertices	Medial-axis	Buffer Dissolve Eliminate Generalize Sample	Conversion: center, dominant area, or priority method
Raster	Conversion	Conversion	Conversion	Resample Aggregation

a. Adapted from: Bonham-Carter, G.F. 1996. *Geographic Information Systems for Geoscientists: Modelling with GIS.* Ontario, Canada: Pergamon Press.

9.5.1 Feature center and centroid

A typical transformation applied to polygons (and to a lesser extent points and polylines) is to find the *center* of a feature. There are four types of feature centers: simple, center of gravity, weighted centroid, and label. The *simple centroid,* or *geographic centroid,* is the center of the geographic extent of a feature, usually found at the center of the smallest rectangle that encloses (minimum bounding rectangle) the geographic feature(s) of interest. The *center-of-gravity centroid* (a.k.a. true centroid) is the "balance point" of a feature. For irregularly shaped features, the center-of-gravity centroid is often a different location than the simple center. For points, the centroid is located at the average x and average y values. For triangles, the center-of-gravity centroid is equivalent to the mean center of the three vertices. Note that the average x and average y of the vertices of a polygon only *approximates* the center-of-gravity centroid.[28] The center-of-gravity centroid is calculated most commonly using the trapezoidal method, which reduces a polygon to a series of overlapping triangles for which the center is found. The

28. Jones, C.B. 1997. *Geographical Information Systems and Computer Cartography.* Longman. Page 66.

weighted centroid is generally applied to a series of points that have some values associated with them. For example, the center of US population can be calculated (Figure 9.3).[29] Finally, the *label center* is a point that approximates the centroid, but is guaranteed to fall inside a polygon, which is a useful property for labeling purposes.

ArcGIS provides a variety of ways to compute feature centers, To transform features to a point feature to capture the centers is a two-step process. First, the x and y coordinates of the center type of choice are computed in fields in the feature attribute table. Next, a new point feature dataset is created from the x,y coordinates in the original feature attribute table. This can be done using the *Add X,Y Data* tool. A second way is to use the Field calculator to calculate either the true centroid (.Centroid) and label center (.LabelCenter) (see Chapter 6). [30] With an ArcInfo license, these can also be computed in ArcToolbox using the *Centroid Labels* tool in the Topology group (though the feature dataset needs to be converted to a coverage first).

FIGURE 9.7. Various feature centers, including simple (center of minimum bounding rectangle), centroid, zonal centroid, and label.

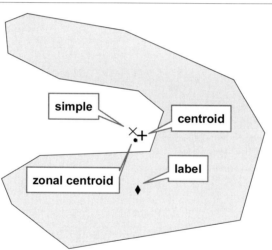

29. Clarke, K. 1990. *Analytical and computer cartography.* Englewood Cliffs, N.J.: Prentice Hall. Page 154.
30. This is an improvement over ArcView v3.x, which had only a single request to find the center (.ReturnCenter), but this returned the label center.

GIS Concepts and ArcGIS Methods

9.5.2 Dissolve

An important operation to simplify line and polygon features is to *dissolve* the shared boundary (or point) between adjacent features with similar attributes. For example, to simplify a land use/cover map that has major and minor categories into major categories, the boundaries of polygons that are adjacent and have the same major land use categories could be removed. The boundary

between the upper-right polygon with a value of 1 and the adjacent polygon with the same value is dissolved, and the boundary between the lower-right polygon with a value of 2 and its adjacent polygon is dissolved.

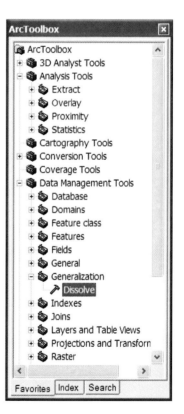

Dissolve replaces multiple features with a single feature by removing unwanted nodes between lines or boundaries between polygons. The output theme contains the shape and the dissolve fields, and fields that contain the average, sum, minimum, maximum, variance, and/or standard deviation of the aggregated features can be added. The primary way to dissolve features in ArcGIS is through the Dissolve tool. Note, however, that this method dissolves all features that have the same attribute into a single feature, regardless of whether the features are adjacent or not (i.e. a single feature with disjoint multiple parts). The polygon and line features appear to be the same, but the attribute table has only one entry per unique feature value. This can be a powerful way to represent feature data (indeed, it mimics zones in a GRID!).[31] A second way to dissolve features, and one that does not result in disjoint multi-part features, is use the *Dissolve tool* found in the Generalization group in ArcToolbox (ArcInfo license required). Again, this requires the input feature dataset to be a coverage.

9.5.3 Eliminate

The *eliminate* operation removes unwanted lines and polygons from a feature theme. This operation is useful when your feature dataset has numerous small polygons

---

31. Just as in ArcView v3.x, dissolving features without creating disjoint multi-part features requires the use of an additional VBA program called *Explode*. This can be acquired from ESRI ArcObjects online: http://arconline.esri.com/arcobjectsonline/.

(a.k.a. sliver polygons) that are artifacts of digitizing and that may cloud subsequent analysis. Elimination of these artifacts can be accomplished using the *Eliminate tool* in ArcToolbox, which merges selected polygons with neighboring polygons that have the largest shared border between them or that have the largest area. Unfortunately, there is no easy way in ArcGIS (with an ArcView license) to emulate this functionality.[32]

9.5.4 Generalization

Frequently, linear and polygonal features need to be simplified by reducing the number of vertices that depict them. The eternal question has been: which points should be removed so that the essential character of feature remains intact? Over the years, cartographers have developed numerous ways to preserve the caricature of a line.[33] An easy method is to remove every n^{th} vertex, but this creates very poor results and is not recommended.[34] One of the most enduring methods is the *Douglas-Peucker* algorithm,[35] and this is used in several places in ArcGIS (e.g., conversion of raster to features). Because generalization can move (or remove) vertices, topology can be corrupted. This is particularly true when generalizing the boundaries of polygons, and therefore generalization can only be accomplished on coverage datasets using the *Simplify Lines tool* in the Generalization group of ArcToolbox (requires ArcInfo license). At v8.3, features can be generalized using the Advanced Editor toolbar (requires ArcEditor or ArcInfo license).

9.5.5 Resampling

Resampling is needed when two raster datasets of different cell size are combined or overlaid, or if two raster datasets with the same cell size are not aligned.

32. One method would be to convert the feature dataset to raster, create regions, identify the regions that are to be eliminated, and then use the Nibble function, then convert back to feature. A very fine resolution GRID would be required, however.

33. Buttenfield, B.P. and R.B. McMaster. 1991. *Map Generalization: Making Rules for Knowledge Representation* (eds). London: Longman.

34. Weibel, R. 1997. Generalization of spatial data: principles and selected algorithms. In: *Algorithmic foundations of geographic information systems*. Berlin: Springer

35. Douglas, D.H. and T.K. Peucker. 1973. Algorithms for the reduction of the number of points required to represent a digitized line or its caricature. *Canadian Cartographer* 10:110-122.

Resampling is automatically performed when using GRIDs with different cell sizes, and ArcGIS identifies the cell that has its center closest to the center of the output cell. The *nearest neighbor* method (left above) is most appropriate for discrete (nominal) data (e.g., land use classes). For continuous data, the *bilinear interpolation* method (center above) is recommended, which uses the weighted distance average of the four nearest input cells. The *cubic convolution* method (right above) is similar to the bilinear, but uses the 16 nearest cells and produces the smoothest output.

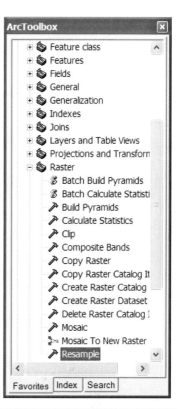

Resampling is also used during display of GRIDs in ArcMap, and nearest neighbor is the default method. Using this method, the cell boundaries are clearly visible (left). When representing a continuous variable (e.g., elevation), it may make sense to change the display

methodology to show a smoother surface by changing the resampling method to bilinear (right) or cubic convolution.

Single-layer analysis

CHAPTER 10   # *Dual-layer analysis*

10.1 Overview

The ability to overlay and compare two or more maps is one of the most powerful analytical features found in a GIS. There are three broad classes of analysis that involve two (or more) maps. The first is *selection*, where the selected features of one layer are used to select features of another layer. *Select by location* was covered in the chapter on spatial queries (Chapter 5) so it will not be discussed further in this chapter. A second type of analysis is *overlay*, where a new layer is generated by performing an overlay operation on two input layers. This type of analysis is probably the premier example of GIS analysis and is discussed in detail below. Related to overlay analysis are spatial join operations, which join the attributes of one feature layer to another based on spatial relationships between the layers' features. More complex models are described in the next chapter.

10.2 Overlay analysis

The idea of conducting an analysis by overlaying two or more maps has no doubt been around for some time. During the American Revolution, General George Washington employed a French cartographer who used hinged overlays to examine the location of Washington's troops in relationship to General Cornwallis' troops.[1] Another example is Dr. John Snow's use of overlay mapping to investigate the cause of cholera, pioneering the field of epidemiology. Dr. Snow superimposed a map of cholera deaths in central London in relation to water pumps, thereby determining the Broad Street pump was the likely source of the 1854 outbreak.[2] An early use of overlays to analyze landscapes was Warren Manning's study of the town of Billerica, Massachusetts in 1912.[3] And perhaps the most widely recognized example of work using overlay analysis is Ian McHarg's classic book *Design with Nature*.[4]

Today, computer technology enables overlay analysis to be conducted rapidly for large study areas that consider many input factors. To enable layers to be overlaid reliably, they first must be georeferenced so that feature geometry is coincident. Note that although layers may appear to line up properly in the display, due to the approximations made by on-the-fly projection, the layers should be in the same coordinate system for the most accurate results.

There are a variety of overlay operations available, and a useful way to organize the possible overlay combinations is to examine which operations can be employed given two input layer types (e.g., point, line, polygon features and raster) (Table 10.1). There are three ways layers can be overlaid, and these can be differentiated based on how the features and attributes are modified (or not) as a result of the overlay process.

TABLE 10.1. Common overlay analyses involving two layers.

From type	On Point	On Line	On/in Polygon	Raster
Point	Merge	Cut lines	Clip/Erase	
Line		Merge	Clip/Erase Intersect Union	
Polygon	Clip/Erase	Clip/Erase	Clip/Erase Intersect Merge Union	
Raster				Map Algebra

1. Wikle, T.A. 1991. Computers, maps, and geographic information systems. *National Forum* (Summer): 37-39.
2. Gilbert, E.W. 1958. Pioneer maps of health and disease in England. *Geographical Journal* 124: 172-183.
3. Steinitz, C., P. Parker, and L. Jordan. 1976. Hand-drawn overlays: Their history and prospective uses. *Landscape Architecture* 56(4):146-157.
4. McHarg, I. 1969. *Design with Nature*. Doubleday/Natural History Press: New York, NY.

First, some overlay operations change the feature geometry of one layer on the basis of another layer, but the attributes of the first layer are not modified. For example, a polygon feature dataset that represents public lands could be used to *clip* or remove the portions of land cover polygons that overlap public lands. Note that an attribute that is based on a feature's geometry (e.g., area, length, compactness, etc.) needs to be re-calculated because the feature geometry has changed. Second, some overlay operations simply append the attributes of one layer based on another. For example, the attributes of a polygon feature dataset (e.g., land cover types) could be joined to the attribute table of a point feature dataset (e.g., soil sample locations), solely on the basis of location. This process is called *spatial join*. Third, some operations cause both feature geometry and attributes to be changed in the output layer (e.g., union). Table 10.2 shows a diagram of these various operations.

10.2.1 Clip

The *clip* operation uses one input layer to change the feature geometry of a second layer. This process works like a cookie cutter and creates a new layer by clipping the first layer, called the *input layer*, with a *clip layer* so that features from the input layer that fall outside of the clip layer are cut away or removed. This operation is used to clip portions of layers that fall outside of a study boundary, thus reducing the size of the original dataset. Another common use of clip is in combination with buffering. For example, to find the land cover types that are within 1 km of a stream, the stream layer would first be buffered by 1 km and then used to clip out the features from the land cover layer. Note that although the input layer can be any feature type (e.g., point, line, or polygon), the clip layer must be a polygon feature type. The input features are clipped so that only those features that are located inside the clip layer are exported to the output layer. As a result, an attribute that is based on feature geometry (e.g., area, length, etc.) should be re-calculated. The attributes of the output layer are the same as the input layer (not the clip layer). Clip uses only the selected features from both the input and clip layer.

TABLE 10.2. Examples of clip, intersect, and union overlay types.

Type	Input layers	Output layer
Clip The output layer's attribute table contains only attributes from the input layer		

Overlay analysis

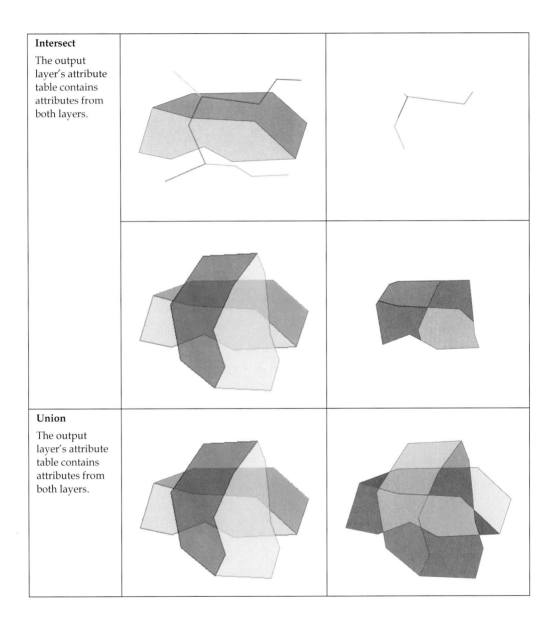

| **Intersect** The output layer's attribute table contains attributes from both layers. | | |

| **Union** The output layer's attribute table contains attributes from both layers. | | |

Although clip retains the features that are inside the clip features (i.e. inclusive), sometimes you may want to remove or *erase* the features that are inside the overlapping portion. Unfortunately, there is not an Erase tool that provides an erase operation. However, for most cases (where the spatial extent of both layers is the same), an erase-like operation using clip can be conducted by first selecting the features *outside* the chosen area in the clip layer and then switching the selected feature set in the clip layer.

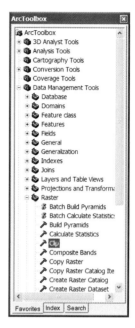

> ### *Clipping (or erasing) features*
>
> 1. Select the desired features to be clipped in the Input layer.
>
> 2. Select the desired features to form the clip area.
>
> 3. Select from ArcToolbox: Analysis Tools -> Extract -> Clip...

A raster dataset can be clipped as well using the Raster tools in Data Management.

10.2.2 *Intersect*

The *intersect* operation is similar to clip in that they both preserve only those features within the spatial extent common to both layers (and those features that are selected). It is different from clip, however, in two ways. First, intersect computes the geometric intersection of the *input* layer and the *overlay layer*. The resulting features and attributes of both are then added to a new dataset.

The features of the *input* layer (line or polygon feature type) are overlaid on the *overlay* layer (polygon only). The *output* layer's attribute table will contain fields from both layers but will be the same feature type as the *input* layer (line or polygon). Second, all of the polygon boundaries (not just the outside ones) are intersected with the feature geometry of the input layer. In this way, boundaries that cross one another are "cut" at their intersection.

Intersecting features

1. Select the desired features to be intersected in the Input layer.

2. Select the desired features to form the Overlay layer.

3. Select from ArcToolbox: Analysis Tools -> Overlay -> Intersect.

Raster datasets also can be combined in such a way that simulates the intersect operation for feature data. The *Combine* function combines two or more raster layers on a cell-by-cell basis and is called in the Raster Calculator using:

Combine ([G1], [G2])

Unique combinations of the input values are given a unique index value, which is assigned to the cells of the output layer. The original value of the input raster dataset is added to the attribute table, one field per input layer (Figure 10.1).

GIS Concepts and ArcGIS Methods

Overlay analysis

FIGURE 10.1. Example of combine function, illustrating *Combine ([G1], [G2])*. Combining G1 (left) with G2 (left center) creates a new GRID (right center) with values indexing unique combinations of G1 and G2. The attribute table (right) has fields with original values of G1 and G2.

										Value	G1	G2
1	2		1	1		1	2		1	1	1
3			3	2		3			2	2	1
									3	3	3

10.2.3 Union

Like the intersect operation, *union* creates a new layer by computing the geometric intersection of features from the *input layer* and the *overlay layer*. The resulting features and the attributes from both layers are added to the new dataset. Union differs from intersect by including features found in the spatial extent of either layer, including those features that may not have overlapped the spatial extent of the other layer (Figure 10.2).

GIS Concepts and ArcGIS Methods   355

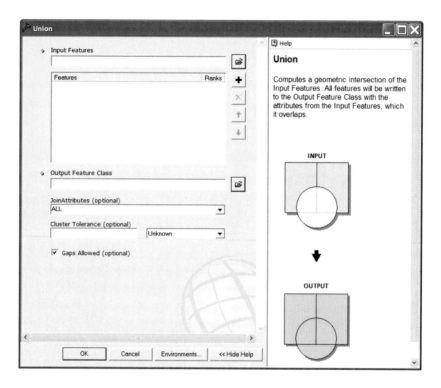

FIGURE 10.2. The difference between intersect and union.

10.2.4 Merge

Although merge is not really considered to be one of the primary overlay operations, it is described here because of its popularity. The *merge* operation combines two or more layers of the same feature type into a single layer that contains all the features from all the input layers. The main intent of this function is to merge a series of adjacent layers that were created as a series of tiles (e.g., quadsheets). This operation, however, does not determine if features touch at the boundary or if features cross lines, it simply merges all the features from the input layers into a new layer. That is, merge does not enforce planar topology, so it does not break features into smaller features if a crossing is found.

A common use of the merge operation is to reconcile GPS points that were collected in two different UTM zones, for example. First, the points are separated by zone into separate layers. Next, the points are projected into a single zone, creating a layer for each zone. Finally, merge is used to combine the reprojected points back into a single layer. A secondary use of this function is to merge layers with features that are spatially coincident, so that linear and polygon features may overlap or cross one another. If the features are points, then merging two layers is a simple way of updating a dataset with more recent information.

Two or more raster datasets (e.g., G1, G2, and G3) can also be merged together using the *Merge* function in the Raster Calculator:

Merge ([G1], [G2], [G3])

If cells overlap, then the priority is determined by the input order (e.g., first G1, then G2, etc.). For raster datasets that represent continuous data, a second function, *mosaic*, is available that averages overlapping cells to create a smooth transition:

Mosaic ([G1], [G2], [G3])

Mosaic uses a weighted average to smooth the cell values at the edges.[5]

---

5. The smoothing is specified by a Hermite Cubic function. See: Franke, R. 1982. Smooth interpolation of scattered data by local thin plate splines. *Computer & Mathematics with Applications* 8(4): 273-281.

10.3 Join by location

A special type of overlay analysis is the ability to associate two layers based on the relationships between their feature locations — without modifying feature geometry — to gain access to attribute information. The *join by location* operation (a.k.a. spatial join) uses relationships between the features in two layers to append the attributes of a layer onto a second layer.

This type of join differs from joining attribute tables via a common field in two important ways. First, joining tables assumes a one-to-one or many-to-one relationship, whereas spatial join provides the means to deal with a one-to-many join. That is, imagine we wanted to know about the cities (points) that are found within a particular county, for example: How many cities are there? What is their average population? What is the largest city's population? In this example, there is one county, but many cities. One-to-many relationships can be handled by either summarizing the *many* aspect (e.g., cities) through some statistic (e.g., average, min, max, etc.) or by selecting only the closest one (or if there are ties, the first one processed is selected). In the latter case, we are using distance as a selection criteria and so a *distance field* is added to the table. A second way spatial join differs is that it creates a new layer with the attributes appended to the new table, rather than being temporarily joined through a dynamic link between two tables. Note that spatial join works on all the features in both layers, not the selected set.

There are many types of relationships or spatial association between features — recall from Chapter 1 the list of *spatial relations*: equivalent, partially equivalent (i.e. overlap), contained, adjacent, or disjoint. The spatial join interface in ArcMap implements only the more common types of relations, though there still is an impressive variety available (Table 10.3). There are three ways to group these methods that cut across feature types: those that find features that are inside a polygon, features that intersect, and the nearest feature.

TABLE 10.3. Spatial join methods organized by feature type.

From type	To point	To line	To polygon
Point	Summarize (closest) Closest (w/distance)	Summarize (intersected or closest) Closest (w/distance)	Summarize (fall inside) Closest (w/distance, if inside=0)
Line	Summarize (intersects) Closest (w/distance)	Summarize (intersected) Part of	Summarize (intersect) Closest (w/distance, if inside=0)
Polygon	Falls inside Closest to (w/distance, if inside = 0)	Summarize (intersected) Completely inside Closest (w/distance)	Summarize (intersect) Completely inside

10.3.1 Nearest feature

The nearest feature method adds a distance field to the attribute table. For example, if you wanted to answer the question; which city is closest to each summit (hill or mountain), then the city layer is joined by location to a summit layer, and we can see that Boulder Mountain is about 8 km (straight-line distance) to the city of Boulder, Colorado (right). Note that if a feature falls on or inside another feature, the distance will be 0. If two or more features have the same distance, the first feature processed will be used to join the attribute data. The nearest or closest feature

can be determined for all but the polygon-to-polygon spatial join.

10.3.2 Intersecting a feature

Another way to examine the relationship between two features is to examine if they intersect. For example, if you wanted to determine the average traffic volume along a stretch of highway, then a layer with point events that have the traffic count could be joined to a layer (line feature) representing the stretch of highway of interest. For each feature (e.g., highways), spatial join finds those features that intersect it. Then, the selected features are summarized to provide the average traffic volume, for example.

10.3.3 Inside a polygon

Perhaps the most common use of spatial join is to find features that fall within a polygon feature. Two of the more common GIS operations are *point in polygon* and *line in polygon* operations. For example, joining by location would be used if you wanted to determine the number of mountains over 3,000 m located in each county of Colorado. If a feature falls within more than one feature (e.g., Lake Tahoe falls in five counties), then the first feature to be processed is used.

Joining by location

1. In ArcMap, right-click on the desired feature layer that another layer's attributes are to be joined to, and select Joins and relates -> Join....

2. At the top drop-down box, select *join data from another layer based on spatial location*.

3. Select the layer to join to this layer.

4. Select the type of join, to either summarize (top) or choose closest (bottom).

5. Specify the output filename and location.

6. Click OK.

Spatial modeling and geoprocessing

11.1 Overview

In this chapter we synthesize what we have learned in the preceeding chapters within the context of building spatial models using Geoprocessing. Modeling as a process has been likened to "peeling back the layers of an onion," where a problem is explored iteratively, typically building on previous models and incorporating additional assumptions or exploring other details. But parsimony should reign when modeling -- it is far too easy to get carried away building more and more complicated (not complex!) models. So, the question is typically raised: how do you know when you have the right model?

It is wise to approach modeling from the perspective that "all models are wrong, but some are useful." Just as the cartographers' mantra in designing maps (what is the purpose of the map), it all hinges on a clear understanding and statement of the purpose of a model. The Geoprocessing tools provided in ArcGIS enable you to easily build models. But remember, just because you *can* doesn't mean you *should*.

Below some basic modeling concepts and ways to represent models will be described. This is followed by a detailed illustration of iterative modeling using an example of modeling accessibility. The basics of the Model Builder are described, followed by a primer of Python and how to write scripts that access ArcGIS.

11.2 Modeling concepts

Why use and build a model? Because a model assists you in thinking about conceptual issues -- about what factors are important, about what assumptions are being made. Too often (especially in GIS), the tendency is to get bogged down in some obscure detail (or in the syntax), that is, not seeing the forest for the trees. Building a model also (typically) forces you to generate an explicit representation of your logical thought process. This is useful to be clear when sharing with others what your model does and how it works. It is also extremely valuable as a way to self-document your work, so that in a few days, weeks, months or even years you can come back to your work and be rapidly productive. This also allows you to leverage your own work -- if you've built a model once, why build it again?

Often a number of maps need to be manipulated and processed to answer a question. Even with seemingly simple models, the logic or work flow can get quite confusing, so that it quickly becomes hard to remember which layer was used to do what when! In a full-fledged *suitability analysis*, the logic can become quite involved indeed. Various means to conceptualize and document the logical flow of a model have been developed, but perhaps the most enduring has been the *flow chart*, which is described below. There are an infinite number of ways to combine various maps to conduct an analysis, but typically these fall within a couple of types: binary, arithmetic, and weighted arithmetic.We'll examine these approaches first, and then dive into a description of how to build models in the Model Builder application.

11.2.1 Flow charts

Diagrams have long been used to depict the flow of logic or steps followed in an analysis. Flow charts are important not only to communicate an idea, but also in that the very act of drawing and diagramming helps us to think about a problem.[1] An early example (1962) of using a flow chart to depict an overlay analysis is Alexander and Mannheim's procedural tree diagram that describes the logical framework and explicit weighting used in their analysis of highway routing.[2]

Although modeling is often an unorganized, ad-hoc process, it is best to think of it as consisting of three stages (Table 11.1). First, in the *development stage* a conceptual model is

1. Edwards, B. 1979. *Drawing on the Right Side of the Brain: a course in enhancing creativity and artistic confidence*. Los Angles: J. P. Tarcher.
2. Alexander, C. and M.L. Manheim.1962. *The Use of Diagrams in Highway Route Location*. Civil Engineering Systems Laboratory, Massachusetts Institute of Technology. Research Report R62-3.

developed that represents the basic structure and assumptions of a particular model. This helps you to create a road map so that you can remain focused and not "lose the forest for the trees." Second, the conceptual model is formalized during the *implementation stage*. At this point it is time to roll up your sleeves and begin to use ArcGIS to implement the conceptual model. Third, the *use stage* occurs when the model is used, either immediately after creating it or perhaps by another person.[3] However, modeling is best seen as an iterative process, where the understanding of a problem is gained by conceptualizing a system, implementing a model, and exploring the behavior of the model under different assumptions. Ideally, these stages of modeling can be integrated with a flow chart that provides, as Joe Berry has written in his *Beyond Mapping* column: "...a succinct expression of a model's logic and an iterative mechanism to execute the model under various interpretations."[4]

A simple flow chart technique to diagram GIS models represents a *dataset* (e.g., an existing map layer) with a rectangle, a *derived dataset* (e.g., new map layer) created in the model with a smoothed rectangle, and a *function* (e.g., process or operation) with an oval. *Models* or components of models are represented by a circle. The *data flow* between these objects is represented by *connectors* (arrows) between data and function objects. Although a number of different flow charting software programs can be used, a simple alternative is to use *AutoShapes* in Microsoft Excel or PowerPoint.

TABLE 11.1. Stages in diagramming a flowchart. Note that these are represented as linear steps, but ideally modeling is an iterative process.

Stage	Comments
I. Conceptualize	1. Start at the end — identify the finished map layer or product and place a data object on the right of the diagram.
	2. Identify the main datasets needed to create the desired product. Place additional source data objects on the left side of the diagram.
	3. Insert main processes needed to create datasets.
	4. Connect data objects to processes with connectors.

3. Theobald, D.M. 1998. A visual programming environment for spatial modeling: The ArcView Spatial Modeler extension. *Proceedings of the ESRI User Conference '98*, San Diego, CA. http://gis.esri.com/library/userconf/proc98/PROCEED/TO150/PAP1010/P101.HTM.

4. Berry, J. 1993. Moving toward a humane GIS. *GeoWorld*. Pg. 22.

TABLE 11.1. Stages in diagramming a flowchart. Note that these are represented as linear steps, but ideally modeling is an iterative process.

II. Implement	1. Start at the beginning—add the necessary source datasets to an ArcMap document.
	2. Create each derivative dataset using the specified process. Often there will be details that need to be worked out to accomplish the function.
	3. Make sure that the details needed to implement a process are recorded and that the flowchart is updated to reflect major changes.
III. Use	1. Examine the flowchart—does it describe the essential characteristics of the model? Separate questions or concerns about the factors considered and assumptions used from basic understanding of the model.
	2. Identify the factors and parameters that are most influential in the model.
	3. Update the flowchart based on feedback about the diagram and through experience of using the model.

An early effort to develop a diagram-based interface that provided dynamic modeling abilities within a spatial framework was the Environmental Modeling Language written in the Extend program (Figure 11.1).[5] Within commercial GIS, flowchart diagrams have been used sparingly, most notably ERDAS's IMAGINE Model Maker. Clark Lab's Idrisi32 Macro Modeler provides a diagram-based modeling environment that allows dynamic modeling. For ESRI GIS products, the *Spatial Modeler* extension for ArcView v3.x GIS was an early suggestion of how a model-building environment might function within the ArcView v3.x GIS environment.[6] And of course ESRI has fully developed the *Model Builder* application within the Geoprocessing framework of ArcGIS. Later in this chapter the Model Builder application for ArcGIS is described in detail. But first, let's investigate two main types of models: boolean and arithmetic.

5. Theobald, D.M. and M. Gross. 1994. EML: A modeling environment for exploring landscape dynamics. *Computers, Environmental, and Urban Systems* 18(3): 193-204. This is an old-time screen snapshot (literally a photo of the CRT monitor)!

6. Theobald, D.M. 1998. A visual programming environment for spatial modeling: The ArcView Spatial Modeler extension. *Proceedings of the ESRI User Conference '98*, San Diego, CA. http://gis.esri.com/library/userconf/proc98/PROCEED/TO150/PAP1010/P101.HTM.

FIGURE 11.1. A dynamic model flowchart describing a fire spread model using the Environmental Modeling Language.

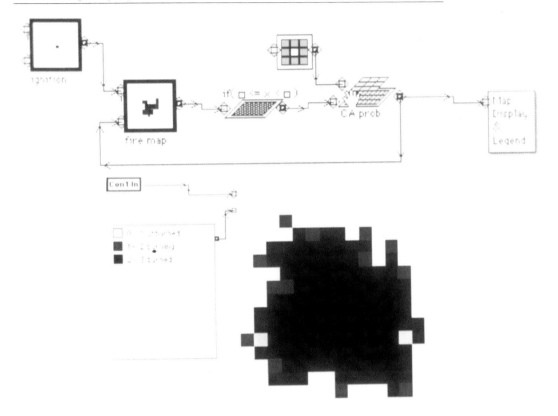

11.2.2 Boolean model

Oftentimes suitability models are expressed using Boolean logic. That is, a number of factors are considered, where each factor can be expressed in terms of *Boolean logic* and converted into a binary map. Boolean models are attractive because they are simple, and it is easy to convert laws or regulations that are expressed in terms of a condition to a binary map. Each of the factors are mapped as yes/no, binary maps, and in the end, the location that satisfies all the conditions comes through. Note that typically a Boolean model is created using raster datasets, where GRID values are 0 or 1 or NoData or 1. However, a Boolean model can also be created using feature datasets, where the logical constraints are implemented through a series of clips or a series of unions with a final attribute query after all layers are combined.

The formula to compute a Boolean model (M_B) is expressed as:

$$M_B = \prod_{i=1}^{m} X_i$$

where pi (Π) denotes that the values X_i in the m input maps (or factors) should be multiplied together.

For example, imagine that a suitable location for a new landfill needs to be found near your town. Typically, a number of factors are considered — for simplicity we'll just consider three here: permeability of surficial geology, proximity to town, and critical wildlife habitat (Figure 11.2). Note, however, that this method does not differentiate the relative quality of different locations that meet the initial criteria. The sensitivity of the model to a given assumption can be tested by bracketing a parameter — that is, specifying a slightly lower and higher value (e g., distance from town > 2 km, >5 km, and >10km) — and re-running the model with the different parameters. A *sensitivity analysis* is helpful to understand how variable the results are given different assumptions. If the results vary to a large degree with different values of a particular parameter, then perhaps more resources (i.e., time, money, effort) should be spent to redefine the estimate of the parameter.

FIGURE 11.2. Flowchart of a Boolean logic model identifying suitable landfill sites. Three layers of evidence are considered.

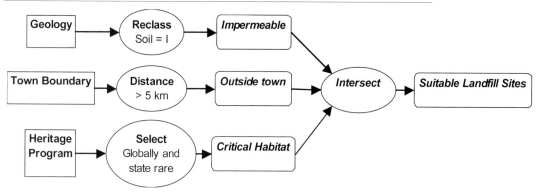

One of the more powerful aspects of using Map Algebra is the ease with which models can be created. For instance, the suitable landfill site model above could be expressed as a series of expressions:

[imperm] = con([geology] == 1, 1, 0)

[out_town] = con (EucDistance([town_bnd]) > 5000, 1, 0)

[critical_hab] = con ([heritage] > 2, 1, 0)

[suitable] = ([imperm] * [out_town] * [critical_hab])

11.2.3 Arithmetic model

A popular method of combining a number of inputs is to score each factor (represented by a layer) and then total the scores. This general model is called the *indexed model* (a.k.a. indexed or arithmetic overlay). The indexed model (M_I) is expressed as:

$$M_I = \sum_{i=1}^{m} X_i$$

where X_i contains the values (in a map). Note that the various factors should have values with similar ranges, otherwise the relative importance between factors becomes difficult to distinguish from the relative importance within a factor. That is, if the Factor A values range from 0 to 10 and Factor B values range from 0 to 20, then the output is biased strongly towards Factor B. The indexed model is based on two important assumptions. First, the additional value of a factor is assumed to increase linearly. That is, the increase in value stepping from 0 to 1 is the same as going from 4 to 5. Second, no interaction between factors is assumed; that is, two factors should not be highly correlated. If there is strong correlation, then locations that are represented by those factors may have an overly strong bias.

Let's examine how an example GIS application can be characterized as an arithmetic model. Scientists at the Wilderness Society mapped *wildness* in the coterminous United States based on the degree of freedom and naturalness.[7] Factors that contribute to freedom are opportunities for solitude, the remoteness of land from mechanical devices, and the degree to which natural processes are left uncontrolled by humans (e.g., no fire suppression). Factors that contribute to naturalness include the degree or level of natural composition, the absence of artificial human structures (e.g., buildings), and the level of pollution. The flowcharts in Figures 11.3, 11.4, and 11.5 describe the model and its parameters, and the final map of wildness is shown in Figure 11.6.

---

7. Aplet, G., J. Thomson, and M. Wilbert. 2000. Indicators of wildness: Using attributes of the land to assess the context of wilderness. In: *Proceedings: Wilderness Science in a Time of Change*. Cole, D.N. and S.F. McCool (eds). U.S. Department of Agriculture, Forest Service, Rocky Mountain Research Station. Also available at: http://www.wilderness.org/wild/network/mapping_wildness.pdf

FIGURE 11.3. Flowchart of *freedom* factors.

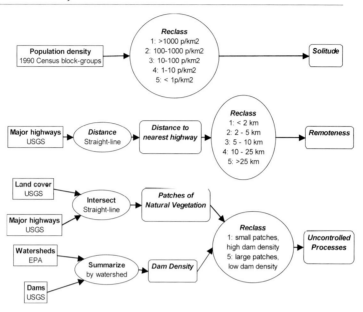

FIGURE 11.4. Flowchart of *naturalness* factors.

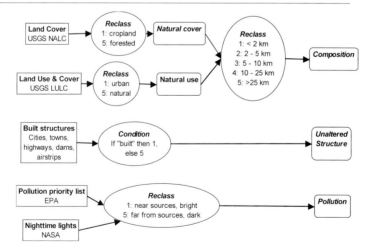

FIGURE 11.5. Flowchart of a wildness model—combining freedom and naturalness (from Figures 10.3 and 10.4).

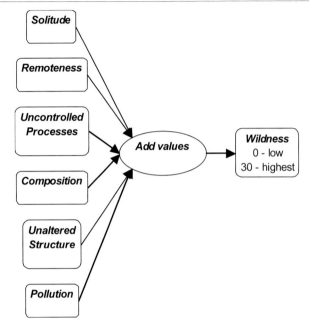

FIGURE 11.6. Final map showing areas of high (blue) and low wildness values (red).

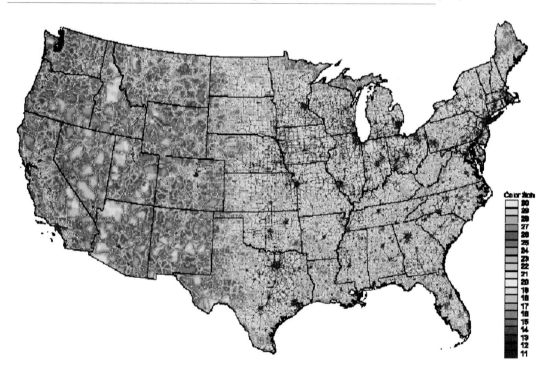

11.2.4 *Weighted arithmetic model*

An extension of the arithmetic model is to weight the relative importance of each factor to reflect the importance placed on each factor by decision makers. This general model is called the *weighted arithmetic model (WA)* (a.k.a. weighted linear combination).[8] The WA model (M_W) is expressed as:

$$M_W = \sum_{i=1}^{m} w_i X_i$$

where X_i contains the values (in a map) and w_i is the weight for factor (map) i. Note that the weights must be normalized so that they sum to 1. The values mapped in each factor should also be normalized, preferably so they range from 0.0 to 1.0 (or 0 to 100).

8. Malczewski, J. 1999. *GIS and multicriteria decision analysis*. John Wiley & Sons.

Again, let's examine an application that has used the weighted arithmetic model approach. A common task in natural resource management is to inventory and prioritize lands based on biological significance and risk of development. The goal of the Lower Gunnison River Basin Conservation Lands Inventory project (completed in 2001) was to identify the portions of the riparian corridor that are valuable for preservation and/or suitable along the Lower Gunnison River and its near tributaries.[9] Four primary factors or conservation criteria were identified: riparian habitat condition, development pressure, level of surrounding protection, and agricultural land. Various GIS data layers were used to represent these factors (Figure 11.7).[10] This type of problem is considered to be a multi-criteria decisionmaking problem[11] and the challenge is to combine multiple factors, including biological significance, threats by development, and land-owner willingness into a single indicator.

In addition, weights were determined through interviews of stakeholders. Stakeholders were interviewed individually to determine their individual weightings, and those were averaged to produce final weights. A useful technique to develop the weights is through a pairwise comparison of the criteria using the *Analytical Hierarchy Process*.[12] Decisionmakers examine pairwise comparisons of all factors and then use a simple mathematical formula to compute the weights. Not only does the process result in weights that reflect the expert opinions of decisionmakers, it helps to identify potential factors that are important that were not considered, and potential factors that were thought to be important but were not. Stakeholders were presented with a series of maps showing each factor and then were asked to estimate the relative importance of each pair of factors by filling out a simple score sheet. The weights were then computed from a matrix of values and a consistency indicator was generated to determine the probability that the matrix ratings were randomly generated.[13] This is useful to identify the degree of agreement and dissension among stakeholders. The weights were as follows: riparian habitat condition = 0.25; development pressure = 0.33; level of surrounding protection = 0.17; and prime agricultural lands = 0.25. Note also that weights were developed by biologists to create the riparian habitat condition map.

9. Molacek, R. 2001. *Lower Gunnison River Basin Conservation Lands Inventory.* Report prepared by Delta Soil Conservation District, Delta, Colorado.
10. Theobald, D.M. 2001. *Documentation of methods to produce factor maps for the Lower Gunnison Basin Conservation Lands Inventory.* Report for the Delta Soil Conservation District, Colorado. 24 August. 4 pages.
11. Carver, S.J. 1991. Integrating multi-criteria evaluation with geographical information systems. *International Journal of Geographical Information Systems* 5(3): 321-339.
12. Saaty, T.L. 1977. A scaling method for priorities in hierarchical structures. *Journal of Mathematical Psychology* 15: 234-291.
13. There are numerous software decision support packages that implement AHP, including: Criterium® Decision Plus®, available as a student version through www.infoharvest.com.

FIGURE 11.7. **Flowchart of a conservation prioritization model for the Lower Gunnison Basin.**

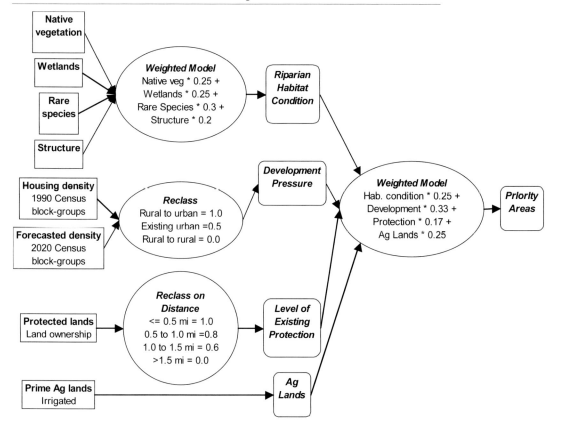

11.3 Evolution of user interfaces in GIS

I began this book with a brief discussion of the evolution of GIS interfaces, from command-line to GUI-based, and here I will end it by returning to that topic. As we have seen, a number of innovations have been developed with ArcGIS, notable among these are the close integration of ArcGIS with Internet mapping and mapping services and the seamless support for meta-data—both innovations will likely change the way GIS data is developed and shared. Yet the way we go about *doing* GIS has remained more or less the same over the past two or three decades. Recently, though there have been significant ways in which this has been improved.

GUI-based interfaces are powerful ways to interact with GIS data and functionality, in particular they allow us to see the data we are working with and manipulate it readily. No wonder the artist in us all is immensely satisfied with the immediate visual stimulation and gratification provided by GUI interfaces in ArcGIS. However, the careful, practical scientist in us all is left grimacing at the lack of documentation of the process. That is, GUI interfaces are notoriously poor at capturing the steps taken to create a map and conduct an analysis in an automated fashion. As a result, creating a map or conducting an analysis once is fun, but doing it twice or more is a chore. And we all have experienced (or will!) that painful realization, when revisiting a map or model a month or two later, that we should have kept better notes about what we did.

So, what does process documentation have to do with modeling and flowcharts? A lot! Typically, modeling is considered to be a purposeful exercise, as I portrayed in the three modeling stages discussed earlier, where the logical framework of a model is carefully constructed. In addition, one might consider the ad hoc tinkering with a GUI as a model, albeit a messy one. In fact, after trimming away the dead-ends and irrelevant steps of a GUI-based work session, what is left at the end of process is the beginnings of a model that can be formalized for repetitive use.[14] The next step in interface design is to simply formalize this model through a flowchart. In this way, a flowchart could be constructed either purposefully through a flowchart interface (e.g., the Model Builder extension), or automatically generated by ArcGIS as one is working through the GUI interface.

Another important advancement of GIS modeling is minimizing the distinction between *doing* GIS from *using* the results of GIS. That is, today a model is constructed and analysis is done typically at a separate time and place from where the information will be used. A vast unrealized opportunity exists to situate GIS analysis directly within the decisionmaking context for which it is needed. Recent interactive whiteboard technology — so called "smart boards" — has developed to enable GIS use in public participatory situations. Again, flowcharts will likely be central to actively engaging a whole new set of users of GIS. This will free GIS analysis from the confines of the office, allowing excursions into the board rooms, hearing rooms, and into the great outdoors.

---

14. Steadfast command-line users of workstation ArcInfo have long had this ability through *watch* files.

11.4 ModelBuilder

11.4.1 Basics of ModelBuilder

The *ModelBuilder* window is an interface that allows you to string a number of processes together to create a model. There are four general mechanical or implementational steps in creating a model in ModelBuilder: creating a new model, adding tools, saving a model, and running it.

First, create a new model. Because models are tied so closely to ArcToolbox, it is in the ArcToolbox window where a new model is created. Recall (from Chapter 1) that models are stored within toolboxes. To create a new toolbox, bring up the ArcToolbox window, then right-click on the root level "ArcToolbox" and select "New Toolbox." Rename it to something meaningful, perhaps "Z_MyModels".[15] Next, right-click on your new toolbox and

select New --> Model. This should bring up the ModelBuilder window (at right). Note that there are menus and toolbars above the model diagram or model display portion of the model.

Second, tools or processes are added to the model display window to construct a model. A model process contains three parts: the input variable(s), the tool itself, and the derived or output variables or datasets. Note that two or more processes are linked together by using the output of one tool as an input to another tool. An *input variable* is used to represent geographic data, such as a data layer that exists as a layer in ArcMap. A *value* is used to represent non-geographic data, such as scalar values that may set the cell size of a raster or cluster tolerance. To capture outputs, a *derived data* element represents output geographic data created by a tool. Other, non-geographic, data that are output from a tool are known as as *derived values*. In the example model above (Model A), *trails* is an input variable, *Line Density* is a tool, and *LinesDen_trai1* is derived data.

The easiest way to add a tool to your model is to locate the desired tool in the ArcToolbox window, then drag and drop it into the model. Open a tool by double-clicking on the tool. Next, specify the input datasets and/or values that are needed, and the output dataset (or value) name as well. (One quirky thing to watch out for -- sometimes when parameterizing a

---

15. It is helpful to keep the system tools separate from your tools, and because tools are sorted alphabetically, starting your tool with a "Z" will place them at the bottom.

tool requiring two or more inputs, a derived data element will be drawn directly and exactly on top of another.)

Third, save your model by clicking Model --> Save. Models are saved within a specific toolbox file (*.tbx). You can find the file location by right-clicking on a model, then select Properties.

Fourth, run your model. Click on the Model menu and select Run (or Run Entire Model). The *Run Entire Model* menu item forces ModelBuilder to run all processes within the model. The other option, *Run*, simply runs processes that have data that have been changed or updated, and so runs only the processes that are needed to generate the final output. Also note that you can run an individual process by right-clicking on a tool. There are numerous tools provided in ArcGIS, which are listed in Table 11.2.

Spatial modeling and geoprocessing

TABLE 11.2. Tools available in ArcToolbox, for ArcView and ArcINFO licenses.

Toolbox	ArcView	ArcInfo
Analysis	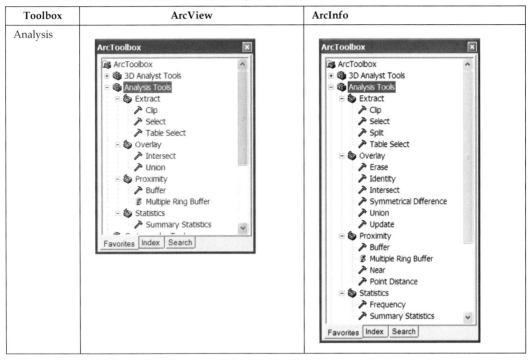	

TABLE 11.2. Tools available in ArcToolbox, for ArcView and ArcINFO licenses.

Toolbox	ArcView	ArcInfo
Cartography		

TABLE 11.2. Tools available in ArcToolbox, for ArcView and ArcINFO licenses.

Toolbox	ArcView	ArcInfo
Conversion		

TABLE 11.2. Tools available in ArcToolbox, for ArcView and ArcINFO licenses.

Toolbox	ArcView	ArcInfo
Coverage - analysis		

TABLE 11.2. Tools available in ArcToolbox, for ArcView and ArcINFO licenses.

Toolbox	ArcView	ArcInfo
Coverage - conversion		

TABLE 11.2. Tools available in ArcToolbox, for ArcView and ArcINFO licenses.

Toolbox	ArcView	ArcInfo
Coverage - data management		

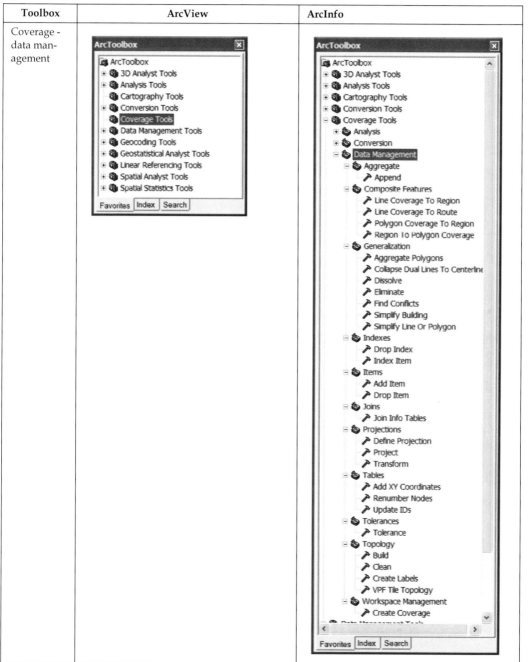

TABLE 11.2. Tools available in ArcToolbox, for ArcView and ArcINFO licenses.

Toolbox	ArcView	ArcInfo
Data management	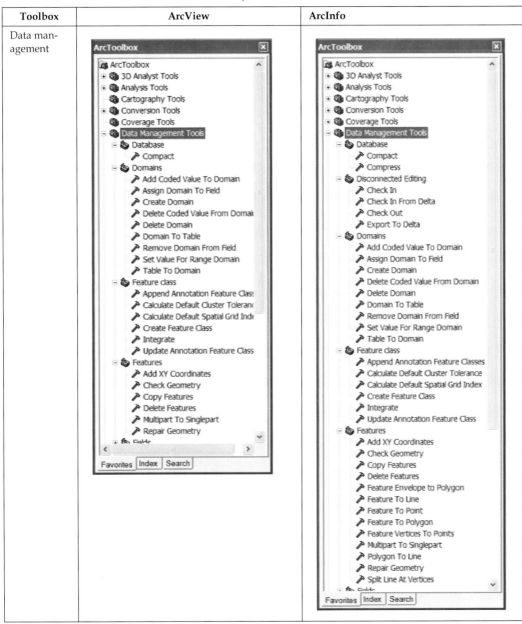	

TABLE 11.2. Tools available in ArcToolbox, for ArcView and ArcINFO licenses.

Toolbox	ArcView	ArcInfo

Data management (cont.)	**ArcToolbox**
	ArcToolbox
	⊞ 3D Analyst Tools
	⊞ Analysis Tools
	Cartography Tools
	⊞ Conversion Tools
	Coverage Tools
	⊟ **Data Management Tools**
	  ⊞ Database
	  ⊞ Domains
	  ⊞ Feature class
	  ⊞ Features
	  ⊟ Fields
	      Add Field
	      Assign Default To Field
	      Calculate Field
	      Delete Field
	  ⊟ General
	      Append
	      Copy
	      Delete
	      Merge
	      Rename
	      Select Data
	  ⊟ Generalization
	      Dissolve
	  ⊟ Indexes
	      Add Attribute Index
	      Add Spatial Index
	      Remove Attribute Index
	      Remove Spatial Index
	  ⊟ Joins
	      Add Join
	      Remove Join
	  ⊟ Layers and Table Views
	      Make Feature Layer
	      Make Query Table
	      Make Raster Catalog Layer
	      Make Raster Layer
	      Make Table View
	      Make XY Event Layer
	      Save To Layer File
	      Select Layer By Attribute
	      Select Layer By Location
	
	Favorites | Index | Search
		ArcToolbox
		⊞ 3D Analyst Tools
		⊞ Analysis Tools
		⊞ Cartography Tools
		⊞ Conversion Tools
		⊞ Coverage Tools
		⊟ **Data Management Tools**
		  ⊞ Database
		  ⊞ Disconnected Editing
		  ⊞ Domains
		  ⊞ Feature class
		  ⊞ Features
		  ⊟ Fields
		      Add Field
		      Assign Default To Field
		      Calculate Field
		      Delete Field
		  ⊟ General
		      Append
		      Copy
		      Delete
		      Merge
		      Rename
		      Select Data
		  ⊟ Generalization
		      Dissolve
		      Eliminate
		      Simplify Line
		      Smooth Line
		  ⊟ Indexes
		      Add Attribute Index
		      Add Spatial Index
		      Remove Attribute Index
		      Remove Spatial Index
		  ⊟ Joins
		      Add Join
		      Remove Join
		  ⊟ Layers and Table Views
		      Make Feature Layer
		      Make Query Table
		      Make Raster Catalog Layer
		      Make Raster Layer
		      Make Table View
		      Make XY Event Layer
		      Save To Layer File
		      Select Layer By Attribute
		      Select Layer By Location
		      Projections and Transformations
		
		Favorites | Index | Search

TABLE 11.2. Tools available in ArcToolbox, for ArcView and ArcINFO licenses.

Toolbox	ArcView	ArcInfo
Data management (cont.)	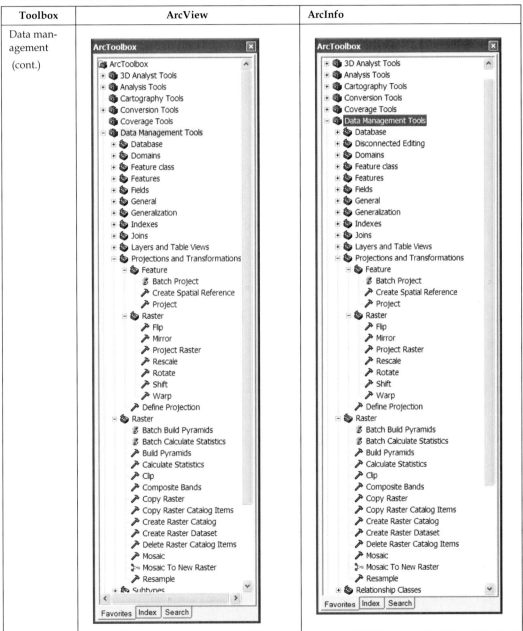	

TABLE 11.2. Tools available in ArcToolbox, for ArcView and ArcINFO licenses.

Toolbox	ArcView	ArcInfo
Data management (cont.)		

TABLE 11.2. Tools available in ArcToolbox, for ArcView and ArcINFO licenses.

Toolbox	ArcView	ArcInfo
Data man-agement (cont.)		

TABLE 11.2. Tools available in ArcToolbox, for ArcView and ArcINFO licenses.

Toolbox	ArcView	ArcInfo
Geocoding		
Geostatistical Analyst		

TABLE 11.2. Tools available in ArcToolbox, for ArcView and ArcINFO licenses.

Toolbox	ArcView	ArcInfo
Linear refer-encing		

TABLE 11.2. Tools available in ArcToolbox, for ArcView and ArcINFO licenses.

Toolbox	ArcView	ArcInfo
Spatial Statistics		

11.4.2 Modeling accessibility -- an illustration of iterative modeling

Imagine, if you will, that your task is to conduct a spatial analysis to better understand the influence of park visitors on the resources of a park. A typical way to visualize the effects of park visitation is the trail network (Figure 11.8).

We'll work through a series of steps or iterations of logic. At each step, we'll consider other models that we have already built and grab tools or process as needed. Often we'll just start another step by copying (and pasting) the model representing the previous step. Building up a model iteratively is a useful way to work because we can build on previous work, we keep track of our logic, we can backtrack in case we do not like the approach we took, and because we can automatically document our work. Also note that in this example a number of tools from raster-based analysis will be used, especially cost-weighted distance tools. Please refer back to the previous chapters for a more detailed discussion.

FIGURE 11.8. The Bear Lake corridor in Rocky Mountain National Park, Colorado, USA. The roads (solid black line), trails (dashed black line), and hydrology (blue lines) are displayed over a hillshade. (Note: Longs Peak is in the lower-right corner.

There are a couple of ways that trails are used to develop a measure of influence. One way is to compute the trail density using a moving window with a given radius, such as 1 km. **Model A** shows a single process, in which the *Line Density* tool (from Spatial Analyst) is used to compute the density from the input layer *trails*.

This initial model identifies locations with high average density of trails (dark purple at right), but does not differentiate locations that are further away from trail heads. Also, because the results are driven largely by the search radius, one must be careful to explicitly state, and provide a rationale for, the search radius.

Another common way is to compute the distance from roads and/or distance from trails. Here we could either generate multiple buffers at incremental distances (e.g., 100, 200, 300, 500, 1000 m, etc.). Instead, **Model B** shows a single-process model using the *Euclidean Distance* tool that allows us to model surfaces using raster datasets. The resulting raster (EucDisttrail1) has, for every cell, the straight line distance back to the nearest trail. Note that the optional Output Direction raster was not computed.

Here, areas in red are short distances, yellow is further away. Again, this gets at part of what we are wanting to measure, but does not distinguish the context of a trail or road. That is, all parts or segments of a trail are the same -- no matter if a portion is directly adjacent to a trailhead (typically with lots of people) or far away from a trailhead (less people). We need to think about the source from which people emanate -- the parking lots and trailheads.

So, a next step is to differentiate parts of trails that are close to the trailhead from those that are far away. Again, we'll use the Euclidean distance tool, but this time we'll compute distance from *trailheads*. To create **Model C**, we'll copy our previous model (Model B), then paste to create a new one and call it "Model C - Distance from trailheads". We simply need to change the input file to *trailheads* and change the output file name to *EucDist_ths*.

Now we can see the distance increasing away (red to yellow to blue) from the trailheads (shown by green circles). This is getting better, but does not differentiate where a trail is or is not.

Our next step is to constrain computation of distance from trailheads to stay *along* the trails. Here, we'll use a tool called *Cost Distance*, which computes distance by accumulating "costs" from specified starting locations. Again, we copy Model C, paste it back into the working toolbox, and rename it "**Model D - Dist from trailheads along trails**." Because we want to count distance along trails (and not off trail), we'll first convert trails to a raster with cell values of 1 (using the *Feature to Raster* tool and a field in *trails* that contains values of 1). The output *trails_r* is the cost-weight input into the Cost Distance tool.

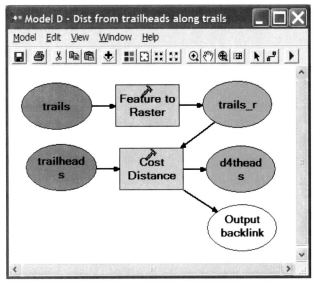

We'll use the trailhead locations as the starting location. The *Cost Distance* tool starts at a trailhead, then accumulates distances using a weight of 1. This will result in the Euclidean distance (because we are using a weight of 1), but it will be computed recognizing the bends and wiggles of the trails. (The tool automatically recognizes the cell size, so our output will be in map units, meters in this case). Be sure that the trailheads are "snapped" to the trails. That is, the trailheads, when converted to raster, need to touch the trails -- otherwise the distances from trailheads will be zero. One other technique (not used in this model) to ensure starting points link to the linework is to first buffer the starting points by some distance.

Because we constrained computation of distance along trails, we see the raster cells depicting distance just along the trails (zoomed in), with increasing distance away from the trailheads (red to orange to yellow). This is valuable because we know, for any location on a trail, the distance back to the closest trailhead.

But, we aren't representing anything about *off-trail* distances. That is, all locations off-trail are the same distance, which doesn't seem to get at what we are trying to measure.

Our next step is to compute the off-trail distance from trails, but this time we'll add the along-trail distance as well. This assumes that to get to a location X that is off-trail (e.g., one of the lakes), a person would hike along the trail to the closest point, then hike off-trail to get to location X. The way that we'll compute the closest along-trail distance is using the *Euclidean Allocation* tool. Here we have added the Euclidean Allocation tool -- but because the output of the Euclidean Distance tool is a floating-point raster (with real values), and the allocation tool requires an integer raster as input, we first use the *Int* tool to convert from a floating point to integer raster. To get to any location off-trail we assume that one must first hike along the trail to the closest point, so we add (using the *Plus* tool) the on-trail and off-trail distances to get a final, off-and-on trail distance raster (called *EucD_onofft*).

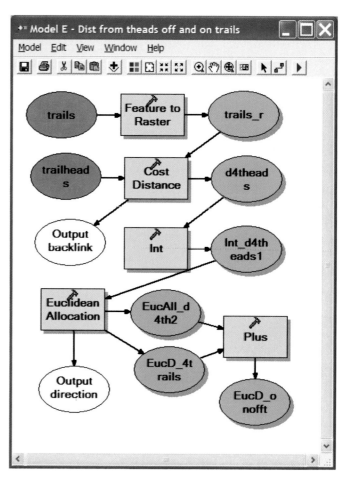

Now this is more like it! We now have, for every location in our study area, the distance back to the nearest trailhead. Note that there are some abrupt differences in distances (shown by non-continuous color gradations, e.g., red to yellow or yellow to blue). These are due to the allocation zones, which simply "grow" from the nearest trail.

This is all good and well and we are making good progress, but on deeper reflection, you might notice that here we have assumed that a person can walk anywhere off-trail with equal ease -- is this realistic? No...

So, our next step (and this is a big, powerful one!) is to adjust distances by the difficulty of moving across a given stretch (or cell). A primary factor influencing this is *slope*. For example, walking up a steep trail takes more energy and time than a flatter trail. We're computing one-way distance, so whether we are hiking up or down a steep slope does not matter too much at this point. First, *trails_r* is multiplied (using the *Times* tool) times the DEM to return a raster with elevation values found only on the trail (*dem_trails*). Then we use the *Slope* tool to compute the slope at each location along the trail (*slope_trail*). We then compute a function (using a map algebra statement in the *Single Output Map* tool) based on slope (see below). We'll use the equation outlined in Chapter 7 (Section 7.9.1.2) that relates a hiker's average velocity in relation to slope. The average velocity is 5.04 km per hour, for flat ground. We'll simply adjust the cost-weight so that distance travelled is expressed as effective distance, where locations that have steeper slopes require more time -- which we can also express as increased distance. In other words, if a person hiking on a steep slope moves at half the velocity as on a flat section, then it is the same as if he/she was walking twice as far on all flat ground. The *slope_wt* raster is then used as the cost-weights in the *Cost Distance* tool.

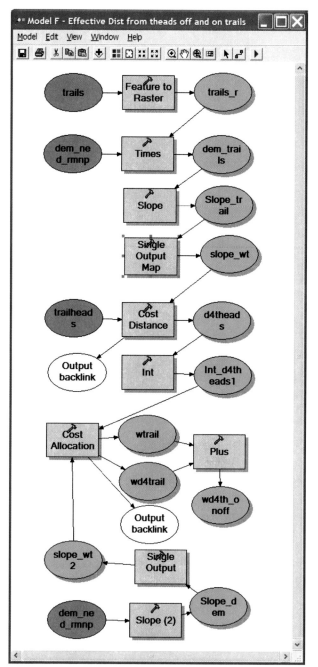

ModelBuilder

The Map Algebra expression from the Single Output Map tool (in Model F) to compute the effective distance weight based on trail slope is provided below.

Single Output Map Algebra

Map Algebra expression

5.04 / (6 * exp (-3.5 * abs(tan (slope_trail / 57.29578) + 0.05)))

Now our model measures effective distance in a way that recognizes the difficulty of hiking, relative to slopes. Note that computing slope along a trail requires extracting the elevation along just the trail, then computing slope. Slope computed on a full DEM provides the slope in the direction of the maximum fall line, which typically exceeds the trail slope (because a trail is typically aligned to cut across a slope). Indeed, trails are likely to become heavily eroded if their alignment follows the "fall-line" of a hillside.

The output from this model is looking pretty good. But one more thing (yes, there's always just one more thing to think about): isn't it slower when walking off-trail than on-trail? And are some off-trail areas easier or harder to hike through? Glad you asked: yes. One situation where this definitely is the case is around lakes (we can climb the highest mountains, but we can't walk on water!). That is, our model should be constrained so that we must walk around a lake to get to the other side (see arrows, right). In addition, other land cover types offer different resistance to walking through an area -- for example think about the difference between an open forest or grassland (tundra in our example) vs. thick shrub cover or dense old-growth forest.

Here in **Model G** we'll adjust the cost-weights to account for the difficulty of off-trail hiking (regardless of the slope), based on land cover types (Table 11.3). We incorporate these weights into our model by the *Single Output* tool that takes *nlcd_rmnp* as an input and creates *nlcd_wts*. This is then multiplied times the *slope_wts* to create cost weights that incorporate both slope and cover type.

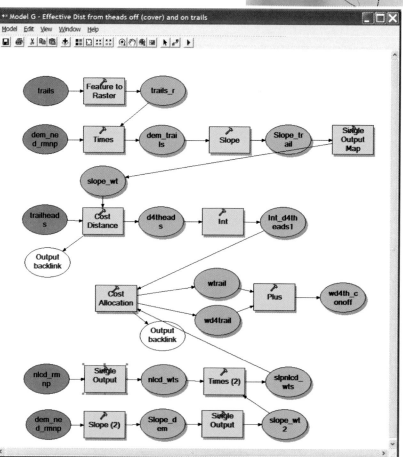

The map algebra expression is used to compute the land cover weights (right). A conditional statement is used here, rather than the *Reclassify* tool, because the output of Reclassify is an integer raster, so only whole values can be generated (e.g., 1, 2, 3...) but not 1.5.

Single Output Map Algebra (3)

Map Algebra expression
con (nlcd_rmnp == 11, 1000.0, con (nlcd_rmnp == 12, 5.0, con (nlcd_rmnp <= 23,
3.0,con (nlcd_rmnp <= 33, 2.0 ,con (nlcd_rmnp <= 43, 3.0,con (nlcd_rmnp == 51, 5.0, con
(nlcd_rmnp == 71,1.5 ,con (nlcd_rmnp <= 85, 2.0, 2.0)))))))

The effective distances computed by Model G (shown right) are able to distinguish the likely busy location near the trailheads (and roads), the farther-flung areas, as well as incorporate different land cover types (the lakes are now visible as pockets of higher distance). Note that the symbology shown here, and in particular the red colors, makes it look like the distances increased. However, the color scheme has simply stretched because of higher distances, thereby shifting some moderate distance values into the red (short) hue range.

One way to portray these distances a little more simply is to convert the effective distance values into something more meaningful, perhaps the number of minutes it would take to travel to a given place. We can do this by simply dividing the effective distance (in meters) by the number of meters that an average person can travel in a minute assuming flat ground and on trail, which is 84 meters per minute (see Figure 11.9).

To summarize, we've gone from a simple model based on computing density of roads and/or trails, to a more sophisticated representation of what we believe are important aspects of park visitation and possible effects on natural resources. Which of these models is "the best"? Again, this can be judged only within the context of the purpose or goal of a model.

FIGURE 11.9. One-way travel time from trailheads (green circles) in the Bear Lake corridor in Rocky Mountain National Park, Colorado, USA. The roads (solid black line), trails (dashed black line), and hydrology (blue lines)

One-way travel
<VALUE>
- 0.5 hrs
- 1 hr
- 2 hrs
- 3 hrs
- 4 hrs
- 6 hrs
- 8 hrs
- >8 hrs

TABLE 11.3. Estimated weights for cost-weights of off-trail travel through land cover types, using National Land Cover Dataset.

Value	Type	Weight
11	Water (lakes, reservoirs)	1000.0
12	Snowfields, glaciers	5.0
21, 22, 23	Urban/built-up (residential, commercial, industrial)	3.0
31, 32, 33	Transitional	2.0
41	Forest - deciduous	3.0
42	Forest - coniferous	3.0
43	Forest - mixed	3.0
51	Shrubland	5.0
61	Orchards	2.0
71	Grasslands	1.5
81, 82, 83, 84, 85	Agricultural	2.0
91, 92	Wetlands	3.0

11.5 Programming models using Python

11.5.1 Why use Python?

Python is a scripting language that provides yet another way to construct models. Python has quickly become the primary language to write geoprocessing tools with ArcGIS. Why? For a variety of reasons:

- Python is easy to learn because it based on simple, clear concepts and clean syntax;

- it supports object-oriented programming;

- Python code is readable and so less documentation is needed;

- it is COM compliant and can be easily integrated with other languages (C++, Fortran, Java, etc.);

- it is platform independent; and

- Python is free and has a broad user community (and can be installed with ArcGIS v9).

One of the best ways to learn how to program spatial Geoprocessing with ArcGIS using Python is to simply generate a model (as we did above) with Model Builder, and then export the model to Python. Then you've got someplace to start from that does something with which you are familiar.[16] So, for example, Model A (right), looks like this in Python code (below).

```
# --------------------------------------------------------------------------
# model_a.py
# Created on: Sat Jun 25 2005 07:10:51 PM
#   (generated by ArcGIS/ModelBuilder)
# --------------------------------------------------------------------------

# Import system modules
import sys, string, os, win32com.client

# Create the Geoprocessor object
gp = win32com.client.Dispatch("esriGeoprocessing.GpDispatch.1")

# Check out any necessary licenses
gp.CheckOutExtension("spatial")

# Load required toolboxes...
gp.AddToolbox("C:/Program Files/ArcGIS/ArcToolbox/Toolboxes/Spatial Analyst Tools.tbx")

# Local variables...
LineDen_trail = "C:\\davet\\projects\\RMNP\\ROMO_data\\lineden_trail"
trails = "trails"

# Process: Line Density...
gp.LineDensity_sa(trails, "NONE", LineDen_trail, \
                "C:\\davet\\projects\\RMNP\\ROMO_data\\eucdist_bear1", "1000", "HECTARES")
```

Another excellent resource for learning about scripting is ESRI's document: *ArcGIS v9: Writing Geoprocessing Scripts*. But before we dive right into some of the nitty-gritty details, a brief primer on Python programming basics is in order. Remember that when you begin programming in Python to do a geoprocessing task, you'll need to keep Python syntax, modules, etc. distinct from the peculiarities of the GpDispatch object (your gateway to ArcGIS).

---

16. This was a powerful feature of ArcView v3 (the Avenue code was available for all menu items, for example), and was missed in ArcGIS v8.

11.5.2 Basics of Python programming

There are a variety of programming techniques, variables, and data structures that are important to know about. These are not so different from other programming languages, so if you know BASIC, Fortran, C, or VBA, Python should be a snap to learn. Here I presume that you have installed Python v2.1[17] and PythonWin (a programming application window), which is provided by the ArcGIS Desktop install program. Note that throughout this section I will provide snippets of Python code (a couple of lines of code, but these does *not* constitute a complete program in and of itself), which will be distinguished by `black, Courier` font. Sections of code that were written as a whole, stand-alone program are portrayed with colored text, as in the following script:

```
#import standard library modules
import win32com.client, sys, os
print "Hello there!"
```

11.5.2.1 PythonWin

PythonWin is an application that allows you to interact with Python through a command-line window (ArcGIS does not need to be running to access geoprocessing tools!). Start up PythonWin through Start --> All programs --> Python 2.1--> Pythonwin. Note that there is an interactive window that allows you to type much of the following code directly, and see the results. Or, you can create a script file (*.py) and run it from within PythonWin. The steps are to:

1) write your script;

2) save it;

3) check it (click on the check mark on the Standard toolbar); and

4) run it (running guy button).

---

17. Hopefully with v9.2 a more recent Python version, v2.4 will be available with the ArcGIS installation. You should check with ESRI to determine the most current version of Python that is supported by the version of ArcGIS that you are using.

Later we'll see how to run a Python script from within ArcGIS.

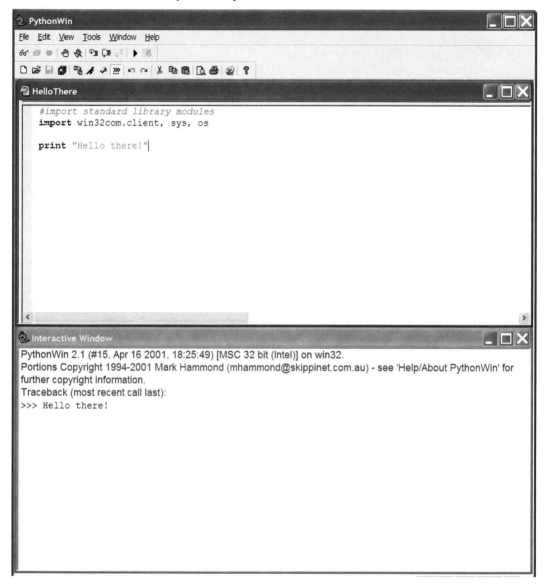

11.5.2.2 Modules

Modules are the way that scripts are organized in Python, similar to libraries in other programming languages. Modules store Python scripts that are somehow related (such as routines to handle strings). To bring a module (and its associated individual scripts, functions, or variables into a program), use the `import` statement. For example, nearly every script that you will write will have the following lines at the beginning of the program:

```
#import standard library modules
import win32com.client, sys, os
```

This code imports the Windows 32, system, and operating system modules. The `win32com` module provides programs to allow Python and the COM IDispatch (aka GpDispatch) to communicate. The `sys` module refers to the Python system, while the `os` module provides access to fundamental functions associated with the operating system, such as filename manipulation tools.

There are many, many other modules available in Python.

11.5.2.3 Peculiarities of Python

Python is fastidious. Python variable names and functions are case-sensitive (so *x* and *X* are two different variables). Moreover, the logical structure of a program is specified by indentations, rather than start/end statements (e.g., if... then/endif in VBA). So, you will need to learn to be neat-and-tidy in your scripting -- and soon you'll appreciate the simplicity and ease of scripting in Python.

11.5.2.4 Comments

It is very important to document your code. Comments are one of the best ways to do this (using variables with meaningful names is another). A comment in Python is distinguished by a special character -- a pound sign ("#"). Everything to the right of the # on the same line is a comment. This means that comments can be on their own line, as in:

```
# This is an example of a comment
```

or a comment can be "in-line", such as:

```
apples = 2        # initialize the number of apples
```

11.5.2.5 Variables

There are a variety of types of variables, but the most frequently-used ones are numbers, strings, lists, and dictionaries. Note that Python does not require you to explicitly identify a variable before it is used (e.g., in VBA one usually must first "dimension" a variable).

Variables names should start with a character (and remember, Python is case sensitive) and contain only alpha-numeric characters. A useful naming convention is to use descriptive variable names (avoid abbreviations) and capitalize the beginning of each word. For example, a variable that stores a list that stores the neighbors of a polygon might be called:

```
lstPolygonNeighbors.
```

Numbers can be assigned to a variable name using the equal sign ("="). For example:

```
lakeAcres = 10
intSqFeetPerAcre = 43560
lakeAcres * intSqFeetPerAcre    #returns 435,600 square feet
```

Note that the divisor operator "/" is an integer divisor if all variables or numbers in an equation are integers. That is, x in the statement below would equal 3, not 3.5.

```
x = 7 / 2
```

If you want real values to be computed, then use:

```
x = 7 / 2.0
```

Strings can also be used to store literal strings. These can be enclose in single or double quotes, but typically double quotes are used so that single quotes can be used within a string to indicate contraction or possesion:

```
strCity = "Winter Park"
strMotto = "Mountain biking fun!"
```

Two strings can be joined together into a single string, or be *concatenated*, by the + operator:

```
strGlued = "Once upon a time" + " " + "in a land far away..."
```

results in:

```
Once upon a time in a land far away...
```

A string can span more than one line by "escaping" it with a back-slash ("\"):

```
strVerse = "I can't seem to face up to the facts. I'm tense \
and nervous and I can't relax."
```

Characters in a string can be accessed through indexes that are offset by square brackets ("[]") rather than parentheses. The first character is indexed by 0. So, strX in the following would be "W":

```
strX = strCity[0]
```

You can also access a range of characters by using a colon, so the following would return "Win".

```
strX = strCity[0:2]
```

Note that common functions in VBA like left() or right() that return all characters to the left or right of a place can be accessed. Getting all characters to the right of the 1st character would result in "inter Park":

```
strX = strCity[1:]
```

11.5.2.6 Common data structures

A *list* is a compound data type that is used to group together a variety of items (strings, numbers, or a mixture). A list is written as a list of comma-separated items between square brackets. For example, a list of states that neighbor California would be:

```
lstCaliforniaNeighbors = ["Arizona", "Nevada", "Oregon"]
```

Getting the first item in a list is the same as getting characters in a string ("Arizona"):

```
strFirstNeighbor = lstCaliforniaNeighbors[0]
```

A list can also contain another list.

A list can be used as a *stack* data structure ("last-in, first-out"). Imagine a stack of fruit-filled pancakes, where the last pancake made and added to the stack is the first one to be eaten. Append() is used to add a new item to the stack, while pop() is used to remove the top item.

```
lstPancake = [ "blueberry", "banana", "raspberry" ]
lstPancake.append( "coconut" )     # new pancake added
x = lstPancake.pop()     # x gets the coconut pancake
```

A list can also be used as a *queue* ("first-in, first-out") data structure. In this case, append() is used again to add new items to the back of a list, but pop(0) retrieves the first item.

A *dictionary* is similar to a list, but it provides a set of unordered key:value pairs. The keys must be unique within a dictionary. Dictionaries are created by using a pair of braces ("{}"), and key:value pairs (items) are separated by commas. To obtain a list of the keys, use keys().

TABLE 11.4. Useful functions for strings and lists. Example variables are: x = 3.1415, strX = "Crested Butte", and lstX = [1, 2, 3, 4, 5, 6]. Note: remember Python is case-sensitive!

Function	Description	Example
append()	Adds or appends an item to the end of the list (to append to a string, use + or concatenate function).	lstX.append(7) >>> 1, 2, 3, 4, 5, 6, 7
Assign value	Assign a value to an individual item of a list	lstX[2] = 10 >>> 1, 2, 10, 4, 5, 6
	Assign values to multiple items (also called a "slice")	lstX[0:2] = [2, 2] >>> 2, 2, 3, 4, 5, 6
count()	Returns the number of times value x occurs in a list or string.	strX.count("t") >>> 3 lstX.count(6) >>> 1
del()	Deletes the value at index x in a list	lstX[1] >>> 1, 3, 4, 5, 6
find()	Returns the position of the first occurrence of value x in a string.	strX.find("e") >>> 3

TABLE 11.4. Useful functions for strings and lists. Example variables are: x = 3.1415, strX = "Crested Butte", and lstX = [1, 2, 3, 4, 5, 6]. Note: remember Python is case-sensitive!

Function	Description	Example
index()	Returns the index or position in a list whose value is x. This returns an error if the value does not exist in the list. Use find() for strings.	lstX.index(1) >>> 0 strX.index("d") >>> 6

insert()	Insert an item into a list. Can use "slice" syntax or insert() function.	lstX[1:1] = [8, 8]
		>>> 1, 8, 8, 2, 3, 4, 5, 6
		lstX.insert(0, 0)
		>>> 0, 1, 2, 3, 4, 5, 6

Left	Return the first x number of characters in a string or items in a list	strX[:5] >>> 'Crest' lstX[:3] >>> 1, 2, 3
len()	Returns the length or number of items in a list or string	len(strX) >>> 13 len(lstX) >>> 6
pop()	Returns and removes an item at a given index, or last index if none specified.	lstX.pop(0) >>> 1 lstX.pop() >>> 6

remove()	Remove items from a list -- can use "slice" syntax or remove() function. Removes the first item from the list whose value is x. This returns an error if no such item exists. Use count() to see if or how many occurences of x there are in a list.	lstX[0:2] = []
		>>> 3, 4, 5, 6
		lstX.remove(1)
		>>> 2, 3, 4, 5, 6

replace()	Replaces a target string with a new string.	strX.replace("Crested", "Snowy") >>> "Snowy Butte"
reverse()	Reverses the elements of a list, keeping them in place.	lstX.reverse() >>> 6, 5, 4, 3, 2, 1
Right	Return the last x number of characters in a string or items from a list.	strX[-5:] >>> 'Butte' lstX[-2:] >>> 5, 6
sort()	Sorts the items of a list, in place, ascending.	lstX.sort() >>> 1, 2, 3, 4, 5, 6
split()	Splits a string into a list based on a separator string.	strX.split(" ") >>> ['Crested', 'Butte']

TABLE 11.4. Useful functions for strings and lists. Example variables are: x = 3.1415, strX = "Crested Butte", and lstX = [1, 2, 3, 4, 5, 6]. Note: remember Python is case-sensitive!

Function	Description	Example
escape sequences	There are a variety of escape sequences or special characters that can be generated in a string, and commonly used ones are listed here.	\n >>> newline \\ >>> backslash \n >>> linefeed \r >>> carriage return \t >>> tab
random functions	The random module provides access to a number of useful functions that access a pseudo-random number generator. Need to import random before calling these functions.	random() >>> uniform random value between 0,1.0 seed(x) >>> initializes the random seed value to x shuffle(x) >>> randomly shuffles or permutes list x

11.5.2.7 Conditional statements (if/then/else)

An important statement is called a *conditional statement* that uses Boolean logic to control program flow. Essentially, it implements "if X occurs, then do Y". Note that there are no matching end statements -- rather indentation and the colons (":") control the blocks of logic. And yes, *elif* is not a typo -- rather it stands for "else if".

For example, the following snippet would help decide flow based on whether x was negative, zero, or positive:

```
if x < 0:
    print "Negative"
elif x == 0:
    print "Zero"
else:
    print "Positive"
```

11.5.2.8 Looping

Loops are powerful structures within a program to do repetative tasks. Combined with conditional statements, loops are very common in programs.

There are a variety of ways to loop, but the most commonly-used loop statements are for and while. *For* iterates over the items of any list (or string), in the order the items appear. *While* loops as long as a condition is true. This statement typically requires three steps: 1) initialize a variable; 2) test the condition of the variable; and 3) increment the variable. (Don't forget this last step, otherwise you'll be stuck in an infinite loop). Here are a couple of examples to show you how loops work.

```
# looping example1
lstX = [ 1, 2, 3]
for x in lstX:
    print x
```

This generates the following list:

```
1
2
3
```

Again, the keywords *for*, *in*, and the colon (":") are required, and indentation controls the structure. That is, all lines of code that are indented will be included in the loop, while those that are outside of the indentation are not. For example:

```
# looping example2
lstX = [1, 2, 3]
for x in lstX:
    print x
    print "Go!"
```

This generates the following output:

```
1
Go!
2
Go!
3
Go!
```

But if a statement is out of the indentation structure, it is *not* included in the loop:

```
# looping example3
lstX = [1, 2, 3]
for x in lstX:
    print x
print "Go!"
```

This results in the following output (note that it is good practice to provide a line between groups of lines of code:

```
1
2
3
Go!
```

The following program uses a while statement to generate the same output ("1 2 3 Go!"):

```
# looping example4
x = 1
while x < 4:
    print x
    x = x + 1


print "Go!"
```

Note that the while loop executes as long as the condition is true. Any non-zero integer value is true, while zero and negative values are false. The *break* statement breaks out of the smallest enclosing for or while loop. The *continue* statement bypasses the rest of the statements in a loop and continues with the next iteration.

11.5.2.9 Short examples

Here are a couple of short examples of Python code to demonstrate some of the basics about lists, dictionaries, and for loops.[18]

```
# example to demonstrate lists, dictionaries, and loops
lstNodes = [ 1, 2, 3, 4, 5, 6 ]
dctNeighbors = { 1: [2, 4, 5], 2: [1, 4, 5], 3: [5, 6], 4: [1,
2, 5], 5: [1, 2, 3, 4], 6: [3] }
print "A list of the Neighbors for each Node:"
for x in lstNodes:
    print x, dctNeighbors[x]
```

This script generates the following output:

---

18. The adjacency lists are a based on an example from: Anselin, L. and O. Smirnov. 1996. Efficient algorithms for constructing proper higher order spatial lag operators. *Journal of Regional Science* 36(1): 67-89.

```
A list of the Neighbors for each Node:
1 [2, 4, 5]
2 [1, 4, 5]
3 [5, 6]
4 [1, 2, 5]
5 [1, 2, 3, 4]
6 [3]
```

The script below generates a list of 1st and 2nd order neighbors.

```
# example to find 1st and 2nd order neighbors
lstNodes = [ 1, 2, 3, 4, 5, 6 ]
dctNeighbors = { 1: [2, 4, 5], 2: [1, 4, 5], 3: [5, 6], 4: [1,
2, 5], 5: [1, 2, 3, 4], 6: [3] }

for x in lstNodes:
    print "1st order of " + str(x) + ": " + str(dctNeighbors[x])
    # find 2nd order neighbors
    z = []
    for y in dctNeighbors[x]:
            print "\t2nd order of " + str(y) + ": " +
str(dctNeighbors[y])
```

The output is:

```
1st order of 1: [2, 4, 5]
    2nd order of 2: [1, 4, 5]
    2nd order of 4: [1, 2, 5]
    2nd order of 5: [1, 2, 3, 4]
1st order of 2: [1, 4, 5]
    2nd order of 1: [2, 4, 5]
    2nd order of 4: [1, 2, 5]
    2nd order of 5: [1, 2, 3, 4]
1st order of 3: [5, 6]
    2nd order of 5: [1, 2, 3, 4]
```

```
    2nd order of 6: [3]
1st order of 4: [1, 2, 5]
    2nd order of 1: [2, 4, 5]
    2nd order of 2: [1, 4, 5]
    2nd order of 5: [1, 2, 3, 4]
1st order of 5: [1, 2, 3, 4]
    2nd order of 1: [2, 4, 5]
    2nd order of 2: [1, 4, 5]
    2nd order of 3: [5, 6]
    2nd order of 4: [1, 2, 5]
1st order of 6: [3]
    2nd order of 3: [5, 6]
```

11.5.3 Arguments

An important way that you can communicate with a Python script is through script *arguments* (or sometimes known as parameters). This allows you to pass in input parameters, such as a shapefile to do some geoprocessing on, or output parameters that details where to save an output file. Arguments are usually assigned to local variables at the beginning of a script, using the variable sys.argv[] list. Note that all arguments are passed in as strings -- so you may need to do some type conversion if other variable types are needed. For example, if you want to pass in an integer, then the argument (e.g., "2") is converted to an integer (note that argv[0] is reserved for the script name itself):

```
# example to demonstrate passing an argument in
strNode = sys.argv[1]
xNode = int(strNode)
lstNodes = [ 1, 2, 3, 4, 5, 6 ]
dctNeighbors = { 1: [2, 4, 5], 2: [1, 4, 5], 3: [5, 6], 4: [1,
2, 5], 5: [1, 2, 3, 4], 6: [3] }
print "Neighbors of node " + str( xNode ) + ": " +
str(dctNeighbors[xNode])
```

11.5.4 Connecting Python with ArcGIS

And now for the part you have been waiting for -- accessing ArcGIS functionality through a Python script. This "magic" is done by declaring an object called the *GpDispatch* object. So, to declare the geoprocessor object, you'll simply copy the following lines into your script (its the fourth line starting with "Gp" that does declares the geoprocessing object:

```
#import standard library modules
import win32com.client, sys, os
from win32com.client import Dispatch
Gp = Dispatch("esriGeoprocessing.GpDispatch.1")
```

There are two main groups of objects that can be called through "Gp": those that access ArcGIS tools directly and are named after a tool (e.g., Gp.Clip...); or methods and properties that are supported through the Gp object itself. The methods and properties of Gp can be further divided into four types: describe objects, enumeration objects, cursor objects, and environment settings.

11.5.4.1 Tools

Every tool in ArcGIS (listed in section 11.4) can be called from Python direction using the Gp object. A helpful way to understand what the code should look like is to: 1) identify the desired tool in ArcToolbox; 2) open the tool; 3) click on the Help button (right side); and 4) examine the Scripting syntax section (and Script example) at the bottom (see below). For example, to call the Select tool, you could call it from Python using:

```
Gp.select_analysis("wells.shp", "gas.shp",'"WELL_TYP" =
\'GAS\'')
```

Also note that a tool can also be called from the Command Line (with slightly different syntax):

```
select_analysis wells.shp wells_Gas.shp "WELL_TYP" = 'GAS'
```

Another useful document is the Quick Reference Guide (*Geoprocessing_Quick_Ref_Gde.pdf*) that comes with the digital documenation library (most likely installed in c:\esri_library\ArcGIS_Desktop\...).

To streamline incorporating ArcGIS tools within Python scripts, I have written a Python script[19] called *Tool2Gp.py*. This allows you to enter the name (or part of, it supports a wildcard search) of a tool to search for, then provides the Usage (a concise description of all

parameters of a tool) and a Python-ready string that can be copied and pasted into a script.[20] For example, a search based on an input argument of "select_analysis" produces the following in the Interactive Window of PythonWin:

```
Tool2Gp: *select_analysis*
### Usage: Select_analysis <in_features> <out_feature_class>
{where_clause}
```

19. Thanks to J. Norman for helping brainstorm how this script could be improved.
20. This, and other scripts from this text, are available electronically from: www.consplan.com.

```
Gp.Select_analysis( "in_features", "out_feature_class",
"where_clause")
### Usage: TableSelect_analysis <in_table> <out_table>
{where_clause}
Gp.TableSelect_analysis(  "in_table",  "out_table",
"where_clause")
```

Note that two tools were found with the search string, and for each tool found, two lines are produced. The first line that is commented out (with "###") shows the full usage to help you recall what parameters are needed. The second line ("Gp.Select....") can be triple-clicked, copied, and then pasted into a *.py script window. You'll need to then set the parameters to tie into the rest of your code. Note that the parameters are already enclosed with double-quotes (which is required by Python).

Also, default parameters are assumed and inserted into the code when there are optional arguments (of course you can change these by editing the text):

```
Tool2Gp: *buffer_analysis*
### Usage: Buffer_analysis <in_features> <out_feature_class>
<buffer_distance or field> {FULL | LEFT | RIGHT} {ROUND | FLAT}
{NONE | ALL | LIST} {dissolve_field;dissolve_field...}
Gp.Buffer_analysis( "in_features", "out_feature_class",
"buffer_distance or field", "FULL", "ROUND", "NONE",
"dissolve_field;dissolve_field...")
```

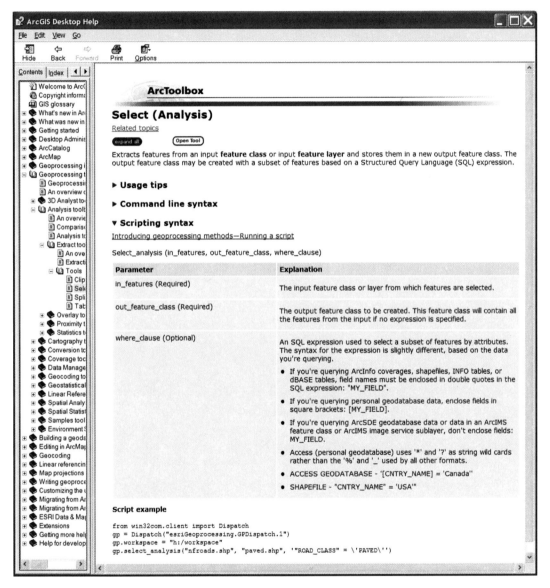

11.5.4.2 Listing and describing objects (enumerations)

The describe objects provide descriptive properties about a dataset (spatial or tabular), and different dataset types have different properties. Accessing these properties allows you to change the logic of a program based on different properties, such as doing different processing on point vs. polyline vs. polygon feature types. This is a two-step process. First, you will need to obtain a dataset that you are interested in, and this is often done by selecting from a list of datasets. Gp recognizes the following different dataset types: feature class, coverage feature class, layer, tableView, datasets, relationship class, table, and workspace. Once you've found the dataset of interest, you can access properties that describe it.

There are a variety of enumerations (sequences or arrays of Gp objects) that are used to generate a list of these objects (see Table 11.6): *datasets, feature classes, raster datasets, tables, and workspaces*. Lists of fields and indexes for a particular table can also be generated. These lists or enumerations are stored as an *array*, and there are a number of functions for arrays (Table 11.5). Note that parameters for these functions are optional, and support using wildcards ("*") for the first optional input.

For example, to get a list of all the polygon feature classes in a particular workspace, you could use the following code. Note seven important steps that are common to enumerations:

1) set the workspace;

2) get the enumeration;

3) reset the enumeration to the beginning;

4) get the first object;

5) enter a while loop, until the objects in the sequence are done;

6) do something with the object; and

7) get the next in the sequence (otherwise you'll be stuck in an infinite loop).

```
# Import COM Dispatch module
from win32com.client import Dispatch
Gp = Dispatch("esriGeoprocessing.GPDispatch.1")
# List all feature classes in workspace
Gp.Workspace= "c:/temp/data.mdb"   #1st
fcs = Gp.ListFeatureClasses("*","polygon") #2st
#list them out to user
fcs.Reset()      #3nd - must reset to start at the first object
fc = fcs.Next() #4rd - get the first object
while fc:        #5th - enter loop
    print fc.Name #6th - do something with it
    fc = fcs.Next()  #7th - get the next in sequence
```

TABLE 11.5. List enumerations of datasets and objects. Typically the workspace must be defined before using any of the list methods (e.g.,: Gp.Workspace ("c:/temp"))

Dataset type	Properties
ListDatasets()	Lists the datasets in the current workspace. ListDatasets({nameWildcard}, {datasetType}). E.g., Gp.ListDatasets ("d*", "All"). Possible dataset types are: *All, CAD, Coverage, Feature, RasterCatalog, TIN, Topology, VPF*
ListEnvironments	Lists the environment variables available. ListEnvironments({nameWildcard}). E.g., Gp.ListEnvironments("").
ListFeatureClasses	Lists the feature classes in a workspace. ListFeatureClasses({nameWildcard}, {featureType}). E.g., Gp.ListFeatureClasses ("*", "Polygon"). Possible feature types are: *All, Arc, Label, Line, Node, Point, Polygon, Region, Route*
ListFields	Lists the fields for a specified table. ListFields (<path/name>, {nameWildcard}, {fieldType}). E.g., Gp.ListFields ("c:/temp/roads.dbf", "*", "Integer"). Field types are: *All, Blob, Date, Double, Geometry, Integer, OID, Single, SmallInteger, String*
ListIndexes	Lists the fields that are indexed for a specified table. ListIndexes (<path/name>, {nameWildcard}). E.g., Gp.ListIndexes ("c:/temp/roads.dbf", "*").
ListRasters	Lists the raster datasets in the specified workspace. ListRasters({nameWildcard}, {rasterType}). E.g., Gp.ListRasters("*", "GRID"). Possible raster types are: *All, ADRG, BIL, BIP, BSQ, BMP, CADRG, CIB, ERS, GIF, GIS, GRID, IMG, JPEG, LAN, NITF, PNG, RAW, SID, SDE, STACK, TIFF*
ListTables	Lists the tables in the current workspace. ListTables(<nameWildcard>, <tableType>). E.g., Gp.ListTables ("d*", "All"). Possible dataset types are: *All, dBASE, INFO*
ListToolboxes	Lists the toolboxes in a workspace. ListToolboxes({nameWildcard}). E.g., Gp.ListToolboxes ("FLoWS").
ListTools	Lists the tools in a workspace. ListTools({nameWildcard}). E.g., Gp.ListTools ("Create*").
ListWorkspaces	Lists the workspaces available in the current workspace. ListWorkspaces(<nameWildcard>, <workspaceType>). E.g., Gp.ListWorkspaces ("d*", "All"). Possible workspace types are: *All, Access, Coverage, SDE, Shapefile*

TABLE 11.6. Functions for the various enumeration objects. Get the array from some list operation (e.g., fc = Gp.List..., then intC = fc.Count

Function	Description
Array	**Add**(k) - adds an object *k* to array at the end of the list.
	Count - returns the number of objects in the array.
	GetObject(i) - gets the object at a specified index *i*.
	Insert(i, k) - insert object *k* at index *i*.
	Next() - returns the next object in array, usually used at the bottom of a while loop.
	Remove(i) - remove object at index i from array.
	RemoveAll() - remove all objects from array.
	Reset() - resets the arary to the first object.

The properties that can be accessed and described depend on the dataset type, and are listed in Table 11.8.

TABLE 11.7. Describe objects and properties associated with each dataset type. Note that these properties are accessed from desc.<property>, where desc = Gp.Describe (<inDataSet>).

Dataset type	Properties
Coverage	**Tolerances.Dangle**
	Tolerances.Edit -
	Tolerances.Fuzzy -
	Tolerances.Grain -
	Tolerances.NodeSnap -
	Tolerances.Snap -
	Tolerances.TicMatch -
	Tolerances.Weed -
Coverage feature class	**Extent** - The xmin, ymin, xmax, ymax of minimum enclosing rectangle.
	FeatureClassType - The feature type: *point, arc, polygon, annotation, file, label, link, node, region, route, tic*
	Fields - List of the fields.
	HasFAT -Boolean indicator of existence of feature attribute table.
	HasOID - Boolean indicator of an OID (object ID) field.
	Indexes - list of the indexed fields.
	OIDFieldName - The name of the OID field.
	Topology - State of topology: *exists, nonapplicable, preliminary, unknown*

TABLE 11.7. Describe objects and properties associated with each dataset type. Note that these properties are accessed from desc.<property>, where desc = Gp.Describe (<inDataSet>).

Dataset type	Properties
Dataset	DatasetType - *coverage, featuredataset, featureclass, table, relationshipclass, rasterdataset, rasterband, rastercatalog, any, caddrawing, container, geo, planargraph, geometricNetwork, topology, text, tin, tool, toolbox*
	Extent - The xmin, ymin, xmax, ymax of minimum enclosing rectangle.
	SpatialReference -
Feature class	**FeatureType** - The type of feature (one of the following constants: *simple, simple_junction, simple_edge, complex_junction, complex_edge, annotation, coverage_annotation, dimension*).
	HasM - Boolean value if feature class has M (measured) values.
	HasZ - Boolean value if feature class has Z (elevational) values.
	HasSpatialIndex - Boolean value if spatial index has been built.
	RelationshipClassNames - A list of the names (";" delimited) of associated relationships.
	ShapeFieldName -The name of the shape field.
	ShapeType -The type of the shape (feature): *point, multipoint, polyline, polygon, null, line, circulararc, ellipticarc, bezier3curve, path, ring, envelope, any, bag, multiPatch, triangleStrip, triangleFan, ray sphere.*
	SpatialReference - The spatial reference object that stores coordinate system information.
	TopologyName -Name of the topology of this feature class.
Layer	**FeatureClass** - The source location of the feature class associated with the layer. Note this is a temporary file stored in memory, and generated during an ArcMap session.
	FIDSet -a list (";" delimited) of record numbers (integers)
	FieldInfo -
	WhereClause - The definition query used to define the layer (SQL where clause).
	NameString - The name of the layer.
Raster band	**Height** - Number of rows.
	IsInteger - Boolean of integer data (1) or float (0)
	MeanCellHeight - Height of cell in map units.
	MeanCellWidth - Width of cell in map units.
	NoDataValue - The value of that represents NoData.
	PixelType - F32 (floating point 32-bit)
	PrimaryField -
	TableType - Indexed
	Width - Number of columns.

TABLE 11.7. Describe objects and properties associated with each dataset type. Note that these properties are accessed from desc.<property>, where desc = Gp.Describe (<inDataSet>).

Dataset type	Properties
Raster catalog	**Dataset Properties** - see Dataset Properties above. **RasterFieldName** - the name of the raster field. **Table Properties** - see Table below.
Raster dataset	**BandCount** - Number of bands in raster dataset. **CompressionType** - None, etc.... **Format** - GRID, IMG or TIFF. **Permanent** - Boolean true or false. **SensorType** -
Relationship class	**IsVersioned** - Boolean for version type. **Fields** - see Fields above.
Table	**Fields** - See Fields above. **HasOID** - Boolean if OID exists. **Indexes** - List of indexes. **OIDFIeldName** - The name of the OID field.
TableView	**Table** - See Table above. **FIDSet** - **FieldInfo** - See FieldInfo. **WhereClause** - **NameString** -
Workspace	**ConnectionString** - **Domains** - **WorkspaceFactoryProgID** - **WorkspaceType** -

TABLE 11.8. Additional describe objects and properties.

Type	Properties
Field (from enumeration of Fields)	**Name** - The name of the field. **AliasName** - The aliased name of a field **Domain** - **IsEditable** - Boolean describing editable state. **HasIndex** - Boolean of existence of index. **IsNullable** - Boolean of nullable. **IsUnique** - Boolean of unqiue field. **Length** - Length of text field. **Type** - Type of data. **Scale** - Places to the right of the decimal for real values. **Precision** - Places to the left of the decimal for real values.
Geometry	**Type** - **Extent** - **Centroid** - **FirstPoint** - **LastPoint** - **Area** - **Length** - **IsMultipart** - **PartCount** - **GetPart** (i) -
Index	**Name** - name of the index. **IsAscending** - Boolean sorting in ascending order. **IsUnique** - Boolean if unique index. **Fields** - Fields object for this index.

TABLE 11.8. Additional describe objects and properties.

Type	Properties
Point	**X** - the horizontal location.
	Y - the vertical location
	Z - the evlevation.
	M - the measure value.
	ID - a long integer providing unique identification
SpatialReference	**Type** - *Unknown, projected, geographic*
	Name -The name of the projection.
	Abbreviation, Remarks -
	FactoryCode - The factory code of the spatial reference
	HasMPrecision, HasXYPrecision, HasZPrecision - Boolean if data stores coordinates as integers
	FalseOriginAndUnits - falseX; falseY; Units.
	MFalseOriginAndUnits - falseM; Units
	ZFalseOriginAndUnits - falseZ; Units
	Domain, MDomain, ZDomain - xmin;ymin;xmax;ymax
	Usage - Notes on common usage of projection
	CentralMeridian - Origin of x coordinates in decimal degrees.
	CentralMeridianInDegrees - Origin of x coordinates in degrees, minutes, seconds.
	LongitudeOfOrigin - Origin of y coordinates in decimal degrees
	LatitudeOf1st - Latitude of first point of a projected coordinate system.
	LatitudeOf2nd - Latitude of second point of a projected coordinate system.
	FalseEasting, FalseNorthing -
	CentralParallel - Defines the origin of the y coordinates.
	StandardParallel1 - Defines latitude where scale is 1:1 for conic projections.
	StandardParallel2 - Defines latitude where scale is 1:1 for conic projections.
	LongitudeOf1st - Longitude of the first point of a projected coordinate system.
	LongitudeOf2nd - Longitude of second point of a projected coordinate system.
	ScaleFactor - A value applied to center point of map projection.
	Azimuth -Defines the center line of a projection.
	Classification - The classification type of a projection.
	SemiMajorAxis - The longer or major radius of an ellipsoid.
	SemiMinorAxis -The shorter or minor radius of an ellipsoid.
	Flattening - The percentage difference between major and minor axes.
	Longitude - The left longitude bounding a 360 degree range.
	RadiansperUnit -The radians per angular unit.

A *cursor* is an object that is used to access rows in tables, or to insert new rows into tables. There are three of types of cursor objects, each tailored to a particular task. Each of these cursors generate an enumeration of row objects that are contained in an array (Table 11.10). Cursors support navigation but only in a forward direction, you cannot back up.

The *search cursor* is a basic cursor object -- it simply returns the rows that have meet a particular condition, specified by a "where clause" or SQL expression (similiar to the Select by Attributes dialog). This allows you to find, for example, all the lakes in a feature class that are larger than a specific size (i.e. described in an "area" field). The other two cursors also use the same search string, but allow you additional functions to change a table. The *insert cursor* is used to insert new rows into a table (or feature class). This is typically used to add new features and associated attributes into a table. The *update cursor* allows you to update (or change) an attribute's value.

```
# Import COM Dispatch module
from win32com.client import Dispatch
Gp = Dispatch("esriGeoprocessing.GPDispatch.1")
Gp.Workspace = "c:/temp/fraser_forest"
# Get fields
fields  =  Gp.ListFields  (  "c:/temp/fraser_forest/
waterbodies.shp")
fields.Reset()
field = fields.Next()
# Get rows
rows  =  Gp.SearchCursor  ("c:/temp/fraser_forest/
waterbodies.shp")
#list them out to user
row = rows.Next()
while row:
     print str( row.GetValue ( field.Name ) )
     row = rows.Next()
```

TABLE 11.9. Cursor types and methods.

Cursor type	Properties
SearchCursor	Retreives the next object in the array. SearchCursor(<dataset>, {whereClause}). E.g., rows = Gp.**SearchCursor**("c:\temp\roads.shp").
	Reset - rows.Reset()
	Next - row = rows.Next() - gets the next row
InsertCursor	Can be used to insert an object in the array. InsertCursor(<dataset>, {whereClause}). E.g., rows = Gp.**InsertCursor**("c:\temp\roads.shp") **Reset** - rows.Reset()
	NewRow - newRow = rows.NewRow()
	InsertRow() - rows.InsertRow(newRow)
UpdateCursor	Can be used to insert an object in the array. InsertCursor(<dataset>, {whereClause}). E.g., rows ⁻ Gp.UpdateCursor("c:\temp\roads.shp").
	Reset() - rows.Reset()
	Next() - row = rows.Next()
	UpdateRow() - rows.UpdateRow(row)
	DeleteRow() - rows.DeleteRow(row)

11.5.5 Debugging tips

The basic *debugging* recipe is one part logic and one part intuition. The strategy is to systematically eliminate possible problems, by developing a series of ways to test if a certain assumption is true or not. It also relies on intuition (and experience), because there are typically a large number of possible things that could go wrong, but some are more likely than others. If you find yourself losing your cool in the heat of the battle with a bug, stop guessing, step away from your computer, and construct a quick list of things to check. Then, order your checklist (ascending) by the things that are most likely to happen.

Easier said than done, so here is a general checklist of things that you might want to check:

1. Determine if the error is due to a pure Python statement or if it occurs when calling a GpDispatch object.

2. If it is a Python error, check consistency of variable names (remember, Python is case-sensitive)

3. If it is a GpDispatch error:

3a. Run the tool manually in the Command Line window with the parameters you are trying to use. The Command Line dialog provides additional error messages that might give you a better clue as to what is causing the problem.

3b. If you believe the dispatch object is acting improperly, at least resort you could quit ArcCatalog and ArcMap applications and run your script from Python.

3c. Create a model in ModelBuilder with the desired tool, then export the tool to Python and examine the code.

11.6 Ten ways to improve your ArcGIS experience

I end this book with 10 suggestions that will (hopefully!) increase your productivity and allow you to have more fun using ArcGIS.

1. Manage your "folder connections" (or short-cuts) that specify where your spatial data are located. Create a folder connection for each major project in which you are involved, and delete ones that point to old or suspended projects. You can do this from either ArcCatalog or in the Add Data dialog in ArcMap.

2. A corrolary to the first tip is to load your most-frequently-used datasets onto local computer drives for faster performance.

3. Save your ArcMap document frequently. At important steps along the way (perhaps after each major modification) save a copy of your document that is time-stamped (e.g., "MyMDX_20050704"). This provides you a sequence of archives of your past work. Use: File -> Save a copy...

4. Turn off the *Field Calculator* warning message (that warns you every single time of changing values in a table outside of an edit session). To do this: Tools --> Options... Tables tab, check off the "Show warning when calculating field values outside edit session".

5. Change the *warning threshold* that triggers the warning message when using the Select All/ Switch Selection buttons. To do this: Selection --> Options, set the value in the Warning Threshold portion (at bottom) to be a really big number (e.g., 999,999).

6. Specify the file formats you wish to see in the Add Data dialog. For raster data, select the formats that you commonly use (probably GRID and IMG), and turn off the ones seldom used (probably GIF, TIFF, BMP, etc.). To do this: Tools --> Options, Raster tab, File formats button...

7. Because there is no "undo" when changing the symbology of a legend, get in the habit of first saving a layer file before you modify an existing one. Another option is to copy the layer (right-click, copy) and then paste a new layer into the data frame.

8. Create a most-frequently-used toolbox that contains a copy of each tool that you use frequently. While the tool approach is powerful, it can be annoying to have to search through hundreds of tools to find your old trusty Phillips-head screwdriver.

9. Build a model to do and document your spatial analysis.

10. When processing with large datasets, first create a very small (e.g., 5-10% of full extent) dataset to test out your processing/model. Make sure it works as a "proof-of-concept" on the small dataset, then go for the whole enchilada.

Symbols

*.ai 151
*.aih 41
*.ain 41
*.apr 11
*.asc 61
*.bil 233
*.bmp 62, 147, 151, 233
*.cal 212
*.cgm 151
*.cib 62
*.csv 61
*.dbf 41
*.dem 314
*.e00 47, 78, 79
*.emf 152
*.eps 151
*.ers 233
*.exp 164
*.gif 63, 233
*.img 233
*.jpg 63, 147, 152, 233
*.Lookup 287
*.lyr 134
*.mxt 148
*.pdf 152
*.pmf 61
*.png 63, 147, 152, 233
*.rlc 63, 233
*.rs 63, 233
*.sbn 41
*.sbx 41
*.shp 41
*.shx 41
*.sid 63, 233
*.svg 152
*.tab 61
*.tif 63, 152, 233
*.txt 61
*.wmf 147

Numerics

3D Analyst 27, 140, 271
3D shapefiles 42

A

absolute pathname 134
absolute x,y 191
accessibility 390
add to current selection 158
Add X,Y Data 342
address matching 209
address tables 209
adjacency 174
Adobe Illustrator Format 151
Alexander, C. 362
allocation 256
Alvi, J. 41
Analysis environment 236
analysis extent 237
analysis mask 237
Analytical Hierarchy Process 371
angle 191
Animation tool 31
annotation 47, 143
Anselin, L. 413
Aplet, G. 367
append 199, 409
Append wizard 199
Arc 49
arc 47
ArcCatalog 9, 19
ArcGIS 9
ArcMap 9, 11
arc-node 45
ArcPress 152
ArcPublisher 154
ArcReader 27, 154
Arcs 49
ArcToolbox 9
are completely within 173
are identical to 172
area 43, 44, 163, 169, 320

center-of-gravity 341
centroid method 240
feature center 341
geographic centroid 341
graduated symbols 126
label center 342
mean center 331
population center 331
radius of neighborhood 249
spatial relation 172
center-of-gravity centroid 341
centroid 341
Centroid Labels 342
chain 47, 49
character marker symbol 132
characters 408
checkerboard 292
Childs, C. 186
choropleth 115
Chou, Y. 240, 325, 332
Chrisman, N. 8, 44, 239
Clarke, K. 342
classification 116
classification statistics 121
classified 125
clip 349
clip features 197
clip layer 349
clip, data frame 136
cluster tolerance 200, 207
CMYK color model 132
coded domain 57, 76
Color hue 131
color model, HSV 131
color model, RGB 131
color ramps 124
Color saturation 131
Color Selector 131, 133
Color value 131
Combine 354
combine 354

command 25
common field 66
completely contain 173
completely within 173
Complex features 39
complex polygon 43
compound queries 164
Computer Graphics Metafile 151
Con 290
concatenated 408
conditional statement 411
conformality 91
connectors 363
Construct Features 208
contain 173
contained by 173
contents view 21
continue 413
contour interval 268
contour lines 2, 112, 139, 265, 266
contour lines, defined 268
contour tool 269
Contours 268
contrast 136
control network 88
Corbett, J. 47
Corson-Rikert, J. 186
cost GRID 259
cost weighted distance 301
Cost-weighted distance 259, 330
Coulson, M. 117
count 409
count field 320
Cova, T. 36
coverage 47
create a new selection 158
create new feature 186
Create Thiessen Polygons tool 340
crossed by the outline 172
cubic convolution 345
CURRENT_DATE 164

cursor 427
cursor coordinates 16
cursor, search 427
Custom stretch 235
cut polygon features 186
cyclic data 65
cyclical 273

D

Dangermond, J. 1, 39
dangle length 185
dangles 205
dangling nodes 185
dasymetric 128
data frame 14
data model 36
data models 55
data structures 37
data view 15
datasets 363
DATE 164
date 70
datum 87
dblbnd.adf 229
debugging 428
defined interval 117
definition query 165
degrees, minutes, seconds 86
del 409
DeMers, M. 198
density surface 263
Dent, B. 116
derived data 374
derived dataset 363
derived values 374
DESC 164
deselect 168
desktop GIS 8
development stage 362
DFAD 79
DiBiase, D. 131
dictionary 409

differential correction 89
DIME 79
direction 329
direction GRID 256
disjoint features 196
display field 160
dissolve 343
Dissolve tool 196, 319, 343
distance
    254
        constrained distance 329
        cost weighted 259
        straight-line 255
distance field 358
Djokic, D. 55
documentation mantra 24
dominant method 240
double 70
double digitized 185
double-precision 41, 42
Douglas, D. 242, 344
Douglas-Peucker 344
DTED 265
dynamic HTML 153
dynamic labels 142

E

e00, also see *.e00 10
easting 98
edges 52, 203
Edit 195
edit cache 189
Edwards, B. 362
effective distance 338
Eicher, C. 128
elif 411
Eliminate tool 199, 344
ellipse 322
Encapsulated PostScript 151
end node 45
Enhanced metafiles 152
entity model 36

Environmental Modeling Language 364
equal interval 116
equator 86
erase 352
ESRI, 1998 43
Euclidean distance 328
exclusion 122
exclusion zones 306
explode 343
Explode tool 208
exploding 196
expression file 164
expression text box 287
Extend 364
extensions 27

F

feature behavior 54
feature class 55
feature data model 36
feature dataset 55
feature service 17
feature services 17
feature state 54
feature-centric digitizing 186
feature-linked annotation 143
features 111
Field Calculator 212, 429
Field Calculator warning message 214
field data model 36, 62, 223
field types 70
field, adding 69
field, precision 70
field, scale 70
fill symbols 133
find 159
Find tool 19
First Law of Geography 254, 259, 277, 334
first-order neighbors 174
Fisher, H. 1
Fisher, W.D. 1958 117
fishnet 140, 292

Float 290
float 62, 70, 76, 226
flow chart 362
Focal 248
focal 250
folder connection 16
Foley, J. 240
for 411
fragmentation index 325
Fragstats 323
Franke, R. 357
Freeman, J. 5
freeze 71
Frolov, Y. 320
FROM 164
function 363
fuzzy tolerance 185

G

gap 200
Gardner, M. 298
Gardner, R. 326
Gatrell, A. 282
generalization 208, 344
geocoding 209
geocoding services 211
geocoding styles 211
geodatabases 54
geographic transformation 87
geographical coordinate system 82
geographical primitives 38
geometric data structure 38
geometric network 52, 56
geoprocessing, introduced 25
Geostatistical Analyst 28, 140, 277, 334
Gersmehl, P. 109
Gesch, D. 266
Gilbert, E. 348
GIRAS 79
GIScience 37
GISFrag 326
Global Positioning System 88

resolution 83, 238
reverse 410
RGB 131
Rhind, D. 320
Rigaux, P. 60
right() 408
ring 42, 43, 47, 56
ring, defined 49
riparian zones 338
Ripple, W. 326
rise over run 272
rnd 217
road density 264
Robinson, A. 96, 107
rook's case 300
root mean square error 279
routes 47
row-major order 292
row-prime order 292
ROYGBIV 131
Run Entire Model 375
run-length encoding 224
Russell, E. 271
Rutovitz, D. 224

S

Saaty, T. 371
salt and pepper 304
Samet, H. 225
satellite constellation 88
saturation 131
Scalable Vector Graphics 152
scale
    coarse 82
    fine 82
    large 82
    small 82
scale range 137
Scholl, M. 60
Schruben, P. 270
script 25
seams 266

search tool 23
Segment 49
SELECT 164
Select By Attributes 160
Select by Location 171
Select Features 167, 168, 174
select from current selection 158
Selectable Layers 167
selected 157
selected set 157
selection methods 160
selection tolerance 168
Selection tool 19
selection, geoprocessing 158
sensitivity analysis 366
shape, symbol property 131
shapefile 41
share a line segment 173
Shared Edit 195
shared features 203
Shih, T. 132
Silverman, B. 263
simple features 39
simple line symbol 132
simple random sampling 306
Simplify Lines tool 344
single symbol 111
size 131
sketch 30
sliver polygons 198, 200
sliver polygons, merge 199
slivers polygons 266
slope 272
slope, trail 399
Smirnov, O. 413
snap extent to 237
snapping 189
snapping properties 189
snapping tolerance 189
Snow, John 348
Snyder, J. 95

TINs 53
Tissot's indicatrix 95
Tobler, W. 83, 109, 254, 259, 334
Tomlin, C. 243
Tomlinson, R. 1
tool 25
Tool2Gp.py 417
toolbox 25
toolbox GIS 8
tools, full listing 375
toolset 25
topological association 186
topological data structure 44
topology 43, 44
Topology Edit Tool 195
Topology Edit tool 207
Topology toolbar 207
touch the boundary of 173
Tracking Analyst 28
transformations 340
transparency 136, 270
Triangulated Irregular Networks 53
TRUNC 164
Turner, M. 326
Tyler, D. 266

U

undershoot 184
union 355
union features 196
unioned 196
unique values 113
universe polygon 50
Unwin, D. 282
update 427
update cursor 427
updating 357
UPPER 164
usage 288
use stage 363
user component 88
USGS National Hydrography Dataset 51

UTM 98

V

validation 202
value 131
Value Attribute Table 76
van Dam, A. 240
van Wagtendonk, J. 261
vat.adf 229
VBA 30
vertical datums 87
vertices 38, 203
viewshed 274
visible layers 159
visualization framework 109
Voisard, A. 60
Voronoi polygons 256

W

w001001.adf 229
w001001x.adf 229
WAAS 90
Wagner, D. 298
warning message 429
warning threshold 429
watch 373
Watson, D. 279
Weibel, R. 344
weighted arithmetic model 370
weighted centroid 342
weighted linear combination 370
weighted mean 317
weird polygons 191
WHERE 164
while 411
White, D. 186
Wide Area Augmentation System 90
Wikle, T. 348
Wilbert, M. 367
Windows Explorer 9
wire-frame 140
within a distance of 173
Wizards 26

Wong, D. 330
Wood, W. 320
Worboys, M. 36, 43, 320
world file 151
Wright, J. 128
X
x, y data 75
x,y centroid 322
XY domain 55
Z
z factor 272
Zeiler, M. 54
zenith 269
Zonal 300
zonal 252
Zonal Statistics 253
ZonalGeometry 322
zone 226, 252